Everyday Mathematics®

The University of Chicago School Mathematics Project

Math Masters

Grade

D1089316

McGraw Hill Education

Chicago, IL • Columbus, OH • New York, NY

The University of Chicago School Mathematics Project (UCSMP)

Max Bell, Director, UCSMP Elementary Materials Component; Director, *Everyday Mathematics* First Edition; James McBride, Director, *Everyday Mathematics* Second Edition; Andy Isaacs, Director, *Everyday Mathematics* Third Edition; Amy Dillard, Associate Director, *Everyday Mathematics* Third Edition; Rachel Malpass McCall, Associate Director, *Everyday Mathematics* Common Core State Standards Edition

Authors

Max Bell, John Bretzlauf, Amy Dillard, Robert Hartfield, Andy Isaacs, James McBride, Kathleen Pitvorec, Denise Porter‡, Peter Saecker, Noreen Winningham*, Robert Balfanz†, William Carroll†

*Third Edition only   †First Edition only   ‡Common Core State Standards Edition only

Technical Art	**UCSMP Editorial**	**Third Edition Teachers in Residence**
Diana Barrie	Rosina Busse, Laurie K. Thrasher, David B. Spangler	Fran Goldenberg, Sandra Vitantonio

Contributors

Tammy Belgrade, Diana Carry, Debra Dawson, Kevin Dorken, James Flanders, Laurel Hallman, Ann Hemwall, Elizabeth Homewood, Linda Klaric, Lee Kornhauser, Judy Korshak-Samuels, Deborah Arron Leslie, Joseph C. Liptak, Sharon McHugh, Janet M. Meyers, Susan Mieli, Donna Nowatzki, Mary O'Boyle, Julie Olson, William D. Pattison, Loretta Rice, Diana Rivas, Michelle Schiminsky, Sheila Sconiers, Kevin J. Smith, Teresa Sparlin, Laura Sunseri, Kim Van Haitsma, John Wilson, Mary Wilson, Carl Zmola, Teresa Zmola

Photo Credits

Cover (l)Steven Hunt/Stone/Getty Images, (c)Martin Mistretta/Stone/Getty Images, (r)Digital Stock/CORBIS, (bkgd)Pier/Stone/Getty Images; **Back Cover Spine** Martin Mistretta/Stone/Getty Images; **iii** Ocean/CORBIS; **iv** C Squared/Photodisc/Getty Images; **v** C Squared Studios/Getty Images; **vi** The McGraw-Hill Companies; **vii** Sean Ellis/Photographer's Choice/Getty Images; **viii** Tatsuhiko Sawada/Getty Images; **ix** (l)The McGraw-Hill Companies, (c r)Tony Freeman/PhotoEdit; **x** Ocean/CORBIS; **xi** The McGraw-Hill Companies; **xii** C Squared Studios/Photodisc/Getty Images; **3 29** The McGraw-Hill Companies; **63** Dave Bartruff/Digital Vision/Getty Images; **98** Photolibrary; **121–184** The McGraw-Hill Companies; **217** Image Source/Getty Images; **290–368** The McGraw-Hill Companies; **403** Alinari Archives/CORBIS; **410A** Robert Glusic/CORBIS.

Permissions

Excerpt from "Arithmetic" in THE COMPLETE POEMS OF CARL SANDBURG, copyright © 1970, 1969 by Lilian Steichen Sandburg, Trustee, reprinted by permission of Harcourt, Inc. This material may not be produced in any form or by any means without the prior written permission of the publisher; Excerpt from "Finding Time" by JoAnne Growney, Mathematics Magazine, vol. 68, no. 4 (October 1995); Second Poem: "123" by Ken Stange, first published in Cold Pigging Poetics (Hypothesis 5), ISBN 0-920424-25-2, 1981, York Publishing, Toronto.

This material is based upon work supported by the National Science Foundation under Grant No. ESI-9252984. Any opinions, findings, conclusions, or recommendations expressed in this material are those of the authors and do not necessarily reflect the views of the National Science Foundation.

---

everyday**math**.com

 **Education**

Send all inquiries to:
McGraw-Hill Education
STEM Learning Solutions Center
P.O. Box 812960
Chicago, IL 60681

ISBN: 978-0-07-657697-5
MHID: 0-07-657697-3

Printed in the United States of America.

2 3 4 5 6 7 8 9 QDB 17 16 15 14 13 12 11

McGraw-Hill is committed to providing instructional materials in Science, Technology, Engineering, and Mathematics (STEM) that give all students a solid foundation, one that prepares them for college and careers in the 21st century.

The McGraw-Hill Companies

Contents

Unit 3

Unit 8

Contents   **vii**

Project Masters

Teaching Masters
and
Study Link Masters

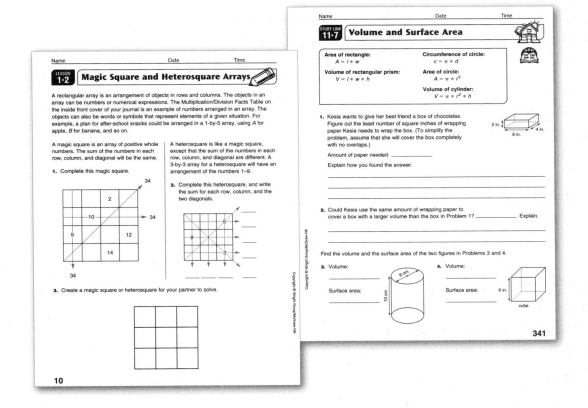

STUDY LINK 1·1

Number Poetry

Many poems have been written about mathematics. They are poems that share some of the ways that poets think about numbers and patterns.

1. Read the examples below.

2. The ideas in the examples are some of the ideas you have studied in *Everyday Mathematics.* Subtraction is one of these ideas. Name as many other ideas from the examples as you can on the back of this page.

Examples:

Arithmetic is where numbers fly like pigeons in and out of your head.
Arithmetic tells you how many you lose or win if you know how many you had before you lost or won.

from "Arithmetic" by Carl Sandburg

A square is neither a line
nor circle; it is timeless.
Points don't chase around
a square. Firm, steady,
it sits there and knows
its place. A circle
won't be squared.

from "Finding Time" by JoAnne Growney

Second Poem: "123"

.
1
12
123
1-32
1-21
1-10
2
21
21-31
2131
21-31-231
121
1
.

How many seconds in an hour?
How many in a day?
What size are the planets in the sky?
How far to the Milky Way?

How fast does lightning travel?
How slow do feathers fall?
How many miles to Istanbul?
Mathematics knows it all!

from "Marvelous Math" by Rebecca Kai Dotlich

from "Asparagus X Plus Y"
by Ken Stange

3. Use a number pattern to make your own poem on the back of this page.

STUDY LINK 1·1

Unit 1: Family Letter

Introduction to *Fifth Grade Everyday Mathematics*

Welcome to *Fifth Grade Everyday Mathematics.* This curriculum was developed by the University of Chicago School Mathematics Project to offer students a broad background in mathematics.

The features of the program described below are to help familiarize you with the structure and expectations of *Everyday Mathematics.*

A problem-solving approach based on everyday situations Students learn basic math skills in a context that is meaningful by making connections between their own knowledge and experience and mathematics concepts.

Frequent practice of basic skills Students practice basic skills in a variety of engaging ways. In addition to completing daily review exercises covering a variety of topics and working with multiplication and division fact families in different formats, students play games that are specifically designed to develop basic skills.

An instructional approach that revisits concepts regularly Lessons are designed to take advantage of previously learned concepts and skills and to build on them throughout the year.

A curriculum that explores mathematical content beyond basic arithmetic Mathematics standards around the world indicate that basic arithmetic skills are only the beginning of the mathematical knowledge students will need as they develop critical-thinking skills. In addition to basic arithmetic, *Everyday Mathematics* develops concepts and skills in the following topics—number and numeration; operations and computation; data and chance; geometry; measurement and reference frames; and patterns, functions, and algebra.

Everyday Mathematics provides you with ample opportunities to monitor your child's progress and to participate in your child's mathematical experiences. Throughout the year, you will receive Family Letters to keep you informed of the mathematical content your child is studying in each unit. Each letter includes a vocabulary list, suggested Do-Anytime Activities for you and your child, and an answer guide to selected Study Link (homework) activities.

Please keep this Family Letter for reference as your child works through Unit 1.

Fifth Grade Everyday Mathematics emphasizes the following content:

Number and Numeration Understand the meanings, uses, and representations of numbers; equivalent names for numbers, and common numerical relations.

Operations and Computation Make reasonable estimates and accurate computations; understand the meanings of operations.

Data and Chance Select and create appropriate graphical representations of collected or given data; analyze and interpret data; understand and apply basic concepts of probability.

Geometry Investigate characteristics and properties of 2- and 3-dimensional shapes; apply transformations and symmetry in geometric situations.

Measurement and Reference Frames Understand the systems and processes of measurement; use appropriate techniques, tools, units, and formulas in making measurements; use and understand reference frames.

Patterns, Functions, and Algebra Understand patterns and functions; use algebraic notation to represent and analyze situations and structures.

Unit 1: Number Theory

In Unit 1, students study properties of whole numbers by building on their prior work with multiplication and division of whole numbers.

Students will collect examples of arrays to form a class Arrays Museum. To practice using arrays with your child at home, use any small objects, such as beans, macaroni, or pennies.

Building Skills through Games

In Unit 1, your child will practice operations and computation skills by playing the following games. Detailed instructions for each game are in the *Student Reference Book.*

Factor Bingo This game involves 2 to 4 players and requires a deck of number cards with 4 each of the numbers 2–9, a drawn or folded 5-by-5 grid and 12 pennies or counters for each player. The goal of the game is to practice the skill of recognizing factors.

Factor Captor See *Student Reference Book,* page 306. This is a game for 2 players. Materials needed include a *Factor Captor* Grid, 48 counters the size of a penny, scratch paper, and a calculator. The

goal of the game is to strengthen the skill of finding the factors of a number.

Multiplication Top-It See *Student Reference Book,* page 334. This game requires a deck of cards with 4 each of the numbers 1–10 and can be played by 2–4 players. *Multiplication Top-It* is used to practice the basic multiplication facts.

Name That Number See *Student Reference Book,* page 325. This game involves 2 or 3 players and requires a complete deck of number cards. *Name That Number* provides practice with computation and strengthens skills related to number properties.

Vocabulary

Important terms in Unit 1:

composite number A counting number greater than 1 that has more than two *factors.* For example, 4 is a composite number because it has three factors: 1, 2, and 4.

divisible by If the larger of two counting numbers can be divided by the smaller with no remainder, then the larger is divisible by the smaller. For example, 28 is divisible by 7 because $28 / 7 = 4$ with no remainder.

exponent The small, raised number in exponential notation that tells how many times the base is used as a *factor.*

Example:

$5^2 \leftarrow$ exponent $\quad 5^2 = 5 * 5 = 25.$

$10^3 \leftarrow$ exponent $\quad 10^3 = 10 * 10 * 10 = 1,000.$

$2^4 \leftarrow$ exponent $\quad 2^4 = 2 * 2 * 2 * 2 = 16.$

factor One of two or more numbers that are multiplied to give a *product.*

$3 * 5 = 15 \qquad 15 * 1 = 15$

Factors Product   Factors Product

factor rainbow A way to show factor pairs in a list of all the factors of a number. A factor rainbow can be used to check whether a list of factors is correct.

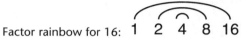

Factor rainbow for 16: 1 2 4 8 16

number model A number sentence or expression that models a number story or situation. For example, a number model for the array below is $4 * 3 = 12.$

prime number A whole number that has exactly two factors: itself and 1. For example, 5 is a prime number because its only factors are 5 and 1.

product The result of multiplying two or more numbers, called *factors.*

rectangular array A rectangular arrangement of objects in rows and columns such that each row has the same number of objects and each column has the same number of objects.

square number A number that is the product of a counting number multiplied by itself. For example, 25 is a square number, because $25 = 5 * 5.$

As You Help Your Child with Homework

As your child brings assignments home, you might want to go over the instructions together, clarifying them as necessary. The answers listed below will guide you through this unit's Study Links.

Study Link 1·2

1. 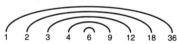 1 * 5 = 5; 5 * 1 = 5

2. 1 * 14 = 14; 14 * 1 = 14
2 * 7 = 14; 7 * 2 = 14

3. 1 * 18 = 18; 18 * 1 = 18; 2 * 9 = 18;
9 * 2 = 18; 3 * 6 = 18; 6 * 3 = 18

4. 795   **5.** 271   **6.** 98   **7.** 984   **8.** 5

Study Link 1·3

1. 24; 24

3. 24; 3, 8; 24

6. 1 * 5 = 5; 1, 5

7. 4   **8.** 3,919   **9.** 2,763   **10.** 159

Study Link 1·4

1. The next number to try is 5, but 5 is already listed as a factor. Also, any factor greater than 5 would already be named because it would be paired with a factor less than 5.

2. 1, 5, 25   **3.** 1, 2, 4, 7, 14, 28

4. 1, 2, 3, 6, 7, 14, 21, 42

5. 1, 2, 4, 5, 10, 20, 25, 50, 100

6. 9,551   **7.** 48   **8.** 41,544   **9.** 441   **10.** 7

Study Link 1·5

1. Divisible by 2: 998,876; 5,890; 36,540; 1,098
Divisible by 3: 36,540; 33,015; 1,098
Divisible by 9: 36,540; 1,098
Divisible by 5: 5,890; 36,540; 33,015

2. Divisible by 4: 998,876; 36,540

3. 1,750   **4.** 8,753   **5.** 250   **6.** 13

Study Link 1·6

1. 11; 1, ⑪;   p
2. 18; 1, ②③ 6, 9, 18;   c
3. 24; 1, ②③ 4, 6, 8, 12, 24;   c
4. 28; 1, ② 4, ⑦ 14, 28;   c
5. 36; 1, ②③ 4, 6, 9, 12, 18, 36;   c
6. 49; 1, ⑦ 49;   c
7. 50; 1, ②⑤ 10, 25, 50;   c
8. 70; 1, ②⑤⑦ 10, 14, 35, 70;   c
9. 100; 1, ② 4, ⑤ 10, 20, 25, 50, 100;   c

10. 9,822   **11.** 234   **12.** 21,448   **13.** 9 R3

Study Link 1·7

1. 16   **2.** 49   **3.** 6   **4.** 64   **5.** 25

6. 81   **7.** 4 * 9 = 36   **8.** 5 * 5 = 25

9. a. 5 * 5 = 25

b. 5 * 5 = 25 shows a square number because there are the same number of rows and columns. A square can be drawn around this array.

Study Link 1·8

1. 36: 1, 2, 3, 4, 6, 9, 12, 18, 36; $6^2 = 36$ The square root of 36 is 6.

1 2 3 4 6 9 12 18 36

3. $11^2 = 121$; the square root of 121 is 11.

5. 6,219   **6.** 3,060   **8.** 8 R2   **9.** 42

Study Link 1·9

1. b. $7^2 = 7 * 7 = 49$

c. $20^3 = 20 * 20 * 20 = 8,000$

2. a. 11^2 **b.** 9^3 **c.** 50^4

3. a. $2 * 3^3 * 5^2 = 2 * 3 * 3 * 3 * 5 * 5 = 1,350$

b. $2^4 * 4^2 = 2 * 2 * 2 * 2 * 4 * 4 = 256$

4. a. $40 = 2 * 2 * 2 * 5 = 2^3 * 5$

b. $90 = 2 * 3 * 3 * 5 = 2 * 3^2 * 5$

5. 5,041   **6.** 720   **7.** 50 R4   **8.** 99,140

9. 12   **10.** 47,668

LESSON 1·1 Following Written Directions

Read the directions *carefully.* Do *not* do anything until you have read all ten instructions.

1. Draw a square inside of a rectangle on this page.
2. Find the sum of the student fingers and toes in your class.
3. Stand up. Cover your eyes with your hands, and turn 90 degrees to the right.
4. Pat the top of your head with your right hand and, at the same time, rub your stomach in a clockwise direction with your left hand. Sit down.
5. As loudly as you can, count backwards from 10.
6. Find the sum of the digits for today's date.
7. Estimate how many miles you walked in the last 2 months.
8. Try to touch the tip of your nose with your tongue.
9. If you reach into a bag where there is a $1 bill, a $5 bill, and a $10 bill, what is the chance that, without looking, you will pull a $10 bill? Whisper your answer to a neighbor.
10. Do not do any of the first 9 activities. Instead, turn over your paper and wait for your teacher's instructions.

✂ -

Name   Date   Time

LESSON 1·1 Following Written Directions

Read the directions *carefully.* Do *not* do anything until you have read all ten instructions.

1. Draw a square inside of a rectangle on this page.
2. Find the sum of the student fingers and toes in your class.
3. Stand up. Cover your eyes with your hands, and turn 90 degrees to the right.
4. Pat the top of your head with your right hand and, at the same time, rub your stomach in a clockwise direction with your left hand. Sit down.
5. As loudly as you can, count backwards from 10.
6. Find the sum of the digits for today's date.
7. Estimate how many miles you walked in the last 2 months.
8. Try to touch the tip of your nose with your tongue.
9. If you reach into a bag where there is a $1 bill, a $5 bill, and a $10 bill, what is the chance that, without looking, you will pull a $10 bill? Whisper your answer to a neighbor.
10. Do not do any of the first 9 activities. Instead, turn over your paper and wait for your teacher's instructions.

STUDY LINK 1·2 | More Array Play

A **rectangular array** is an arrangement of objects in rows and columns. Each row has the same number of objects, and each column has the same number of objects. We can write a multiplication number model to describe a rectangular array.

$4 * 3 = 12$

For each number below, use pennies or counters to make as many different arrays as possible. Draw each array on the grid with dots. Write the number model next to each array.

1. 5

2. 14

3. 18

Practice

4. $487 + 308 =$ _____

5. $679 - 408 =$ _____

6. $14 * 7 =$ _____

7. $164 * 6 =$ _____

8. $45 \div 9 =$ _____

8

LESSON 1·2   Rows and Columns

A rectangular array is an arrangement of objects in rows and columns. Each row has the same number of objects, and each column has the same number of objects.

Work with a partner to build arrays. For each array, take turns rolling dice. The first die is the number of rows. Write this number in the table under Rows. The second die is the number of cubes in each row. Write this number under Columns. Then use centimeter cubes to build the array on the dot grid. How many cubes are in the array? Write this number under Array Total on the dot grid table.

Rows	Columns	Array Total

Rows	Columns	Array Total

LESSON 1·2 — Magic Square and Heterosquare Arrays

A rectangular array is an arrangement of objects in rows and columns. The objects in an array can be numbers or numerical expressions. The Multiplication/Division Facts Table on the inside front cover of your journal is an example of numbers arranged in an array. The objects can also be words or symbols that represent elements of a given situation. For example, a plan for after-school snacks could be arranged in a 1-by-5 array, using *A* for apple, *B* for banana, and so on.

A magic square is an array of positive whole numbers. The sum of the numbers in each row, column, and diagonal will be the same.

1. Complete this magic square.

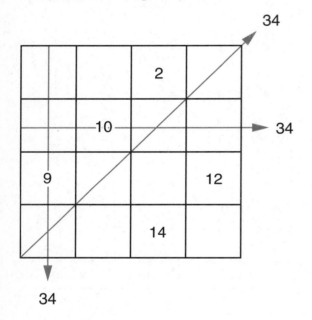

A heterosquare is like a magic square, except that the sum of the numbers in each row, column, and diagonal are different. A 3-by-3 array for a heterosquare will have an arrangement of the numbers 1–9.

2. Complete this heterosquare, and write the sum for each row, column, and the two diagonals.

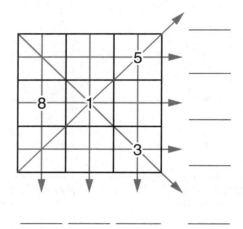

3. Create a magic square or heterosquare for your partner to solve.

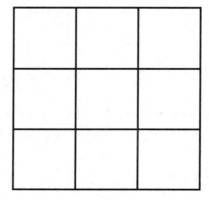

LESSON 1·3   **Multiplication Facts**

A List					
3 * 6 = 18					
6 * 3 = 18					
3 * 7 = 21					
7 * 3 = 21					
3 * 8 = 24					
8 * 3 = 24					
3 * 9 = 27					
9 * 3 = 27					
4 * 6 = 24					
6 * 4 = 24					
4 * 7 = 28					
7 * 4 = 28					
4 * 8 = 32					
8 * 4 = 32					
4 * 9 = 36					
9 * 4 = 36					
5 * 7 = 35					
7 * 5 = 35					
5 * 9 = 45					
9 * 5 = 45					
6 * 6 = 36					
6 * 7 = 42					
7 * 6 = 42					
6 * 8 = 48					
8 * 6 = 48					
6 * 9 = 54					
9 * 6 = 54					
7 * 7 = 49					
7 * 8 = 56					
8 * 7 = 56					
7 * 9 = 63					
9 * 7 = 63					
8 * 8 = 64					
8 * 9 = 72					
9 * 8 = 72					
9 * 9 = 81					

B List					
3 * 3 = 9					
3 * 4 = 12					
4 * 3 = 12					
3 * 5 = 15					
5 * 3 = 15					
4 * 4 = 16					
4 * 5 = 20					
5 * 4 = 20					
5 * 5 = 25					
5 * 6 = 30					
6 * 5 = 30					
5 * 8 = 40					
8 * 5 = 40					
6 * 10 = 60					
10 * 6 = 60					
7 * 10 = 70					
10 * 7 = 70					
8 * 10 = 80					
10 * 8 = 80					
9 * 10 = 90					
10 * 9 = 90					
10 * 10 = 100					

Bonus Problems					
11 * 11 = 121					
11 * 12 = 132					
5 * 12 = 60					
12 * 6 = 72					
7 * 12 = 84					
12 * 8 = 96					
9 * 12 = 108					
10 * 12 = 120					
5 * 13 = 65					
15 * 7 = 105					
12 * 12 = 144					
6 * 14 = 84					

11

Number Models for Arrays

SRB
10

Complete the chart. You will need to find each missing part and write it in the correct space.

	Array	Number Model	Factors	Product
1		6 * 4 = _____	6, 4	
2			2, 12	
3		3 * 8 = _____		
4			1, 15	
5				15
6				5

Reminder: Look for examples of arrays and bring them to school.

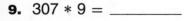

Practice

7. 12 / 3 = _____

8. 1,288 + 2,631 = _____

9. 307 * 9 = _____

10. 306 − 147 = _____

LESSON 1·3 | **Factoring Numbers with Cube Arrays**

Use centimeter cubes to build arrays for the following numbers. With each array write the **factor pair.** Remember that the number of rows in the array is one **factor** and that the number of columns in the array is the other **factor.**

Continue to build every possible array until you have all of the factors for the number.

1. 14

Factors: _____

2. 8

Factors: _____

3. 10

Factors: _____

4. 20

Factors: _____

5. 33

Factors: _____

6. Can you tell when you have all of the factors for a number before you have built every possible array?

_____ Explain. _____

_____

_____

_____

_____

___

Try This

7. Write three true statements about factors.

_____

_____

_____

_____

_____

STUDY LINK 1·4 | **Factors**

To find the factors of a number, ask yourself: *Is 1 a factor of the number?*
Is 2 a factor? Is 3 a factor? Continue with larger numbers. For example, to
find all the factors of 15, ask yourself these questions.

	Yes/No	**Number Sentence**	**Factor Pair**
Is 1 a factor of 15?	Yes	1 * 15 = 15	1, 15
Is 2 a factor of 15?	No		
Is 3 a factor of 15?	Yes	3 * 5 = 15	3, 5
Is 4 a factor of 15?	No		

1. You don't need to go any further. Can you tell why?

_____

_____

_____

_____

So the factors of 15 are 1, 3, 5, and 15.

List as many factors as you can for each of the numbers below.

2. 25 _____

3. 28 _____

4. 42 _____

5. 100 _____

| **Practice** |

6. 8,417 + 1,134 = _____   **7.** 73 − 25 = _____

8. 6,924 * 6 = _____   **9.** 634 − 193 = _____

10. 56 / 8 = _____

STUDY LINK 1·5 · Divisibility Rules

◆ All even numbers are divisible by 2.

◆ A number is divisible by 3 if the sum of its digits is divisible by 3.

◆ A number is divisible by 6 if it is divisible by both 2 and 3.

◆ A number is divisible by 9 if the sum of its digits is divisible by 9.

◆ A number is divisible by 5 if it ends in 0 or 5.

◆ A number is divisible by 10 if it ends in 0.

1. Use divisibility rules to test whether each number is divisible by 2, 3, 5, 6, 9, or 10.

Number	Divisible...					
	by 2?	by 3?	by 6?	by 9?	by 5?	by 10?
998,876						
5,890						
36,540						
33,015						
1,098						

A number is divisible by 4 if the tens and ones digits form a number that is divisible by 4.

Example: 47,8**36** is divisible by 4 because 36 is divisible by 4.

It isn't always easy to tell whether the last two digits form a number that is divisible by 4. A quick way to check is to divide the number by 2 and then divide the result by 2. It's the same as dividing by 4, but is easier to do mentally.

Example: 5,3**84** is divisible by 4 because 84 / 2 = 42 and 42 / 2 = 21.

2. Place a star next to any number in the table that is divisible by 4.

Practice

3. 250 * 7 = _____

4. 1,931 + 4,763 + 2,059 = _____

5. (20 + 30) * 5 = _____

6. 78 ÷ 6 = _____

LESSON 1·5

Divisibility by 4

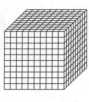

1,000 cubes

100 cubes

10 cubes

⬚

1 cube

1. What number is shown by the base-10 blocks? _____

2. Which of the base-10 blocks could be divided evenly into 4 groups of cubes?

_____

_____

3. Is the number shown by the base-10 blocks divisible by 4? _____

4. Circle the numbers that you think are divisible by 4.

324   5,821   7,430   35,782,916

Use a calculator to check your answers.

5. Use what you know about base-10 blocks to explain why you only need to look at the last two digits of a number to decide whether it is divisible by 4.

_____

_____

_____

_____

_____

_____

STUDY LINK
1·6
Prime and Composite Numbers

A **prime number** is a whole number that has exactly two factors—1 and the number itself. A **composite number** is a whole number that has more than two factors.

For each number:

◆ List all of its factors.

◆ Write whether the number is prime or composite.

◆ Circle all of the factors that are prime numbers.

Number		Factors	Prime or Composite?
1	11		
2	18		
3	24		
4	28		
5	36		
6	49		
7	50		
8	70		
9	100		

Practice

10. $4,065 + 2,803 + 2,954 =$ _____

11. $392 - 158 =$ _____

12. $1,532 * 14 =$ _____

13. $39 / 4 \rightarrow$ _____

14. $48 * 15 =$ _____

LESSON 1·6 Goldbach's Conjecture

1. Write each of the following numbers as the sum of two prime numbers.

   Examples: $56 = \underline{43 + 13}$ $\qquad$ $26 = \underline{13 + 13}$

   a. $6 = $ _____

   b. $12 = $ _____

   c. $18 = $ _____

   d. $22 = $ _____

   e. $24 = $ _____

   f. $34 = $ _____

The answers to these problems are examples of **Goldbach's Conjecture.** A **conjecture** is something you believe is true even though you can't be certain that it is true. Goldbach's Conjecture might be true, but no one has ever proven it. Anyone who can either prove or disprove Goldbach's Conjecture will become famous.

2. Work with a partner. Find and write as many of the addition expressions as you can for the numbers in the grid on page 19.

3. Can any of the numbers in the grid be written as the sum of two prime numbers in more than one way? If so, give an example. Show all possible ways.

   _____

   _____

   _____

Try This

4. Write 70 as the sum of two primes in as many ways as you can.

   _____

   _____

LESSON 1·6 **Goldbach's Conjecture** *continued*

Write each number below as the sum of two prime numbers.

4	6	8	10	12
2 + 2 _____	_____	_____	_____	_____
14 _____	16 _____	18 _____	20 _____	22 _____
24 _____	26 _____	28 _____	30 _____	32 _____
34 _____	36 _____	38 _____	40 _____	42 _____
44 _____	46 _____	48 _____	50 _____	52 _____
54 _____	56 _____	58 _____	60 _____	62 _____
64 _____	66 _____	68 _____	70 _____	72 _____
74 _____	76 _____	78 _____	80 _____	82 _____
84 _____	86 _____	88 _____	90 _____	92 _____
94 _____	96 _____	98 _____	100 _____	102 _____

STUDY LINK 1·7 Exploring Square Numbers

A **square number** is a number that can be written as the product of a number multiplied by itself. For example, the square number 9 can be written as 3 * 3.

$9 = 3 * 3 = 3^2$

Fill in the missing numbers.

1. 4 * 4 = _____   **2.** _____ = 7 * 7   **3.** _____ * 6 = 36

4. 8^2 = _____   **5.** 5^2 = _____   **6.** _____ = 9^2

Write a number model to describe each array.

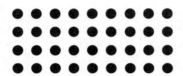   

7. Number model: _____   **8.** Number model: _____

9. a. Which of the arrays above shows a square number? _____

b. Explain your answer.

_____

_____

_____

Practice

10. 97 * 43 = _____   **11.** 4,006 − 2,675 = _____

12. 1,416 + 8,348 = _____   **13.** 725 − 414 = _____

LESSON 1·7 | **Completing Patterns**

Build these patterns with counters. Draw the dot pattern that comes next and record the number of dots in the pattern.

Example:

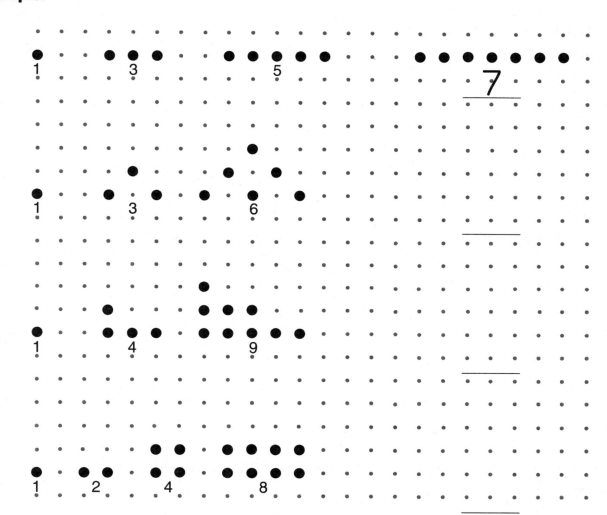

1.

2.

3.

4. Write a description of the pattern in Problem 3.

_____

_____

_____

Factor Rainbows, Squares, and Square Roots

1. List all the factors of each square number. Make a **factor rainbow** to check your work. Then fill in the missing numbers.

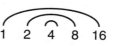

Reminder: In a factor rainbow, the product of each connected factor pair should be equal to the number itself. For example, the factor rainbow for 16 looks like this:

$1 * 16 = 16$ $2 * 8 = 16$ $4 * 4 = 16$

Example:	9:
4: $1, 2, 4$ ⌢124 $2^2 = 4$ The square root of 4 is 2.	$\underline{}^2 = 9$ The square root of 9 is ___.
25: $\underline{}^2 = 25$ The square root of 25 is ___.	36: $\underline{}^2 = 36$ The square root of 36 is ___.

2. Do all square numbers have an odd number of factors? _____

Unsquare each number. The result is its square root. Do not use the square root key $\boxed{\sqrt{}}$ on your calculator.

3. $\underline{}^2 = 121$

   The square root of 121 is _____.

4. $\underline{}^2 = 2,500$

   The square root of 2,500 is _____.

Practice

5. $\begin{array}{r} 4,318 \\ +\ 1,901 \\ \hline \end{array}$

6. $\begin{array}{r} 36 \\ \times\ 85 \\ \hline \end{array}$

7. $\begin{array}{r} 2,852 \\ \times\ \ \ \ 5 \\ \hline \end{array}$

8. $50 \div 6 \rightarrow$ _____

9. $333 - 291 =$ _____

LESSON 1·8 | Comparing Numbers with Their Squares

1. **a.** Unsquare the number 1. $\underline{}^2 = 1$

   b. Unsquare the number 0. $\underline{}^2 = 0$

2. **a.** Is 5 greater than or less than 1? _____

   b. $5^2 =$ _____

   c. Is 5^2 greater than or less than 5? _____

3. **a.** Is 0.50 greater than or less than 1? _____

   b. Use your calculator. $0.50^2 =$ _____

   c. Is 0.50^2 greater than or less than 0.50? _____

4. **a.** When you square a number, is the result always greater than the number you started with? _____

   b. Can it be less? _____

   c. Can it be the same? _____

5. Write 3 true statements about squaring and unsquaring numbers.

   _____

   _____

   _____

   _____

   _____

   _____

STUDY LINK 1·9 | **Exponents**

An **exponent** is a raised number that shows how many times the number to its left is used as a factor.

Examples:

5^2 ← exponent	5^2 means 5 * 5, which is 25.
10^3 ← exponent	10^3 means 10 * 10 * 10, which is 1,000.
2^4 ← exponent	2^4 means 2 * 2 * 2 * 2, which is 16.

1. Write each of the following as a factor string. Then find the product.

Example: $2^3 = \underline{2*2*2} = \underline{8}$ **a.** $10^4 = $ _____ = _____

b. $7^2 = $ _____ = _____   **c.** $20^3 = $ _____ = _____

2. Write each factor string using an exponent.

Example: $6 * 6 * 6 * 6 = \underline{6^4}$ **a.** $11 * 11 = $ _____

b. $9 * 9 * 9 = $ _____   **c.** $50 * 50 * 50 * 50 = $ _____

3. Write each of the following as a factor string that does *not* have any exponents. Then use your calculator to find the product.

Example: $2^3 * 3 = \underline{2*2*2*3} = \underline{24}$

a. $2 * 3^3 * 5^2 = $ _____ = _____

b. $2^4 * 4^2 = $ _____ = _____

4. Write the prime factorization of each number. Then write it using exponents.

Example: $18 = \underline{2*3*3} = \underline{2*3^2}$

a. $40 = $ _____ = _____

b. $90 = $ _____ = _____

Practice

5. $6,383 - 1,342 = $ _____   **6.** $48 * 15 = $ _____

7. $7\overline{)354} \rightarrow$ _____   **8.** $50,314 + 48,826 = $ _____

9. $84 \div 7 = $ _____   **10.** $701 * 68 = $ _____

Using Factor Trees

Factor Trees

One way to find all the prime factors of a number is to make a **factor tree.** First write the number. Then, underneath, write any two factors whose product is that number. Then write factors of each of these factors. Continue until all the factors are prime numbers.

Below are three factor trees for 36.

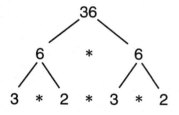 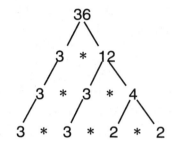 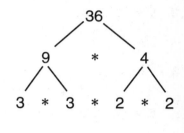

It does not matter which two factors you begin with. You always end with the same prime factors—for 36, they are 2, 2, 3, and 3. The **prime factorization** of 36 is 2 * 2 * 3 * 3.

Make a factor tree for each number. Then write the prime factorization for each number.

24   50

24 = _____   50 = _____

48   100

48 = _____   100 = _____

LESSON 1·9 | # The Sieve of Eratosthenes

The mathematician Eratosthenes, born in 276 B.C., developed this method for finding prime numbers. Follow the directions below for *Math Masters,* page 27. When you have finished, you will have crossed out every number from 1 to 30 in the grid that is not a prime number.

1. Since 1 is not a prime number, cross it out.

2. Circle 2 with a colored marker or crayon. Then count by 2, crossing out all multiples of 2—that is, 4, 6, 8, 10, and so on.

3. Circle 3 with a color different from Step 2. Cross out every third number after 3 (6, 9, 12, and so on). If a number is already crossed out, make a mark in a corner of the box. The numbers you have crossed out or marked are multiples of 3.

4. Skip 4 on the grid because it is already crossed out, and go on to 5. Use a new color to circle 5 and cross out the multiples of 5.

5. Continue. Start each time by circling the next number that is not crossed out. Cross out all multiples of that number. If a number is already crossed out, make a mark in a corner of the box. If there are no multiples for a number, start again. Use a different color for each new set of multiples.

6. Stop when there are no more numbers to be circled or crossed out. The circled numbers are the prime numbers from 1 to 30.

7. List the prime numbers from 1 to 30.

_____

_____

LESSON 1·9

The Sieve of Eratosthenes *continued*

1	2	3	4	5
6	7	8	9	10
11	12	13	14	15
16	17	18	19	20
21	22	23	24	25
26	27	28	29	30

LESSON 1·9 | Palindromic Squares

Palindrome numbers are numbers that read the same forward or backward. A single-digit number is also a palindrome. The two-digit palindrome numbers are 11, 22, 33, 44, 55, 66, 77, 88, and 99. The table below lists samples of 3-digit and 4-digit palindromes.

1. Find 3-digit and 4-digit numbers to add to the table.

Palindrome Numbers	
3-digit	**4-digit**
101, 111	1,001; 1,111
202, 222	2,002; 2,222
303, 333	3,003; 3,333

Sometimes finding the square of a palindrome number results in a square number that is also a palindrome number—a palindromic square. For example, $111^2 = 12,321$.

2. Which 3 single-digit numbers have palindromic squares? _____

3. Which 2-digit numbers have palindromic squares? _____

4. Find the numbers from the table that have a palindromic square and write the number model.

Example: $101^2 = 10,201$

_____

_____

STUDY LINK 1·10 | Unit 2: Family Letter

Estimation and Calculation

Computation is an important part of problem solving. Many of us were taught that there is just one way to do each kind of computation. For example, we may have learned to subtract by borrowing, without realizing that there are many other methods of subtracting numbers.

In Unit 2, students will investigate several methods for adding, subtracting, and multiplying whole numbers and decimals. Students will also take on an Estimation Challenge in Unit 2. For this extended problem, they will measure classmates' strides, and find a median length for all of them. Then they will use the median length to estimate how far it would take to walk to various destinations.

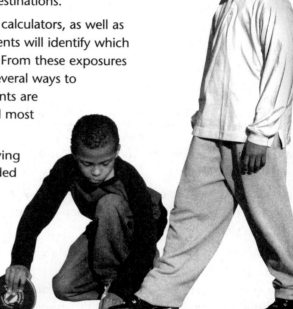

Throughout the year, students will practice using estimation, calculators, as well as mental and paper-and-pencil methods of computation. Students will identify which method is most appropriate for solving a particular problem. From these exposures to a variety of methods, they will learn that there are often several ways to accomplish the same task and achieve the same result. Students are encouraged to solve problems by whatever method they find most comfortable.

Computation is usually not the first step in the problem-solving process. One must first decide what numerical data are needed to solve the problem and which operations need to be performed. In this unit, your child will continue to develop his or her problem-solving skills with a special focus on writing and solving equations for problems.

Please keep this Family Letter for reference as your child works through Unit 2.

Vocabulary

Important terms in Unit 2:

Estimation Challenge A problem for which it is difficult, or even impossible, to find an exact answer. Your child will make his or her best estimate and then defend it.

magnitude estimate A rough estimate. A magnitude estimate tells whether an answer should be in the tens, hundreds, thousands, and so on.

Example: Give a magnitude estimate for 56 * 32

Step 1: Round 56 to 60.

Step 2: Round 32 to 30.

60 * 30 = 1,800, so a magnitude estimate for 56 * 32 is in the thousands.

10s	100s	(1,000s)	10,000s

maximum The largest amount; the greatest number in a set of data.

mean The sum of a set of numbers divided by the number of numbers in the set. The mean is often referred to simply as the average.

median The middle value in a set of data when the data are listed in order from smallest to largest or vice versa. If there is an even number of data points, the median is the *mean* of the two middle values.

minimum The smallest amount; the smallest number in a set of data.

partial-sums addition A method, or algorithm, for adding in which sums are computed for each place (ones, tens, hundreds, and so on) separately and are then added to get a final answer.

```
                        268
                      + 483
1. Add 100s           600
2. Add 10s            140
3. Add 1s           +  11
4. Add partial sums.  751
```

Partial-sums algorithm

place value A number system that values a digit according to its position in a number. In our number system, each place has a value ten times that of the place to its right and one-tenth the value of the place to its left. For example, in the number 456, the 4 is in the hundreds place and has a value of 400.

range The difference between the *maximum* and *minimum* in a set of data.

reaction time The amount of time it takes a person to react to something.

trade-first subtraction A method, or algorithm, for subtracting in which all trades are done before any subtractions are carried out.

Example: 352 − 164

100s	10s	1s		100s	10s	1s
	4	12			14	
3	5̸	2̸		2	4̸	12
− 1	6	4		3̸	5̸	2̸
				− 1	6	4
				1	8	8

Trade 1 ten for 10 ones.

Trade 1 hundred for 10 tens and subtract in each column.

Building Skills through Games

In Unit 2, your child will practice computation skills by playing these games. Detailed instructions are in the *Student Reference Book.*

Addition Top-It See *Student Reference Book,* page 333. This game for 2 to 4 players requires a calculator and 4 each of the number cards 1–10, and provides practice with place–value concepts and methods of addition.

High-Number Toss See *Student Reference Book,* pages 320 and 321. Two players need one six-sided die for this game. *High-Number Toss* helps students review reading, writing, and comparing decimals and large numbers.

Multiplication Bull's-Eye See *Student Reference Book,* page 323. Two players need 4 each of the number cards 0–9, a six-sided die, and a calculator to play this game. *Multiplication Bull's Eye* provides practice in estimating products.

Number Top-It See *Student Reference Book,* page 326. Two to five players need 4 each of the number cards 0–9 and a Place-Value Mat. Students practice making large numbers.

Subtraction Target Practice See *Student Reference Book,* page 331. One or more players need 4 each of the number cards 0–9 and a calculator. In this game, students review subtraction with multidigit whole numbers and decimals.

Do-Anytime Activities

To work with your child on the concepts taught in Units 1 and 2, try these activities:

1. When your child adds or subtracts multidigit numbers, talk about the strategy that works best. Try not to impose the strategy that works best for you! Here are some problems to try:

    467 + 343 = _____   _____ = 761 + 79

    894 − 444 = _____   842 − 59 = _____

2. As you encounter numbers while shopping or on license plates, ask your child to read the numbers and identify digits in various places—thousands place, hundreds place, tens place, ones place, tenths place, and hundredths place.

As You Help Your Child with Homework

As your child brings assignments home, you might want to go over the instructions together, clarifying them as necessary. The answers listed below will guide you through this unit's Study Links.

Study Link 2·1

Answers vary for Problems 1-5.

6. 720 **7.** 90,361 **8.** 12 **9.** 18

Study Link 2·2

Sample answers:

1. 571 and 261 **2.** 30, 20, and 7

3. 19 and 23 **4.** 533 and 125

5. 85.2 and 20.5, or 88.2 and 17.5; Because the sum has a 7 in the tenths place, look for numbers with tenths that add to 7: $85.2 + 20.5 = 105.7$; and $88.2 + 17.5 = 105.7$.

6. 4,572 **7.** 4.4 **8.** 246 **9.** 1.918

10. 47 **11.** 208 **12.** 3 **13.** 8 R2

Study Link 2·3

1. 451 and 299 **2.** 100.9 and 75.3

3. Sample answer: 803 and 5,000

4. 17 and 15 **5.** 703 and 1,500

6. 25 and 9 **7.** 61 **8.** 137 **9.** 5.8

10. 18.85 **11.** 6 **12.** 84,018 **13.** $453.98

14. 98 **15.** 14

Study Link 2·4

1. a. 148 and 127 **b.** Total number of cards

c. $148 + 127 = b$ **d.** $b = 275$

e. 275 baseball cards

2. a. 20.00; 3.89; 1.49 **b.** The amount of change

c. $20.00 - 3.89 - 1.49 = c$, or $20 - (3.89 + 1.49) = c$

d. $c = 14.62$ **e.** $14.62

3. a. 0.6; 1.15; 1.35; and 0.925

b. The length of the ribbons

c. $b = 0.6 + 1.15 + 1.35 + 0.925$

d. $b = 4.025$ **e.** 4.025 meters

Study Link 2·5

Answers vary for Problems 1–5.

6. 5,622 **7.** 29,616 **8.** 518 **9.** 13

Study Link 2·6

1. Unlikely: 30% Very likely: 80%
Very unlikely: 15% Likely: 70%
Extremely unlikely: 5%

2. 30%: Unlikely 5%: Extremely unlikely
99%: Extremely likely 20%: Very unlikely
80%: Very likely 35%: Unlikely
65%: Likely 45%: 50-50 chance

Study Link 2·7

1. 1,000s; $70 * 30 = 2,100$

2. 1,000s; $10 * 700 = 7,000$

3. 10,000s; $100 * 100 = 10,000$

4. 10s; $20 * 2 = 40$

5. 10s; $3 * 4 = 12$

6. Sample answers: $45 * 68 = 3,060$; $684 * 5 = 3,420$; and $864 * 5 = 4,320$

Study Link 2·8

1. 152; 100s; $8 * 20 = 160$

2. 930; 100s; $150 * 6 = 900$

3. 2,146; 1,000s; $40 * 60 = 2,400$

4. 21; 10s; $5 * 4 = 20.$

5. 26.04; 10s; $9 * 3 = 27$

Study Link 2·9

1. 6,862; 1,000s **2.** 88.8; 10s **3.** 33.372; 10s

4. 100,224; 100,000s **5.** 341.61; 100s

6. 9,989 **7.** 5 R2 **8.** 91 **9.** $19.00

Study Link 2·10

1. 390.756 **2.** 3,471.549 **3.** 9,340

4. 244 **5.** 44,604 **6.** 19 R2

STUDY LINK 2·1 | **Estimation**

SRB 247

Class Medians for: Step Length _____ Steps in 1 Minute _____

A group of fifth-grade students in New Zealand are going camping. They will hike from Wellington to Ruapehu. Then they will follow a trail for another $\frac{1}{2}$ mile to their campsite. Use the map on this page (Scale: 1 inch = 400 miles) as well as your class median step length, and number of steps in 1 minute, to make the following estimates. (*Reminder:* 1 mile = 5,280 feet)

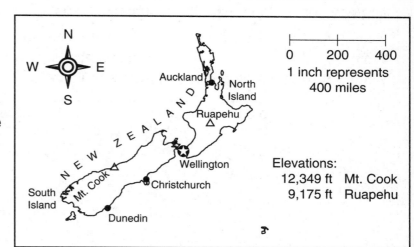

1. About how many miles is it from Wellington to Ruapehu? _____
   (unit)

2. About how many miles is it from Wellington to the campsite? _____
   (unit)

3. About how long would it take the students to arrive at their campsite, if they don't make any stops? _____
   (unit)

4. Each day, the students will hike for 12 hours and take 12 hours for stops to eat, rest, and sleep. If they leave at 7:00 A.M. on a Monday morning, at about what time, and on what day would you expect them to arrive at their campsite?

   Time: About _____ Day: _____

Try This

5. Suppose the students take a bus from Wellington to Mt. Cook and then hike to a campsite at the top of the mountain. Would they have to hike more or less than the distance they hiked to their campsite at Ruapehu?

Practice

6. 48 * 15 = _____

7. 24,029 + 26,840 + 39,492 = _____

8. 36 / 3 = _____

9. 35 − 17 = _____

33

**LESSON
2·1**   **Estimation Strategies**

1. Rosie wants to estimate the number of flowers in this picture. Her estimation strategy has 3 steps. Find the 3 steps in the list of strategies below.

   Write 1 next to the step that you think should be done 1st.
   Write 2 next to the step that you think should be done 2nd.
   Write 3 next to the step that you think should be done 3rd.

_____ Count every flower.

_____ Count the number of flowers in one section.

_____ Make a guess.

_____ Multiply this number by 4.

_____ Ask someone how many flowers are in the picture.

_____ Draw lines to divide the picture into four equal sections.

2. Could you use Rosie's strategy to estimate only
   the number of all-black flowers in the picture? _____

3. Explain why or why not.

_____

_____

_____

_____

_____

LESSON 2·1 Estimating

Work with a partner. Use a sample page from the residential section of a telephone book to estimate the total number of names listed on 10 pages of the telephone book. Develop an estimation strategy by answering the following questions.

1. How might dividing the page into equal portions be useful?

_____

_____

2. What information could you get from the sample page that would let you know how many names are on 10 pages without counting them all?

_____

_____

Record your estimate.

3. About _____ names are on
1 page of the telephone book.

4. About _____ names are on
10 pages of the telephone book.

Work with a partner. Use your sample page from the residential section of a telephone book to estimate the total number of names listed on 10 pages of the telephone book. Develop an estimation strategy by answering the following questions.

1. How might dividing the sample page into four equal sections be useful?

_____

_____

2. What information could you get from the sample page that would let you know how many names are on 10 pages without counting them all?

_____

_____

Record your estimate.

3. About _____ names are on
1 page of the telephone book.

4. About _____ names are on
10 pages of the telephone book.

35

STUDY LINK 2·2

Number Hunt

Reminder: A means *Do not use a calculator.*

Use the numbers in the following table to answer the questions below. You may not use a number more than once.

1. Circle two numbers whose sum is 832.

2. Make an X in the boxes containing three numbers whose sum is 57.

3. Make a check mark in the boxes containing two prime numbers whose sum is 42.

19	85.2	533	571
88.2	525	20	17.5
400	261	20.5	125
7	23	901	30

4. Make a star in the boxes containing two numbers whose sum is 658.

5. Make a triangle in the boxes containing two numbers whose sum is 105.7. Explain how you found the answer.

_____

_____

_____

_____

Solve Problems 6–9 using any method you want. Show your work in the space below.

6. 3,804 + 768 = _____

7. 2.83 + 1.57 = _____

8. 33 + 148 + 65 = _____

9. 1.055 + 0.863 = _____

Practice

10. 73 − 26 = _____

11. 727 − 519 = _____

12. 27 ÷ 9 = _____

13. 4)‾34‾ → _____

LESSON 2·2

Modeling with Base-10 Blocks

Example:

	100s	10s	1s
	2	3	1
+	3	4	5
Add 100s	5	0	0
Add 10s		7	0
Add 1s			6
	5	7	6

100s	10s	1s

500 + 70 + 6

Work with a partner. Choose a problem below. Use the base-10 blocks to model the problem. Have your partner solve the problem and record the answer using the partial-sums method. Compare your model with your partner→s solution. Reverse roles and continue until all problems are solved.

1.   456
     + 53

Add 100s

Add 10s

Add 1s

2.   764
     + 208

Add 100s

Add 10s

Add 1s

3.   271
     + 653

Add 100s

Add 10s

Add 1s

4.   521
     + 455

Add 100s

Add 10s

Add 1s

37

**LESSON
2·2**

Place-Value Strategies

Use your favorite addition algorithm to solve the first problem in each column. Then use the answer to the first problem in each column to help you solve the remaining problems.

1.   3,058
      + 2,182

2.   7,401
      + 2,659

a.   3,058
      + 2,282

a.   7,401
      + 2,679

b.   3,058
      + 2,082

b.   7,401
      + 2,669

c.   3,058
      + 2,582

c.   7,401
      + 2,689

d.   3,058
      + 2,181

d.   7,401
      + 2,699

3. Explain the strategy you used to solve the problem sets above.

_____

_____

_____

_____

_____

STUDY LINK 2·3 | Another Number Hunt

Use the numbers in the following table to answer the questions below.
You may not use a number more than once.

17	15	9	75.03
100.9	803	25	451
1,500	5,000	1	3,096
299	703	75.3	40.03

1. Circle two numbers whose difference is 152.

2. Make an X in the boxes of two numbers whose difference is 25.6.

3. Make a check mark in the boxes of two numbers whose difference is greater than 1,000.

4. Make a star in the boxes of two numbers whose difference is less than 10.

5. Make a triangle in the boxes of two numbers whose difference is equal to the sum of 538 and 259.

6. Use diagonal lines to shade the boxes of two numbers whose difference is equal to 4^2.

Subtract. Show your work for one problem on the grid below.

7. $247 - 186 =$ _____

8. _____ $= 405 - 268$

9. $24.5 - 18.7 =$ _____

10. _____ $= 62.7 - 43.85$

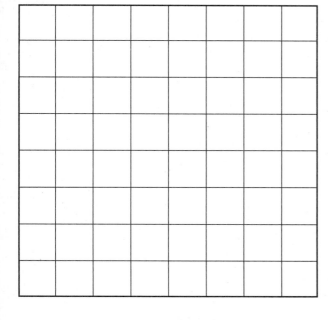

Practice

11. $48 \div 8 =$ _____

12. $81,447 + 2,571 =$ _____

13. $\$451.17 + \$2.81 =$ _____

14. $14 * 7 =$ _____

15. $98 \div 7 =$ _____

LESSON 2·3

Make and Break Apart

Directions

◆ Make 10s by putting your wooden craft sticks or straws into bundles of 10.

◆ Use these bundles to model the subtraction problems.

◆ Then use your models to solve the problems.

Example: 22 − 7

To begin, you need
2 bundles of 10 and
2 ones.

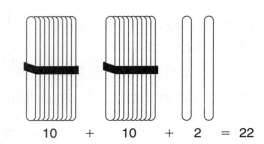

$$10 \ + \ 10 \ + \ 2 \ = \ 22$$

To subtract 7, you need
to break apart one bundle.
Now you have 12 ones.
Remove 7 ones.

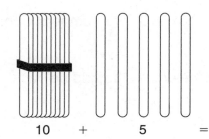 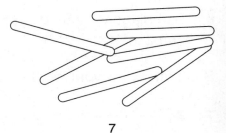

$$10 \ + \ 5 \ = \ 15 \qquad\qquad 7$$

Solution: _____ *15* _____

1. 10 − 4 = _____   **2.** 32 − 6 = _____

3. 71 − 23 = _____   **4.** 22 − 9 = _____

5. 56 − 38 = _____   **6.** 110 − 62 = _____

LESSON 2·4 | **Situation Diagrams**

Total	
Part	**Part**

Total		
Part	**Part**	**Part**

Start	**Change** _____	End

Quantity

Quantity	
	_____
	Difference

_____	**per** _____	_____
		in all

LESSON 2·4 | **Using Open Number Sentences**

Problem 1: At breakfast, the temperature outside was 47°F. By lunchtime, the temperature was 63°F. How many degrees warmer was it by lunchtime?

Open number sentence: _____

Solution: _____   Answer: _____
                                              (unit)

Problem 2: Mary had $32.50 in her savings account. After she withdrew some money, she had $17.25 left. How much money did she withdraw?

Open number sentence: _____

Solution: _____   Answer: _____
                                              (unit)

Problem 3: The school library has 486 fiction books and 321 nonfiction books. How many books does the library have in all?

Open number sentence: _____

Solution: _____   Answer: _____
                                              (unit)

Problem 4: Mrs. Snow is 49 years old. Her son, Kevin, is celebrating his 24th birthday today. Mr. Snow is 6 years older than Mrs. Snow. How old was Mrs. Snow when Kevin was born?

Open number sentence: _____

Solution: _____   Answer: _____
                                              (unit)

STUDY LINK 2·4 Open Sentences and Number Stories

Read each problem. Fill in the blanks and solve the problem.

1. Althea and her brother collect baseball cards. Althea has 148 cards. Her brother has 127 cards. How many cards do they have altogether?

   a. List the numbers needed to solve the problem. _____

   b. Describe what you want to find. _____

   c. Open number sentence: _____

   d. Solution: _____ **e.** Answer: _____
   (unit)

2. Mark bought a hamburger for $3.89 and a drink for $1.49. If he paid with a $20 bill, how much change did he receive?

   a. List the numbers needed to solve the problem. _____

   b. Describe what you want to find. _____

   c. Open number sentence: _____

   _____

   d. Solution: _____ **e.** Answer: _____
   (unit)

3. Fran has four pieces of ribbon. Each piece of ribbon is a different length: 0.6 meters long, 1.15 meters long, 1.35 meters long, and 0.925 meters long. How many meters of ribbon does Fran have in all?

   a. List the numbers needed to solve the problem.

   _____

   b. Describe what you want to find. _____

   c. Open number sentence:

   _____

   d. Solution: _____

   e. Answer: _____
   (unit)

43

LESSON 2·4 **Using Situation Diagrams**

◆ Use the information in each problem to fill in the diagram.

◆ Use a ? to show the missing number.

◆ Write an open number sentence with the information from the diagram.

1. Two angles of a triangle measure 45° and 55°.
What is the sum of the measures of the two angles?

Open number sentence: _____

Total	
Part	**Part**

2. There are 64 tennis balls in a basket. If 35 of them are orange and the rest are green, how many tennis balls are green?

Open number sentence: _____

Total	
Part	**Part**

3. Elvin had $15.00 to spend at the school bazaar. He spent $12.75. How much money did he have left?

Open number sentence:

_____

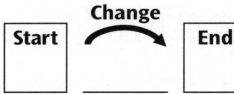

Change

| Start | | End |

4. a. At 7 A.M., the temperature is 76°F. The temperature is expected to drop by 17° by 4 P.M. What will the temperature be at 4 P.M.?

Open number sentence:

_____

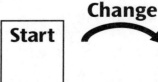

Change

| Start | | End |

b. What would the temperature be at 4 P.M. if the temperature increased by 17°?

Open number sentence:

_____

Change

| Start | | End |

Writing Open Number Sentences

Write an open number sentence and solve the problem.

1. Chan brought his collection of 1,500 sports cards to school. He has 156 basketball cards and 625 football cards. The rest were baseball cards. How many baseball cards did Chan bring?

   a. Open number sentence: _____

   _____

   b. Solution: _____ **c.** Answer: _____

   (unit)

2. Abdul took a bus downtown to see a movie. The bus ride to the theater took 15 minutes. If the movie was $2\frac{1}{4}$ hours long, how many hours and minutes was Abdul away from home?

   a. Open number sentence: _____

   _____

   b. Solution: _____

   c. Answer: _____

   (unit)

3. Julie paid $14.08 to fill her gas tank with 10 gallons of gas before starting a trip from Chicago to Topeka, Kansas. After driving about 305 miles, she bought 10 more gallons of gas in Iowa and paid $11.85. How much more did she pay for a gallon of gas in Chicago than in Iowa?

   a. Open number sentence: _____

   _____

   b. Solution: _____ **c.** Answer: _____

   (unit)

45

Comparing Reaction Times

STUDY LINK
2·5

SRB
114

Use your Grab-It Gauge. Collect reaction-time data from two people at home. At least one of these people should be an adult.

1.

Person 1	
Left	**Right**

2.

Person 2	
Left	**Right**

3. Median times:

Left hand _____

Right hand _____

4. Median times:

Left hand _____

Right hand _____

5. How do the results for the two people compare to your class data?

_____

_____

_____

Practice

6. $2,683 + 2,939 =$ _____

7. $3,702 * 8 =$ _____

8. $604 - 86 =$ _____

9. $39 \div 3 =$ _____

LESSON 2·5 | **Decimal Number-Line Puzzles**

Step 1: Clear your calculator. Look at the number line.

Step 2: Enter the end number, subtract the start number, and divide by the number of jumps between. The result is the interval number.

Step 3: Enter the start number and add the interval number. This is the first missing number. Add the interval again to get the next missing number, and so on.

Example:

End number − start number = difference $6 - 4 = 2$

Difference ÷ hops = interval $2 ÷ 5 = 0.4$

$4 + 0.4 = 4.4;\ 4.4 + 0.4 = 4.8;\ 4.8 + 0.4 = 5.2;\ 5.2 + 0.4 = 5.6;\ 5.6 + 0.4 = 6.0$

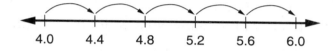

4.0   4.4   4.8   5.2   5.6   6.0

1. Jumps: _____

6   6.8

_____ _____ _____ _____ _____ _____ _____

2. Jumps: _____

1.4   4.2

_____ _____ _____ _____ _____

3. Jumps: _____

4.2 number line

1.34   9.38

_____ _____ _____ _____ _____

Try This

4. Jumps: _____

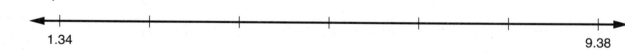

4.568   31.976

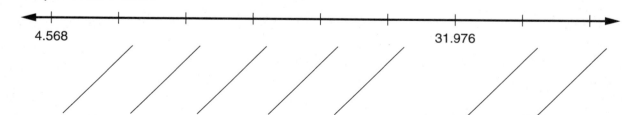

LESSON 2·5 · Interpreting Data

1. Organize the median reaction times for right and left hands for your class by gender—one set of data for girls and one set of data for boys.

Data Landmarks	Girls	Boys
Minimum		
Maximum		
Range		
Mode		
Median		
Mean		

Use the questions below to interpret the data. Write your answers on a separate sheet of paper.

2. **a.** Who has the faster reaction times, boys or girls? _____

   b. Which landmark did you use to decide? _____ **c.** Why?

3. **a.** Suppose you put names in a hat and, without looking, pulled the name of one boy and one girl. How would you use the data from your class to predict who would be faster?

   b. Which landmark would you use to decide? _____ **c.** Why?

4. **a.** What true statements can you make about the data?

   b. How might these statements, called findings, be used by your class?

   c. Could your findings have importance to activities outside of school?

   d. What kind of picture or graph would help people understand your findings?

STUDY LINK 2·6 How Likely Is Rain?

Many years ago, weather reports described the chances of rain with phrases such as *very likely*, *unlikely*, and *extremely unlikely*. Today, the chances of rain are almost always reported as percents. For example, "There is a 50% chance of rain tonight."

1. Use the Probability Meter Poster to translate phrases into percents.

Phrase	Percent
Unlikely	30%
Very likely	
Very unlikely	
Likely	
Extremely unlikely	

2. Use the Probability Meter Poster to translate percents into phrases.

Percent	Phrase
30%	*Unlikely*
5%	
99%	
20%	
80%	
35%	
65%	
45%	

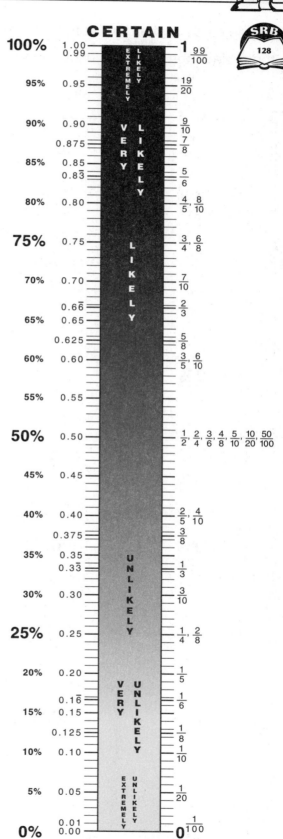

CERTAIN

100%	1.00 / 0.99	EXTREMELY LIKELY	1 99/100
95%	0.95		19/20
90%	0.90	VERY LIKELY	9/10
	0.875		7/8
85%	0.85		5/6
	0.83̄		
80%	0.80		4/5 8/10
75%	0.75	LIKELY	3/4 6/8
70%	0.70		7/10
	0.66̄		2/3
65%	0.65		
	0.625		5/8
60%	0.60		3/5 6/10
55%	0.55		
50%	0.50		1/2, 2/4, 3/6, 4/8, 5/10, 10/20, 50/100
45%	0.45		
40%	0.40		2/5 4/10
	0.375		3/8
35%	0.35 / 0.33̄	UNLIKELY	1/3
30%	0.30		3/10
25%	0.25		1/4, 2/8
20%	0.20		1/5
	0.16̄	VERY UNLIKELY	1/6
15%	0.15		
	0.125		1/8
10%	0.10		1/10
5%	0.05	EXTREMELY UNLIKELY	1/20
0%	0.01 / 0.00		0 1/100

IMPOSSIBLE

SRB 128

49

LESSON 2·6 Order Fractions, Decimals, Percents

Cut out the cards and order them from smallest to largest.

Use the table in the front of the journal to help you.

✂

$\frac{1}{2}$	$33\frac{1}{3}\%$	0.25	$\frac{3}{4}$
20%	0.60	$\frac{4}{5}$	0.10
30%	0.70	$\frac{9}{10}$	$12\frac{1}{2}\%$
0.625	$87\frac{1}{2}\%$	$\frac{2}{3}$	$16\frac{2}{3}\%$

LESSON 2·6

Making Spinners

Choosing a Pants Color

There is a 30% chance of choosing blue pants.

There is a $\frac{1}{4}$ chance of choosing black pants.

There is a 0.1 chance of choosing white pants.

There is twice the probability of choosing red pants as there is of choosing white pants.

There is a 15 out of 100 chance of choosing brown pants.

Choosing a Favorite Color

28% of the people said red was their favorite color.

$\frac{1}{3}$ of the people reported that blue was their favorite color.

One-half as many people favored white as favored blue.

0.1 of the people chose brown as their favorite color.

3 out of 25 people named black as their favorite color.

Drawing Colored Chips from a Bag

There is a 1 out of 5 chance of drawing a white chip.

There is a 20% chance of drawing a blue chip.

The probability of drawing black is 0.3.

The chance of drawing a red chip is 15%.

A brown chip is as likely to be drawn as a red chip.

Choosing a Car Color

7 out of 70 people chose white.

25% of the people chose black.

0.15 of the people chose red.

$\frac{4}{12}$ of the people chose blue.

$\frac{1}{6}$ of the people chose brown.

Choosing a Notebook Color

3 out of 20 people favored brown.

20% of the people favored blue.

$\frac{1}{4}$ of the people favored black.

0.3 of the people favored red.

Half as many people favored white as favored blue.

Choosing a Sock Color

1 out of 8 socks sold are red.

$\frac{5}{25}$ of the socks sold are blue.

$37\frac{1}{2}$% of the socks sold are black.

0.2 of the socks sold are white.

Half as many brown socks are sold as white socks.

LESSON 2·6

Making Spinners *continued*

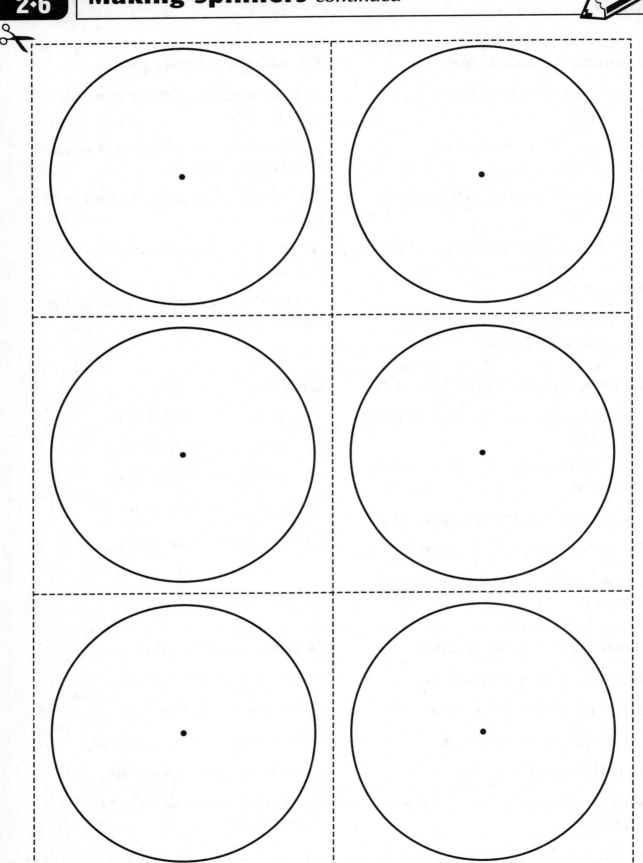

STUDY LINK 2·7 | Magnitude Estimates

A **magnitude estimate** is a very rough estimate. It tells whether the exact answer falls in the tenths, ones, tens, hundreds, thousands, and so on. For each problem, make a magnitude estimate. Ask yourself: *Is the answer in the tenths, ones, tens, hundreds, thousands, or ten-thousands?* Circle the appropriate box. Do not solve the problems.

SRB
250

Example: 18 * 21

| 10s | (100s) | 1,000s | 10,000s |

$$20 * 20 = 400$$

How I estimated

1. 73 * 28

| 10s | 100s | 1,000s | 10,000s |

_____

How I estimated

2. 12 * 708

| 10s | 100s | 1,000s | 10,000s |

_____

How I estimated

3. 98 * 105

| 10s | 100s | 1,000s | 10,000s |

_____

How I estimated

4. 17 * 2.2

| 10s | 100s | 1,000s | 10,000s |

_____

How I estimated

5. 2.6 * 3.9

| 0.1s | 1s | 10s | 100s |

_____

How I estimated

Try This

6. Use the digits 4, 5, 6, and 8. Make as many factor pairs as you can that have a product between 3,000 and 5,000. Use a calculator to solve the problems.

_____

_____

LESSON 2·7 Extended Facts

Directions

◆ Shuffle the deck and draw two cards.

◆ Record and multiply the numbers shown on the cards.

◆ Then use your solution to write extended facts.

Example:

$5 * 7 = 35$

$35 * 10 = 350$

$35 * 100 = 3,500$

$35 * 1,000 = 35,000$

1. _____ * _____ = _____

_____ * 10 = _____

_____ * 100 = _____

_____ * 1000 = _____

2. _____ * _____ = _____

_____ * 10 = _____

_____ * 100 = _____

_____ * 1000 = _____

3. _____ * _____ = _____

_____ * 10 = _____

_____ * 100 = _____

_____ * 1000 = _____

4. Explain how you use multiplication facts to help you solve problems with larger numbers.

_____

_____

_____

_____

STUDY LINK 2·8 Estimating and Multiplying

◆ For each problem, make a magnitude estimate.

◆ Circle the appropriate box. Do not solve the problem.

◆ Then choose 3 problems to solve. Show your work on the grid.

1. 8 * 19 _____

| 10s | 100s | 1,000s | 10,000s |

_____

How I estimated

2. 155 * 6 _____

| 10s | 100s | 1,000s | 10,000s |

_____

How I estimated

3. 37 * 58 _____

| 10s | 100s | 1,000s | 10,000s |

_____

How I estimated

4. 5 * 4.2 _____

| 10s | 100s | 1,000s | 10,000s |

_____

How I estimated

5. 9.3 * 2.8 _____

| 10s | 100s | 1,000s | 10,000s |

_____

How I estimated

LESSON 2·8

Model the Partial-Products Method

Materials ☐ array grid (*Math Masters,* pp. 416 and 417)

☐ base-10 blocks

Directions

◆ Draw a line around rows and columns on the grid to model each problem.

◆ Cover the array you made using as few base-10 blocks as possible.

◆ Solve using the partial-products method.

◆ Then match each part of the array with a partial product.

◆ Record the solution, filling in the sentences to match the blocks you used.

1. 6 * 23 = _____

In each of 6 rows there are…	_____ longs, so there are _____ cubes.	Write the problem showing the partial products.
	_____ cubes, so there are _____ cubes.	_____
	There are _____ cubes in all.	

2. 26 * 18 = _____

In each of 20 rows there are…	_____ longs, so there are _____ cubes.	Write the problem showing the partial products.
	_____ cubes, so there are _____ cubes.	_____
In each of 6 rows there are…	_____ longs, so there are _____ cubes.	_____
	_____ cubes, so there are _____ cubes.	
	There are _____ cubes in all.	

LESSON 2·8 A Mental Calculation Strategy

When you multiply a number that ends in 9, you can simplify the calculation by changing it into an easier problem. Then adjust the result.

Example 1:   2 * 99 = ?

◆ Change 2 * 99 into 2 * 100.

◆ Find the answer: 2 * 100 = 200

◆ Ask: *How is the answer to 2 * 100 different from the answer to 2 * 99?*
100 is 1 more than 99, and you multiplied by 2.
So 200 is 2 more than the answer to 2 * 99.

◆ Adjust the answer to 2 * 100 to find the answer to 2 * 99:
200 − 2 = 198. So 2 * 99 = 198.

Example 2:   3 * 149 = ?

◆ Change 3 * 149 into 3 * 150.

◆ Find the answer: 3 * 150 = (3 * 100) + (3 * 50) = 450.

◆ Ask: *How is the answer to 3 * 150 different from the answer to 3 * 149?*
150 is 1 more than 149, and you multiplied by 3.
So 450 is 3 more than the answer to 3 * 149.

◆ Adjust: 450 − 3 = 447. So 3 * 149 = 447.

Use this strategy to calculate these products mentally.

1. 5 * 49 _____

2. 5 * 99 _____

3. 8 * 99 _____

4. 4 * 199 _____

5. 2 * 119 _____

6. 3 * 98 _____

Name   Date   Time

LESSON 2·9   Lattice Multiplication Table

	9	8	7	6	5	4	3	2	1	0	
	0/0	0/0	0/0	0/0	0/0	0/0	0/0	0/0	0/0	0/0	0
	0/9	0/8	0/7	0/6	0/5	0/4	0/3	0/2	0/1	0/0	1
	1/8	1/6	1/4	1/2	1/0	0/8	0/6	0/4	0/2	0/0	2
	2/7	2/4	2/1	1/8	1/5	1/2	0/9	0/6	0/3	0/0	3
	3/6	3/2	2/8	2/4	2/0	1/6	1/2	0/8	0/4	0/0	4
	4/5	4/0	3/5	3/0	2/5	2/0	1/5	1/0	0/5	0/0	5
	5/4	4/8	4/2	3/6	3/0	2/4	1/8	1/2	0/6	0/0	6
	6/3	5/6	4/9	4/2	3/5	2/8	2/1	1/4	0/7	0/0	7
	7/2	6/4	5/6	4/8	4/0	3/2	2/4	1/6	0/8	0/0	8
	8/1	7/2	6/3	5/4	4/5	3/6	2/7	1/8	0/9	0/0	9

Multiply with the Lattice Method

For each problem:

◆ Make a magnitude estimate. Circle the appropriate box.

◆ Solve using the lattice method. Show your work in the grids.

1. 94 * 73 = _____

| 10s | 100s | 1,000s | 10,000s |

2. 24 * 3.7 = _____

| 0.1s | 1s | 10s | 100s |

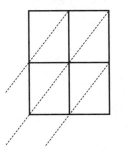

3. 5.4 * 6.18 = _____

| 0.1s | 1s | 10s | 100s |

4. 384 * 261 = _____

| 100s | 1,000s | 10,000s | 100,000s |

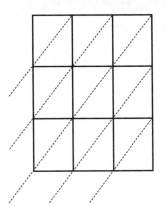

5. 17.7 * 19.3 = _____

| 0.1s | 1s | 10s | 100s |

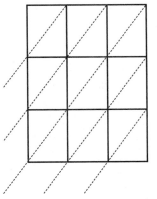

Practice

6. 7,402 + 2,587 = _____

7. 37 ÷ 7 → _____

8. 328 − 237 = _____

9. $15.75 + $3.25 = _____

An Ancient Multiplication Method

LESSON 2·9

Over 4,000 years ago, the Egyptians developed one of the earliest multiplication methods. This method, with some modifications, was then used by the ancient Greeks, and in the Middle Ages, by people living in other parts of Europe.

Study the examples of the Egyptian method below. Each problem has been solved by this method of multiplication. Try to figure out how the method works.

13 * 25 = _325_	**18 * 17 =** _306_	**26 * 31 =** _806_
✔ 1 25 (1 * 25)	~~1~~ ~~17~~	~~1~~ ~~31~~
~~2~~ ~~50~~ ~~(2 * 25)~~	✔ 2 34	✔ 2 62
✔ 4 100 (4 * 25)	4 68	~~4~~ ~~124~~
✔ 8 200 (8 * 25)	8 136	✔ 8 248
325 (13 * 25)	✔ 16 272	✔ 16 496
	306	806

Make up a multiplication problem. Solve it using the Egyptian method. Then explain how the method works, using your problem as an example.

_____

_____

_____

_____

_____

_____

_____

_____

Place-Value Puzzles

Millions			Thousands			Ones		
Hundred-millions	Ten-millions	Millions	Hundred-thousands	Ten-thousands	Thousands	Hundreds	Tens	Ones

Use the clues to solve the puzzles.

Puzzle 1

◆ The value of the digit in the **thousandths** place is equal to the sum of the measures of the angles in a triangle (180°) divided by 30.

◆ If you multiply the digit in the **tens** place by 1,000; the answer will be 9,000.

◆ Double 35. Divide the result by 10. Write the answer in the **tenths** place.

◆ The **hundreds**-place digit is $\frac{1}{2}$ the value of the digit in the thousandths place.

◆ When you multiply the digit in the **ones** place by itself, the answer is 0.

◆ Write a digit in the **hundredths** place so that the sum of all six digits in this number is 30.

What is the number? _____ _____ _____ . _____ _____ _____

Puzzle 2

◆ Double 12. Divide the result by 8. Write the answer in the **thousands** place.

◆ If you multiply the digit in the **hundredths** place by 10, your answer will be 40.

◆ The **tens**-place digit is a prime number. If you multiply it by itself, the answer is 49.

◆ Multiply 7 and 3. Subtract 12. Write the answer in the **thousandths** place.

◆ Multiply the digit in the hundredths place by the digit in the thousands place. Subtract 7 from the result. Write the digit in the **tenths** place.

◆ The digit in the **ones** place is an odd digit that has not been used yet.

◆ The value of the digit in the **hundreds** place is the same as the number of sides of a quadrilateral.

What is the number? _____ _____ _____ _____ . _____ _____ _____

Check: The sum of the answers to both puzzles is 3,862.305.

Practice

3. 7,772 + 1,568 = _____

4. 472 − 228 = _____

5. 826 * 54 = _____

6. 59 / 3 → _____

61

LESSON 2·10 **Number Stories and Estimation**

◆ Read each number story carefully.
◆ Write an open number sentence to use in estimating.
◆ Answer the question.

Example:

It is said that the Aztec king, Montezuma, drank about 50 cups of chocolate per day. Did he drink *more* or *less* than 10 gallons of chocolate in a week? (Hint: 16 cups = 1 gallon)

Open number sentence: $10 * 16 = $ Number of cups in 10 gallons

Answer: *more*

1. Certain varieties of seahorses can move 10.5 inches per minute. At this rate, could these seahorses be able to travel 6 yards in 1 hour?

   a. Open number sentence:

   _____

   b. Answer: _____

2. Orville Wright completed the first airplane flight on December 17, 1903. He traveled 120 feet in 12 seconds. If he had been able to stay in the air for a full minute, would he have traveled 1 mile? (Hint: 1 mile = 5,280 feet)

   a. Open number sentence:

   _____

   b. Answer: _____

3. In 1960, the Triton became the first submarine to circumnavigate the world. It covered 36,014 miles in 76 days. Is that more or less than 100 miles per day?

   a. Open number sentence:

   _____

   b. Answer: _____

Source: *The Kids' World Almanac of Records and Facts*

**STUDY LINK
2·11**

Unit 3: Family Letter

Geometry Explorations and the American Tour

In Unit 3, your child will set out on the American Tour, a yearlong series of mathematical activities examining historical, demographic, and environmental features of the United States. The American Tour activities will develop your child's ability to read, interpret, critically examine, and use mathematical information presented in text, tables, and graphics. These math skills are vital in our technological age.

Many American Tour activities rely on materials in the American Tour section of the *Student Reference Book.* This section—part historical atlas and part almanac—contains maps, data, and other information from a wide range of sources: the U.S. Census Bureau, the National Weather Service, and the National Geographic Society.

Unit 3 also will review some geometry concepts from earlier grades while introducing and expanding on others. In *Fourth Grade Everyday Mathematics,* students used a compass to construct basic shapes and create geometric designs. In this unit, your child will extend these skills and explore concepts of congruent figures (same size, same shape), using a compass and straightedge. In addition, students will use another tool, the Geometry Template. It contains protractors and rulers for measuring, as well as cutouts for drawing a variety of geometric figures.

Finally, students will explore the mathematics and art of tessellations—patterns of shapes that cover a surface without gaps or overlaps. They will use math tools to create their own designs.

You can help your child by asking questions about information presented in newspaper and magazine tables and graphics. Also, the world is filled with many 2-dimensional and 3-dimensional geometric forms: angles, line segments, curves, cubes, cylinders, spheres, pyramids, and so on. Many wonderful geometric patterns can be seen in nature as well as in the things that people create. It will be helpful for you and your child to look for and talk about geometric shapes throughout the year.

Please keep this Family Letter for reference as your child works through Unit 3.

Vocabulary

Important terms in Unit 3:

acute angle An angle with a measure greater than 0 degrees and less than 90 degrees.

Acute angle

adjacent angles Two angles with a common side and vertex that do not otherwise overlap. In the diagram, angles 1 and 2 are adjacent angles. Angles 2 and 3, angles 3 and 4, and angles 4 and 1 are also adjacent.

Adjacent angles

congruent Having exactly the same shape and size.

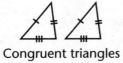
Congruent triangles

diameter A line segment that passes through the center of a circle (or sphere) and has endpoints on the circle (or sphere); also, the length of this line segment. The diameter of a circle or sphere is twice the length of its radius.

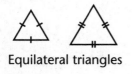

equilateral triangle A triangle with all three sides the same length. In an equilateral triangle, all three angles have the same measure.

Equilateral triangles

obtuse angle An angle with a measure greater than 90 degrees and less than 180 degrees.

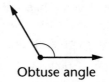
Obtuse angle

radius A line segment from the center of a circle (or sphere) to any point on the circle (or sphere); also, the length of this line segment.

right angle An angle with a measure of 90 degrees.

Right angle

tessellation An arrangement of shapes that covers a surface completely without overlaps or gaps. Also called *tiling*.

A tessellation

vertical (opposite) angles The angles made by intersecting lines that do not share a common side. Vertical angles have equal measures. In the diagram, angles 2 and 4 are a pair of vertical angles. Angles 1 and 3 are another pair of vertical angles.

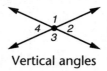
Vertical angles

Building Skills through Games

In Unit 3, your child will practice geometry and computation skills by playing the following games. For detailed instructions, see the *Student Reference Book.*

Angle Tangle See *Student Reference Book,* page 296
Two players will need a protractor and a straightedge to play this game. Playing *Angle Tangle* gives students practice in drawing and measuring angles.

High-Number Toss: Decimal Version See *Student Reference Book,* page 321
This game practices concepts of place value and standard notation. It requires 2 players and number cards 0–9 (4 of each).

Multiplication Top-It See *Student Reference Book,* page 334
This game practices the basic multiplication facts. It requires a deck of cards with 4 each of the numbers 1–10, and can be played by 2–4 players.

Polygon Capture See *Student Reference Book,* page 328
This game uses 16 polygons and 16 Property Cards, and is played by partners or 2 teams each with 2 players. *Polygon Capture* practices identifying properties of polygons related to sides and angles.

Do-Anytime Activities

To work with your child on the concepts taught in this unit and in previous units, try these interesting and rewarding activities:

1. Together, read the book *A Cloak for the Dreamer* by Marilyn Burns.

2. When you are at home or at a store, ask your child to identify different types of polygons such as triangles, squares, pentagons, and hexagons.

3. Visit the Web site for the U.S. Bureau of the Census at http://www.census.gov/. Have your child write three interesting pieces of information that he or she learned from the Web site.

4. Look for examples of bar graphs in newspapers or magazines. Ask your child to explain the information shown by a graph.

As You Help Your Child with Homework

As your child brings assignments home, you may want to go over the instructions together, clarifying them as necessary. The answers listed below will guide you through this unit→s Study Links.

Study Link 3·1

1. Illinois

2. 851,000; 4,822,000; 8,712,000; 12,051,000

3. 3,971,000   4. 3,890,000   5. 3,339,000

6. The population increases by about 4,000,000 every fifty years.

7. About 16,000,000   8. About 14,000,000

Study Link 3·2

1. A   2. 5,472,000   3. H

4. a. About 250,000,000   b. About 55%

Study Link 3·3

1. 60°; 90°; 60°   2. 120°; 60°; 60°

3. 90°; 135°; 135°   4. 30°; 75°

Study Link 3·4

1. 70°   2. 50°   3. 110°   4. 130°

5. 60°   6. 180°   7. 120°   8. 90°

9. 50°   10. 150°   11. 170°

Study Link 3·5

1. acute; 12°   2. acute; 65°   3. obtuse; 103°

4. Sample answer: Angle *D* and angle *E*

5. Sample answer: Angle *D* and angle *F*

6. Sample answer: Angle *G* and angle *H*

9. 14,670   11. 11R1

Study Link 3·6

1. scalene   2. isosceles   3. isosceles; right

4. equilateral; isosceles

5. Objects and types of angles vary.

6. 11,761   7. 5,750   8. 42,405   9. 11

Study Link 3·7

Sample answers are given for Problems 1–5.

1. The pentagon is the only shape that is not regular.

2. The oval is the only shape that is curved.

3. The crossed-out shape is the only shape that is not convex.

4. The trapezoid is the only shape without two pairs of parallel sides.

Study Link 3·8

1.–3. Samples of tessellations vary.

Study Link 3·9

1. Sample answer: Draw a line between two of the vertices to create two triangles. Since the sum of the angles in each triangle is 180°, the sum of the angles in a quadrangle is 360°.

2. 360°

3. a.–b.   c.–d.

Study Link 3·10

1. Sample answers are given.

a.   b.

c.   d.

2.

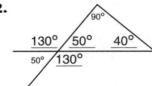

3. a. 2   b. 70°   c. 360°   d. trapezoid

LESSON 2·7 | **Using Multiplication Patterns**

Find information about **Powers of 10** on page 5 of your *Student Reference Book.* Study the example below. Then try to use the same strategy to solve Problems 1 and 2.

20 * 300 = (2 * 10) * (3 * 100)	Write each factor in expanded form.
= 2 * 10 * 3 * 100	Remove the parentheses.
= 2 * 3 * 10 * 100	Use the Commutative Property so that the powers of 10 are together.
= (2 * 3) * (10 * 100)	Multiply the basic fact, and multiply the powers of 10.
= 6 * 1,000	Multiply the partial products.
= 6,000	

Solve the problems. Show your work.

1. 900 * 70 = _____   **2.** 500 * 6,000 = _____

3. Explain why you think counting zeros works in solving multiplication problems involving powers of 10.

_____

_____

_____

_____

4. Use what you know about counting zeros in multiplication to help you figure out the missing numbers below.

4,200 * _____ = 840,000

_____ * 40 = 2,000,000

250 * _____ = 50,000,000

5. On the back of this page, write two problems of your own that can be solved by counting zeros.

Using Place Value to Compare Powers of 10

1 meter	10 decimeters	100 centimeters	1,000 millimete
1 centimeter	0.01 meter	0.1 decimeter	10 millimeters

Use the information in the conversion table to respond to each statement below. Complete each statement with one of the following phrases:

10 times, 100 times, $\frac{1}{10}$ of, $\frac{1}{100}$ of

1. 1 meter is _____ the size of a decimeter.

2. 1 centimeter is _____ the size of a meter.

3. 1 centimeter is _____ the size of a millimeter.

4. 1 decimeter is _____ the size of a meter.

5. 1 millimeter is _____ the size of a decimeter.

Write two of your own statements using the information in the table.

6. _____

_____

7. _____

_____

Complete the table below by making the appropriate conversions.

	millimeters	centimeters	decimeters	meters
8.	9,743			
9.				3
10.		175		

11. In Problem 10, explain what happens to the value of the digit 5 when you go from millimeters to centimeters, and then from decimeters to meters.

_____

_____

_____

_____

LESSON 3·1 | U.S. Census Questions

Here are some of the questions from both the short and long forms of the U.S. Census. Answer the questions *for yourself.* Mark and fill in the boxes with your answers. Then put this sheet in the collection box.

1. What is this person's sex?
Mark one box.

☐ Male ☐ Female

2. a. What is this person's date of birth?
Print numbers in boxes.

Month   Day
☐☐   ☐☐

Year of birth
☐☐☐☐

b. What was this person's age on April 1 of this year?

☐☐☐

3. Where was this person born?

☐ In the United States—*Print name of state.*

☐☐☐☐☐☐☐☐☐☐☐☐

☐ Outside the United States— *Print name of foreign country, or Puerto Rico, Guam, etc.*

☐☐☐☐☐☐☐☐☐☐☐☐

4. a. Does this person speak a language other than English at home?

☐ Yes ☐ No → *Skip to 5.*

b. What is this language?

☐☐☐☐☐☐☐☐☐☐☐☐☐☐

(For example: Korean, Italian, Spanish, Vietnamese)

5. Is there telephone service available in this house, apartment, or mobile home from which you can both make and receive calls?

☐ Yes ☐ No

67

STUDY LINK 3·1 ## Population Data

State	1850	1900	1950	2000
Ohio	1,980,000	4,158,000	7,947,000	11,319,000
Indiana	988,000	2,516,000	3,934,000	6,045,000
Illinois	851,000	4,822,000	8,712,000	12,051,000
Michigan	398,000	2,421,000	6,372,000	9,679,000
Wisconsin	305,000	2,069,000	3,435,000	5,326,000
Minnesota	6,000	1,751,000	2,982,000	4,830,000
Iowa	192,000	2,232,000	2,621,000	2,900,000
Missouri	682,000	3,107,000	3,955,000	5,540,000

1. Which state had the largest population growth from 1850 to 2000? _____

2. Record the population figures for this state below the timeline.

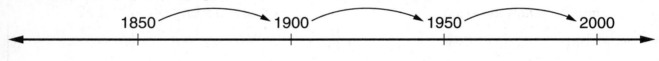

1850   1900   1950   2000

_____   _____   _____   _____

Find the increases for this state for each of the following time spans:

3. 1850–1900 _____   **4.** 1900–1950 _____

5. 1950–2000 _____

6. Are these increases similar or different? Explain.

_____

_____

Estimate the state's population:

7. In 2050 _____   **8.** In 2025 _____

| **Practice** | |

9.   69,452
    + 15,679

10.   178
    − 139

11.   43
    * 14

12. 58 ÷ 7 → _____

LESSON 3·1 Reading for Information

1. Turn to page 361 in your *Student Reference Book.*

   What is the title of this page?

   _____

   _____

2. Take a minute to look at this page. Based on the title, the tables, and the
   graphs, describe the information you expect to find on this page.

   _____

   _____

   _____

3. Look at the tables and graphs on the page. Which table or graph would you
   use to find the mean number of days in school per student, by region?

   _____

   Explain why.

   _____

   _____

4. Look at the tables and graphs on the page. What graph would you use to find
   the median days in school for all states?

   _____

5. Write three questions that you could answer by reading this page, or by using the
   tables and charts on this page.

   _____

   _____

   _____

   _____

LESSON 3·1 Education and Earnings

The table below contains information from surveys by the U.S. Census Bureau. The information describes householders who were at least 25 years old. A *householder* is the person in whose name a home is owned or rented. If a house is owned jointly by a husband and wife, the householder could be either the husband or the wife.

Education and Earnings

Years of School Completed	1980			1990		
	Number of House-holders (thousands)	Percent of House-holders	Median Income	Number of House-holders (thousands)	Percent of House-holders	Median Income
Elementary (less than 9 years)	14,012	18%	$8,875	10,146	11%	$13,523
High School (1–3 years)	10,547	14%	$13,213	10,007	11%	$18,191
High School (4 years)	25,454	34%	$19,638	32,043	36%	$28,744
College (1–3 years)	11,480	15%	$21,740	16,451	19%	$35,724
College (4 years)	7,862	10%	$27,339	11,443	13%	$47,083
College (5 or more years)	6,661	9%	$30,684	9,269	10%	$54,636
Total	76,016	100%	$18,383	89,359	100%	$30,757

Source: *March Current Population Survey,* prepared by Income Statistics Branch/HHES Division U.S. Bureau of the Census

LESSON 3·1 | **Education and Earnings** *continued*

Use the Education and Earnings table to answer the following questions.

1. Describe the relationship between number of years of education and income.

_____

_____

2. Compare the number of householders who did not graduate from high school in 1980 with the number in 1990. Describe any changes that occurred.

_____

_____

_____

_____

3. What would you expect to be the number of householders who do not graduate from high school in 2010?

_____

_____

_____

4. How does the number of householders who did not graduate from high school in 1990 compare to the number of householders who graduated from college?

_____

_____

_____

_____

An Unofficial Census

In 1991, author Tom Heymann took an unofficial U.S. census. The table shows how many people believed various common sayings, based on the sample of the population that he surveyed.

	Saying	Number Who Believe Saying Is True
A	Look before you leap.	175,104,000
B	The grass is always greener on the other side of the fence.	69,312,000
C	Haste makes waste.	153,216,000
D	Beauty is only skin deep.	149,568,000
E	Don't cry over spilled milk.	160,512,000
F	The early bird catches the worm.	136,800,000
G	A penny saved is a penny earned.	155,040,000
H	Don't count your chickens before they hatch.	169,632,000

Source: *The Unofficial U.S. Census,* by Tom Heymann. Ballantine Books, 1991

1. Which saying had the largest number of believers? _____

2. How many more people believed saying E than saying G? _____

3. Which saying had about 100 million more believers than saying B? _____

4. **a.** About $\frac{7}{10}$ of the U.S. population in 1991 believed saying A to be true. What was the total population? _____

   b. About what percent of the total population believed saying F to be true? _____

Practice

5.   256
   − 148

6.   26,551
   + 2,558

7.   36
   * 27

8. 54 ÷ 3 = _____

9. 74 ÷ 8 → _____

72

LESSON 3·2

Solving Place-Value Puzzles

Hundred (100) Billions	Ten (10) Billions	One (1) Billions	Hundred (100) Millions	Ten (10) Millions	One (1) Millions	Hundred (100) Thousands	Ten (10) Thousands	One (1) Thousands	Hundred (100) Units	Ten (10) Units	One (1) Units
BILLIONS			MILLIONS			THOUSANDS			UNITS		
4	2	3	9	8	5	1	0	3	2	6	7

1. Color each section label with a different color.

2. For each puzzle below:

♦ Read the clues to write the digits in the chart.

♦ Write each number in **number-and-word notation** and **standard notation.**

Puzzle 1

♦ Write 4s in the 100-billions and 100-millions place.

♦ Write 5s in the 100s place and 100-thousands place.

♦ Write 6 in the 1-millions place and half of 6 in the 10-millions place.

♦ Write 0s where you need them to complete the number.

Number-and-word notation:

_____

Standard notation:

_____

Puzzle 2

♦ Write 3 in the 10-thousands place and double it in the 10-millions place.

♦ Write 8 in the 100-millions place and half of 8 in the 10s place.

♦ Write 9 in the 1-thousands place.

♦ Write 2s where you need them to complete the number.

Number-and-word notation:

_____

Standard notation:

_____

LESSON 3·2 **Interpreting Patterns from Data**

Use the map on page 349 of the *Student Reference Book*.

1. Choose a region and record the region name. _____

The dates for exploration, settlement, and statehood can be thought of as three data sets. Identify and record the minimum, maximum, median, and range for each data set.

2.

Region: _____		Data Set: Exploration Dates	
Data:			
Minimum		Median	
Maximum		Range	

3.

Region: _____		Data Set: Settlement Dates	
Data:			
Minimum		Median	
Maximum		Range	

4.

Region: _____		Data Set: Statehood Dates	
Data:			
Minimum		Median	
Maximum		Range	

On the back of this page, use the information represented by the landmarks to write one true statement about each data set.

Finding Angle Measures

Figure out the angle measures for the labeled angles in the patterns below. Remember that there are 360° in a circle and 180° in a straight line. Use the Geometry Template, or cut out the shapes at the bottom of this page to help you. Do not use a protractor.

1.

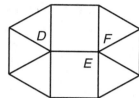

m∠D = _____

m∠E = _____

m∠F = _____

2.

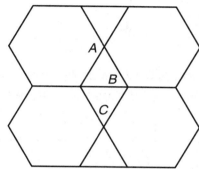

m∠A = _____

m∠B = _____

m∠C = _____

3.

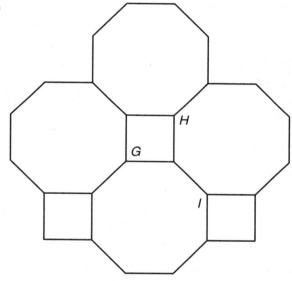

m∠G = _____

m∠H = _____

m∠I = _____

4.

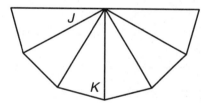

m∠J = _____

m∠K = _____

5. On the back of this page, explain how you found the measure of ∠I.

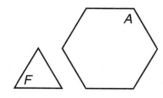

LESSON 3·3

Segments, Lengths, and Collinear Points

141

In geometry, there are conventions used to name a figure and to name the measure of that figure. For example, ∠N names an angle with the vertex N, while the notation m ∠N represents the measure of that angle. For line segments, the notation NM names the line segment with the endpoints N and M, and the notation NM represents the length of that line segment.

M •——• N

The notation NM = 4 inches means *line segment $\overline{NM}$ is 4 inches long.*
Use the points and measures shown on the line below to answer Problems 1 and 2.

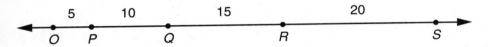

```
          5      10         15          20
◄———————•———•———————•——————————•—————————•———————►
        O   P       Q          R         S
```

1. Which of the following statements show the correct use of these naming conventions for line segments and the measures of line segments? Circle your answer.

   a. $PQ + QR + RS = PS$

   b. $\overline{OP} + \overline{PQ} = OQ$

   c. $OP * 2 = \overline{PQ}$

   d. $\overline{OP} + \overline{QR} + \overline{RS} = 35$

2. For each statement with errors, write the corrections.

   _____

   _____

3. Points that lie on the same line are called **collinear points.** The points H, S, D, K, L, and B are collinear. Use the following information to locate them on the line and label the points accordingly.

   $KS + SB = KB$

   $DH + HS = DS$

   $DH + HK = DK$

   Points L and B are not between any other labeled points on the line.

```
◄———————•———————————•—————————————•———————————•———————————•———————————•————————►
    ___         ___           ___         ___         ___         ___
```

LESSON 3·3   **Measuring the Parts**

Use the figure at the right to help you think about the total number of degrees in a circle.

Then use what you know about angles and the total number of degrees in a circle to answer the following questions.

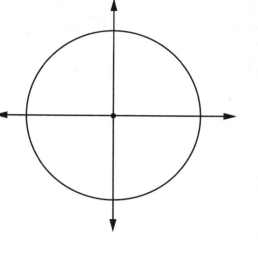

1. How many degrees are in a circle? _____

2. What is the degree measure for each of the 4 angles in the circle above? _____

3. If a circle is divided into 8 equal parts, what is the degree measure for each of the 8 angles formed? _____

4. If a circle is divided into 12 equal parts, what is the degree measure for each of the 12 angles formed? _____

5. If a circle is divided into 6 equal parts, what is the degree measure of each of the 6 angles formed? _____

6. If a circle is divided into equal parts so that the angles have a degree measure of 120°, how many angles would be formed? _____

7. If a circle is divided into 360 equal parts, what is the degree measure of each of the 360 angles? _____

LESSON 3·4 — Measuring and Drawing Angles

Sarah used her half-circle protractor to measure the angle at the right. She said it measures about 35°. Theresa measured it with her half-circle protractor. Theresa said it measures about 145°. Devon measured it with his full-circle protractor. Devon said it measures about 325°.

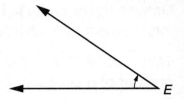

3. a. Use both your template protractors to measure the angle. Do you agree with Sarah, Theresa, or Devon?

_____

   b. Why? _____

_____

Use your half-circle protractor. Measure each angle as accurately as you can.

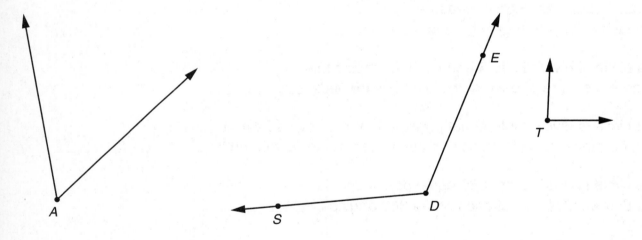

4. a. m∠A is about _____. **b.** m∠EDS is about _____. **c.** m∠T is about _____.

LESSON 3·4 Measuring and Drawing Angles *continued*

Use your full-circle protractor to measure each angle.

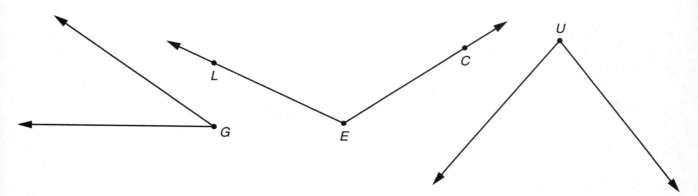

5. a. m∠G is about _____.   **b.** m∠LEC is about _____.   **c.** m∠U is about _____.

Draw and label the following angles. Use your half-circle protractor.

6. a. ∠CAT: 62°   **b.** ∠DOG: 135°

STUDY LINK 3·4 Angle Measures

Find the approximate measure of each angle at the right.

1. measure of ∠CAT = _____

2. m∠BAR = _____

3. m∠RAT = _____

4. m∠CAB = _____

5. m∠BAT = _____

6. m∠CAR = _____

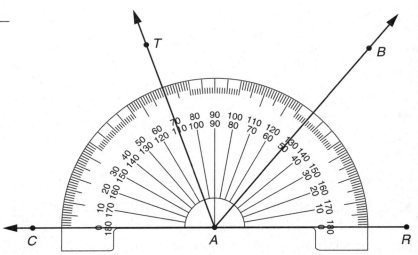

Find the approximate measure of each angle at the right.

7. m∠MEN = _____

8. m∠DEN = _____

9. m∠MET = _____

10. m∠MED = _____

11. m∠TEN = _____

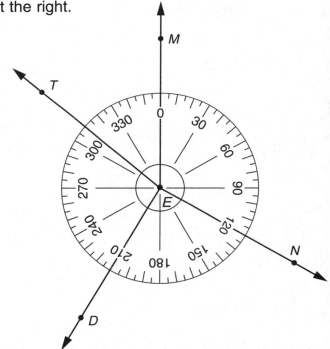

Practice

12.   5,844
         + 2,399

13.   238
         − 129

14.   234
         * 22

15. 60 ÷ 5 = _____

16. 50 ÷ 6 → _____

LESSON 3·4

Points, Lines, and Angles

Identify the terms and objects in the riddles below. Use the words and phrases from the Word Bank to complete the table.

Word Bank			
point	line segment	ray	line
angle	parallel lines	parallel line segments	intersecting lines
vertices	perpendicular lines	perpendicular line segments	vertex

	Clues	What Am I?
1	I am a location in space. It takes only one letter to name me.	
2	My length cannot be measured, but I am named by two of my points.	
3	I do not curve. I have only one end point.	
4	I am measured in degrees. I have a vertex. My sides are two rays.	
5	We have endpoints. When two of us meet, we form one or more right angles.	
6	There are always at least two of us. We have endpoints. We always stay the same distance apart.	
7	I am the point where two rays meet to form an angle.	
8	Two of us meet.	
9	Our lengths cannot be measured. When two of us meet, we form right angles.	
10	I am the endpoint where two sides of a polygon meet.	
11	My length can be measured. I have two endpoints.	
12	Our lengths cannot be measured. There are always at least two of us. We always stay the same distance apart.	

LESSON 3·4 Baseball Angles

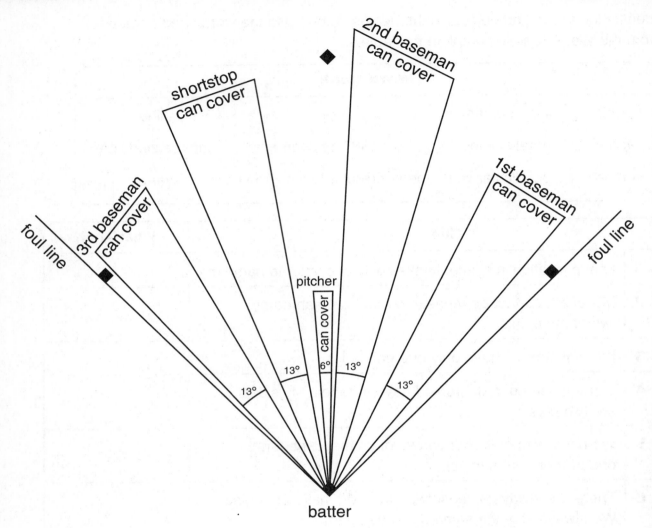

The playing field for baseball lies between the foul lines, which form a 90° angle.
Suppose that each of the four infielders can cover an angle of about 13° on a hard-hit
ground ball, and that the pitcher can cover about 6°. (See the diagram above.)

Source: *Applying Arithmetic,* Usiskin, Z. and Bell, M. © 1983 University of Chicago

1. How many degrees are left for the batter to hit through? _____

Angles in Figures

SRB
138 139

Circle *acute, right,* or *obtuse* for each angle in triangle *ABC*.
Then measure each angle.

1. ∠*ABC*   acute   right   obtuse   m∠*ABC* = _____

2. ∠*CAB*   acute   right   obtuse   m∠*CAB* = _____

3. ∠*BCA*   acute   right   obtuse   m∠*BCA* = _____

Use the figure at the right to do Problems 4–6.

4. Name a pair of adjacent angles.

_____ and _____

5. Name a pair of vertical angles.

_____ and _____

6. Name a pair of opposite angles.

_____ and _____

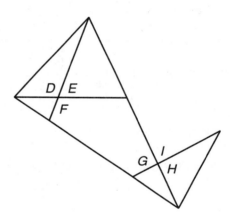

Practice

7.   7,568
        + 9,217
       _____

8.   415
        − 207
       _____

9.   326
        * 45
       _____

10. 68 ÷ 4 = _____   **11.** 78 ÷ 7 → _____

LESSON 3·5 Reading a Ruler

On rulers, inches are usually divided into halves, quarters, eighths, and sixteenths with marks that are different sizes. There are different ways to name a length. Look at the ruler to the right and give two other names for $\frac{1}{2}$ inch.

This space is $\frac{1}{16}$ in. long.   This space is $\frac{4}{16}$ in. or $\frac{1}{4}$ in. long.

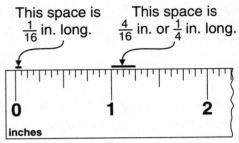

_____

Fill in the blank spaces on each ruler. Identify these marks on your ruler.

1.

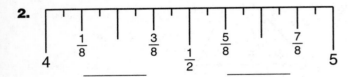

Scale: 6 inches represents 1 inch

2.

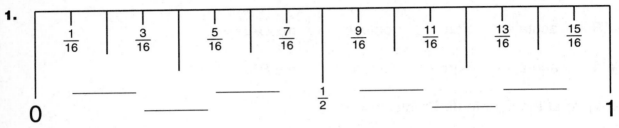

Scale: 3 inches represents 1 inch

Use your ruler to measure the line segments. Give two names for each line segment.

3. _____

_____

4. _____   _____

_____

Use the ruler pictured to determine the length of the line segment. Give two names for the length of the line segment.

5. _____   _____

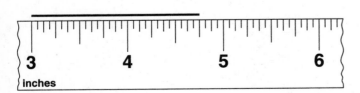

LESSON 3·5   **Designs with a Compass and a Straightedge**

If you know how to inscribe a hexagon in a circle, you can make a 6-pointed star, or **hexagram,** inside a circle.

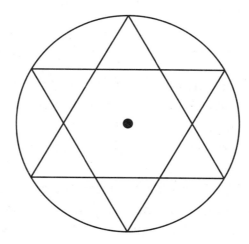

1. On a separate piece of paper, make a 6-pointed star. (*Hint:* Mark the circle as you do for a hexagon. Connect every other mark.)

2. Divide the angles of your star in half as shown below.

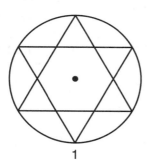

1

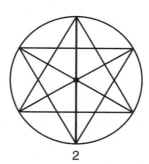

2

3. Color your design in some pattern.

4. Reproduce the following designs, using a compass and a straightedge to draw hexagons and hexagrams. Then find patterns and color them. (*Hint:* Use a pencil and draw lightly so you can erase unwanted lines.)

 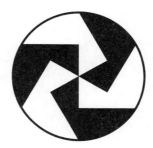

STUDY LINK 3·6 Triangle and Angle Review

For each triangle below, fill in the ovals for all the names that apply.

1.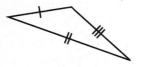

○ equilateral
○ isosceles
○ right
○ scalene

2.

○ equilateral
○ isosceles
○ right
○ scalene

3.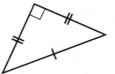

○ equilateral
○ isosceles
○ right
○ scalene

4.

○ equilateral
○ isosceles
○ right
○ scalene

On the back of this page, draw three angles of different sizes that you find at home. (For example, you could trace one corner of a book.) For each angle, name the object that has the angle. Then use words from the Word Bank to name each angle.

5. a. Object _____

Type of angle _____

b. Object _____

Type of angle _____

c. Object _____

Type of angle _____

Word Bank		
acute	obtuse	right
adjacent	reflex	straight

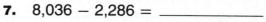

Practice

6. 4,117 + 3,682 + 3,962 = _____

7. 8,036 − 2,286 = _____

8. 8,481 * 5 = _____

9. 99 ÷ 9 = _____

STUDY LINK 3·7 | Odd Shape Out

In each set of shapes, there is one shape that doesn't belong. Cross out that shape and tell why it doesn't belong. (There may be more than one possible reason. What's important is having a good reason for crossing out a shape.)

1.

Reason: _____

_____

2.

Reason: _____

_____

3.

Reason: _____

_____

4.

Reason: _____

_____

5. Make up your own "Odd Shape Out" problem on the back of this page.

Practice

6. $1,042 + 2,834 + 4,096 =$ _____

7. $9,062 - 3,718 =$ _____

8. $9,109 * 9 =$ _____

9. $58 \div 6 \rightarrow$ _____

87

LESSON 3·7 — Classifying Quadrangles

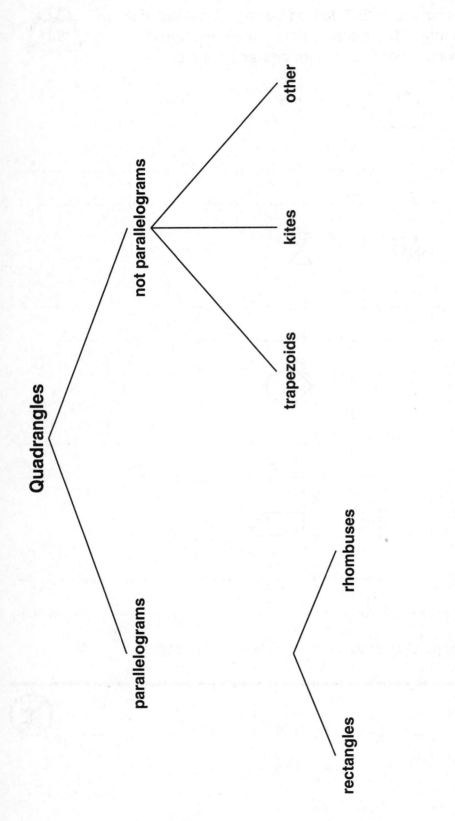

Quadrangles

- **parallelograms**
  - **rectangles**
  - **rhombuses**
    - **squares**
- **not parallelograms**
  - **trapezoids**
  - **kites**
  - **other**

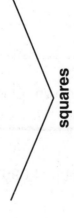

LESSON 3·7 Quadrangles

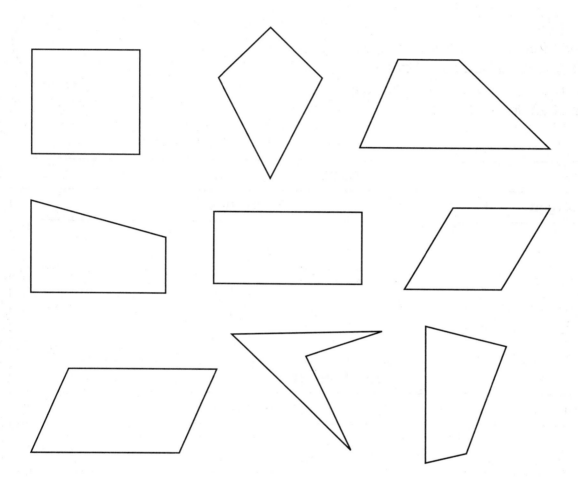

LESSON 3·7   Vertex Connection

If you draw a line segment from one vertex of a polygon to any other vertex that does not share a common side, new shapes will be formed inside the polygon. Connect pairs of vertices in these polygons. Name the new shapes as they are formed.

Write the name of each new polygon and as many true statements as you can about the polygons. Be sure to use what you know about the definitions of angles and lines.

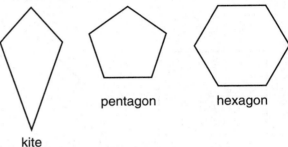

pentagon   hexagon

kite

kite	
New Polygon	**Properties**

pentagon	
New Polygon	**Properties**

hexagon	
New Polygon	**Properties**

LESSON 3·8

Regular Polygons

Cut along the dashed lines. Fold the page like this along the solid lines.

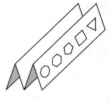

Cut out the polygons. You will be cutting out four of each shape at once.

Tessellation Museum

A **tessellation** is an arrangement of repeated, closed shapes that completely covers a surface, without overlaps or gaps. Sometimes only one shape is used in a tessellation. Sometimes two or more shapes are used.

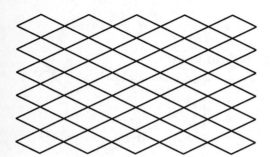 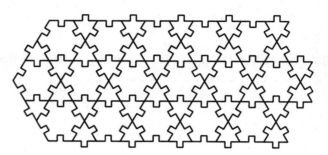

1. Collect tessellations. Look in newspapers and magazines. Ask people at home to help you find examples.

2. Ask an adult whether you may cut out the tessellations. Tape your tessellations onto this page in the space below.

3. If you can't find tessellations in newspapers or magazines, look around your home at furniture, wallpaper, tablecloths, or clothing. In the space below, sketch the tessellations you find.

Practice

4. 1,987 + 6,213 + 2,046 = _____

5. 4,615 − 3,148 = _____

6. 3,714 * 8 = _____

7. 39 / 7 → _____

90

LESSON 3·8   Naming Tessellations

Regular tessellations are named by giving the number of sides in each polygon around a vertex point. A vertex point of a tessellation is a point where vertices of the shapes meet.

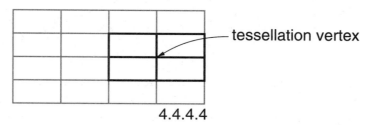

— tessellation vertex

4.4.4.4

For example, the name of the rectangular tessellation above is 4.4.4.4. There are four numbers in the name, so there are four polygons around each vertex. Each of those numbers tells the number of sides in each of the polygons around a vertex point. The numbers are separated by periods. There are four 4-sided polygons around each vertex point.

Look at the tessellation below.

Choose a vertex.

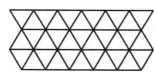

1. How many shapes meet at the vertex point? _____

2. How many sides does each polygon have? _____

3. **a.** What is the name of this regular tessellation? _____

   b. Why? _____

   _____

4. Make a tessellation for each regular polygon on your geometry template. Use the back of this page if necessary. Name each regular tessellation.

STUDY LINK 3·9 Sums of Angle Measures

1. Describe one way to find the sum of the angles in a quadrangle without using a protractor. You might want to use the quadrangle at the right to illustrate your explanation.

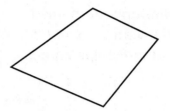

_____

_____

_____

_____

_____

2. The sum of the angles in a quadrangle is _____.

3. Follow these steps to check your answer to Problem 2.

   a. With a straightedge, draw a large quadrangle on a separate sheet of paper.

   b. Draw an arc in each angle.

   c. Cut out the quadrangle and tear off part of each angle.

   d. Tape or glue the angles onto the back of this page so that the angles touch but do not overlap.

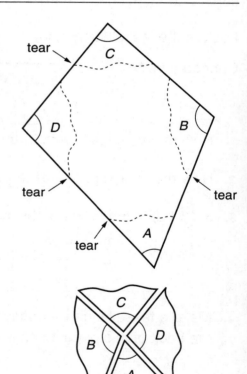

Practice

4. $3,007 + 1,251 + 980 =$ _____

5. $4,310 - 1,290 =$ _____

6. $3,692 * 6 =$ _____

7. $67 \div 8 \rightarrow$ _____

92

LESSON 3·9 — A Quadrangle Investigation

The sum of the angles in a quadrangle is equal to 360°. Since there are 360° in a circle, you might predict that every quadrangle will tessellate. Follow the procedure below to investigate this prediction.

1. Fold a piece of paper ($8\frac{1}{2}$" by 11") into six parts by first folding it into thirds and then into halves.

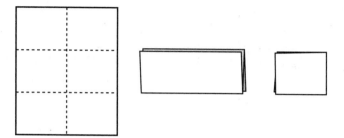

2. Using a straightedge, draw a quadrangle on the top layer of the folded paper. Label each of the four vertices with a letter *inside the figure*—for example, *A, B, C,* and *D.*

3. Cut through all six layers so that you have six identical quadrangles. Label the vertices of each quadrangle in the same manner as the quadrangle on top.

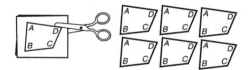

4. Arrange the quadrangles so that they tessellate.

5. When you have a tessellating pattern, tape the final pattern onto a separate piece of paper. Color it if you want to.

6. Talk with other students who did this investigation. Were their quadrangles a different shape than yours? Do you think that any quadrangle will tessellate?

Option To make a pattern that has more than six quadrangles, draw your original quadrangle on a piece of cardstock, cut it out, and use it as a stencil. By tracing around your quadrangle, you can easily cover a half-sheet of paper with your pattern. Label the angles on your stencil so you can be sure you are placing all four angles around points in the tessellation. Color your finished pattern.

LESSON 3·9 | **Angle Measures in Polygons**

The measure of the interior angles of a triangle is 180°. The number of triangles within a polygon is 2 less than the number of sides of the polygon.

---

1. Fill in the chart below using this pattern.

Polygons		
Number of Sides	**Number of Triangles**	**Sum of Angles**
4	2	2 * 180° = 360°
5	3	3 * 180° = _____
6	4	4 * 180° = _____
7	5	____ * 180° = _____
13		____ * 180° = _____
26		____ * _____ = _____
51		____ * _____ = _____
63		____ * _____ = _____
85		____ * _____ = _____

2. Use expressions to complete the statement.

If *n* equals the number of sides in a polygon, _____ equals the number

of triangles within the polygon, and _____ equals the
sum of the angles in the polygon.

STUDY LINK 3·10   **Polygons and Their Measures**

1. Draw each of the following figures.

    a. a polygon

    b. a triangle with no equal sides

    c. a quadrangle with one right angle

    d. a quadrangle with no pairs of parallel sides

2. Without using a protractor, record the missing angle measurements in the figure to the right.

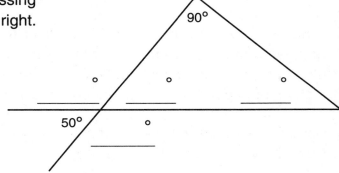

3. Use the figure to the right to answer the questions.

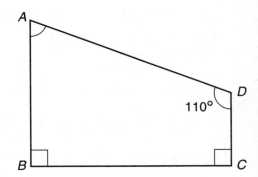

    a. How long is line segment *CD*? _____ cm

    b. What is the measure of angle *A*? _____

    c. What is the sum of the measures of all

       the angles? _____

    d. What is a geometric name for the figure? _____

Practice

4. $1,476 + 2,724 + 3,241 =$ _____

5. $4,002 - 1,361 =$ _____

6. $5,031 * 4 =$ _____

7. $27 \div 9 =$ _____

95

LESSON 3·10 — Geometry Template Problems

Record your solutions on *Math Masters,* page 97. Include the problem numbers.

Challenging   **Examples:**

1. Without using a ruler to measure, enlarge the octagon on the Geometry Template to approximately 2 times its size and 3 times its size. (6 points for the double-size octagon and 9 points for the triple-size octagon)

2. Using the triangles on the template, draw three different **kites.** Describe your procedure. Remember, a kite has two pairs of equal sides, but not four equal sides. The equal sides must share an endpoint. (3 points each)

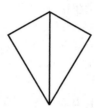

3. Describe how you would draw the largest circle possible with the Geometry Template, without tracing any of the circles on the template. Draw this circle if you have a sheet of paper that is large enough. (15 points)

4. Use your template to draw at least four **parallel lines.** Describe your procedure. (10 points)

5. Each side of the hexagon is 1 unit long. Each side of the equilateral triangle is 1 unit long. Use at least one hexagon and at least one equilateral triangle to make each of the following:

   ◆ An equilateral triangle with sides 3 units long

   ◆ An equilateral triangle with sides 4 units long

   ◆ An equilateral triangle with sides 5 units long
     (10 points each)

6. Draw as many polygons as you can inside each box on *Math Masters,* page 97. The polygons must not overlap. None of the polygons may be used more than once. (1 point for each polygon used)

LESSON 3·10

Geometry Template Problems *continued*

Solutions

6.

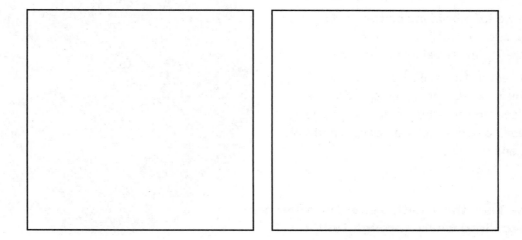

STUDY LINK 3·11

Unit 4: Family Letter

Division

Unit 4 begins with a review of division facts and the relationship between division and multiplication. Emphasis is on fact families. A person who knows that $4 * 5 = 20$ also knows the related facts $5 * 4 = 20$, $20 \div 4 = 5$, and $20 \div 5 = 4$.

These notations for division are equivalent:	
$12\overline{)246}$	$246 \div 12$
$246 / 12$	$\dfrac{246}{12}$

We will develop strategies for dividing mentally. Challenge your child to a game of *Division Dash* to help him or her practice. You'll find the rules in the *Student Reference Book,* page 303.

In *Fourth Grade Everyday Mathematics,* students were introduced to a method of long division called the partial-quotients division algorithm. This algorithm is easier to learn and apply than the traditional long-division method. It relies on "easy" multiplication, and it can be quickly employed by students who struggle with traditional computation.

In this method, a series of partial answers (partial quotients) are obtained, and then added to get the final answer (the quotient). After your child has worked with this method, you might ask him or her to explain the example below:

$$
\begin{array}{r|r}
12\overline{)158} & \\
-120 & 10 \\
\hline
38 & \\
-36 & 3 \\
\hline
2 & 13 \\
\uparrow & \uparrow \\
\textbf{Remainder} & \textbf{Quotient}
\end{array}
$$

In the coming unit, we will review the partial-quotients algorithm and extend it to decimals.

Your child will practice using this division algorithm, as well as others, if he or she chooses. The partial-quotients division algorithm and another method called column division are described in the *Student Reference Book.*

When we solve division number stories, special attention will be placed on interpreting the remainder in division.

The American Tour will continue as the class measures distances on maps and uses map scales to convert the map distances to real-world distances between cities, lengths of rivers, and so on.

Please keep this Family Letter for reference as your child works through Unit 4.

Vocabulary

Important terms in Unit 4:

dividend In division, the number that is being divided. For example, in 35 ÷ 5 = 7, the dividend is 35.

divisor In division, the number that divides another number. For example, in 35 ÷ 5 = 7, the divisor is 5.

map legend (map key) A diagram that explains the symbols, markings, and colors on a map.

map scale The ratio of a distance on a map, globe, or drawing to an actual distance.

number sentence Two expressions with a relation symbol (=, <, >, ≠, ≤, or ≥). For example, 5 + 5 = 10 and 6 * (43 + 7) = 300 are number sentences. Compare to *open sentence*.

open sentence A *number sentence* with one or more *variables*. For example, $x + 3 = 5$ is an open sentence.

quotient The result of dividing one number by another number. For example, in 35 ÷ 5 = 7, the quotient is 7.

remainder The amount left over when one number is divided by another number. For example, if 38 books are divided into 5 equal piles, there are 7 books per pile, with 3 books remaining. In symbols, 38 ÷ 5 → 7 R3.

variable A letter or other symbol that represents a number. A variable can represent one specific number. For example, in the number sentence $5 + n = 9$, only $n = 4$ makes the sentence true. A variable may also stand for many different numbers. For example, $x + 2 < 10$ is true if x is any number less than 8.

Do-Anytime Activities

To work with your child on the concepts taught in this unit and in previous units, try these interesting and rewarding activities:

1. Provide your child with opportunities to look at maps from various parts of the country. Ask him or her to explain the map legend and map scale, and to find the distances between two cities or places of interest.

2. Read the book *A Remainder of One,* by Elinor J. Pinczes.

3. Play *Division Dash, First to 100, Divisibility Dash, Division Top-It* or *Name that Number* as described in the *Student Reference Book.*

4. Ask your child to write number stories that can be solved using division. Help your child solve those problems, and then identify how the quotient and remainder are used to answer the question in the number story.

Building Skills through Games

In Unit 4, your child will practice division as well as other skills by playing these and other games. For detailed instructions, see the *Student Reference Book.*

Divisibility Dash See *Student Reference Book,* page 302
This is a game for two to three players and requires a set of number cards. Playing *Divisibility Dash* provides practice recognizing multiples and using divisibility rules in a context that also develops speed.

Division Dash See *Student Reference Book,* page 303
This is a game for one or two players. Each player will need a calculator. Playing *Division Dash* helps students practice division and mental calculation.

Division Top-It See *Student Reference Book,* page 334
This is a game for two to four players and requires number cards. Playing Division Top-It provides practice recognizing multiples and applying division facts and extended facts.

First to 100 See *Student Reference Book,* page 308
This is a game for two to four players and requires 32 Problem Cards and a pair of six-sided dice. Players answer questions after substituting numbers for the variable on Problem Cards. The questions offer practice on a variety of mathematical topics.

Name That Number See *Student Reference Book,* page 325
This is a game for two or three players using the Everything Math Deck or a complete deck of number cards. This game provides a review of operations with whole numbers.

As You Help Your Child with Homework

As your child brings assignments home, you may want to go over the instructions together, clarifying them as necessary. The answers listed below will guide you through this unit's Study Links.

Study Link 4·1

1. 19; Sample answer: 30 and 27

2. 12; Sample answer: 80 and 16

3. 2,000 mi   **4.** 5 lb

5. 878; $1,803 - 878 = 925$; $925 + 878 = 1,803$; $878 + 925 = 1,803$

6. 875; $377 + 498 = 875$; $875 - 377 = 498$; $875 - 498 = 377$

Study Link 4·2

1. 10, 10, 10, and 3   **2.** 27 R4   **3.** 42 R4

4. 32 R5   **5.** 24

6. 3,985; $3,985 - 168$, or $3,817 = 3,817$, or 168

7. 52,236; 281, or $52,236 + 52,236$ or $281 = 52,517$

Study Link 4·3

1. a. About 1 mi   **b.** About $1\frac{1}{2}$ mi

2. a. About $3\frac{3}{4}$ in.   **b.** About $1\frac{7}{8}$ mi

3. 188; $188 + 188 = 376$

4. 4,148; $4,148 - 3,997$, or $151 = 151$, or 3,997

Study Link 4·4

1. 71   **2.** 53   **3.** 82 R22

4. 26 R10 **5.** 83 pages

6. 2,814; $2,814 - 2,746 = 68$ (or $2,814 - 68 = 2,746$)

7. 3,296; $3,296 + 165 = 3,461$ (or $165 + 3,296 = 3,461$)

Study Link 4·5

Estimates vary. Sample estimates are given for Problems 1–6.

1. The 10s box should be circled; $60 \div 6 = 10$; 13.1

2. The 100s box should be circled; $300 \div 3 = 100$; 129

3. The 1s box should be circled; $30 \div 10 = 3$; \$3.69

4. The 10s box should be circled; $800 \div 40 = 20$; 23

5. The 100s box should be circled; $1,000 \div 5 = 200$; 169

6. The 1s box should be circled; $18 \div 9 = 2$; 1.76

7. 14.544; $14.544 - 8.54$, or $6.004 = 6.004$, or 8.54

Study Link 4·6

1. \$6.25; Reported it as a fraction or decimal; Sample answer: The cost per game is exact, so the answer needs to be exact.

2. 7; Ignored it; Sample answer: The remaining \$4.00 is not enough to buy another pizza, and is ignored.

3. 15 R1   **4.** 52,836

Study Link 4·7

1. 49   **2.** 780   **3.** 610

Answers vary for Problems 4–11.

12. 3,985   **13.** 52,236

Uses of Division

Use multiplication and division facts to solve the following problems mentally.
Remember: Break the number into two or more friendly parts.

Example: How many 4s in 71?

Break 71 into smaller, friendly numbers. Here are two ways.

◆ 40 and 31. Ask yourself: *How many 4s in 40?* (10) *How many 4s in 31?* (7 and 3 left over) Think: *What multiplication fact for 4 has a product near 31?* (4 * 7 = 28) Total = 17 and 3 left over.

◆ 20, 20, 20, and 11. Ask yourself: *How many 4s in 20?* (5) *How many 4s in three 20s?* (15) *How many 4s in 11?* (2 and 3 left over) Total = 17 and 3 left over.

So 71 divided by 4 equals 17 with 3 left over.

1. 57 divided by 3 equals _____.

_____
(friendly parts for 57)

2. 96 divided by 8 equals _____.

_____
(friendly parts for 96)

3. The diameter of Earth, about 8,000 miles, is about 4 times the diameter of the moon. What is the approximate diameter of the moon?

8,000 mi

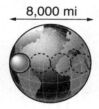

_____
unit

4. The weight of an object on Earth is 6 times heavier than its weight on the moon. An object that weighs 30 lb on Earth weighs how many pounds on the moon?

_____
unit

Practice

Solve. Then write the other problems in the fact families.

5. 1,803 − 925 = _____

_____

_____

_____

6. 498 + 377 = _____

_____

_____

_____

LESSON 4·1 Testing for Divisibility by 7, 11, and 13

Use these divisibility rules to test large numbers.

To test if a number is divisible by 7:

◆ Take the rightmost digit.	25,80<u>9</u>
◆ Double it.	$9 * 2 = 18$
◆ Subtract the result from the remaining digits.	$2,580 - 18 = 2,562$
◆ Repeat, each time doubling the rightmost digit and subtracting, until the result is small enough to know that it is, or is not, divisible by 7.	2,56<u>2</u> $2 * 2 = 4$ $256 - 4 = 252$ 25<u>2</u> $2 * 2 = 4$ $25 - 4 = 21$ 21 is divisible by 7, so 25,809 is divisible by 7.

1. Is 33,992 divisible by 7? _____

To test if a number is divisible by 11:

◆ Find the sum of every other digit.	<u>1</u>0,<u>6</u>4<u>8</u> $1 + 6 + 8 = 15$
◆ Find the sum of the digits that are left.	$0 + 4 = 4$
◆ Subtract.	$15 - 4 = 11$ 11 is divisible by 11, so 10,648 is divisible by 11.◆

2. Is 9,723 divisible by 11? _____

To test if a number is divisible by 13:

◆ Multiply the rightmost digit by 4.	1,166,93<u>2</u> $2 * 4 = 8$
◆ Add the result to the remaining digits.	$116,693 + 8 = 116,701$
◆ Repeat, each time multiplying the rightmost digit and adding, until the result is small enough to know that it is, or is not, divisible by 13.	116,70<u>1</u> $1 * 4 = 4$ $11,670 + 4 = 11,67\underline{4}$ $4 * 4 = 16$ $1,167 + 16 = 1,18\underline{3}$ $3 * 4 = 12$ $118 + 12 = 130$ $130 = 13 * 10$, so 1,166,923 is divisible by 13.

3. Is 89,362 divisible by 13? _____

103

STUDY LINK 4·2   Division

Here is the partial-quotients algorithm using a friendly numbers strategy.

$$7\overline{)237}$$

Rename dividend (use multiples of the divisor):
$237 = 210 + 21 + 6$

How many 7s are in 210? 30
-210 30   The first partial quotient. $30 * 7 = 210$
$\overline{27}$ Subtract. 27 is left to divide.

How many 7s are in 27? 3
-21 $\underline{3}$ The second partial quotient. $3 * 7 = 21$
   Subtract. 6 is left to divide.

6 33   Add the partial quotients: $30 + 3 = 33$

↑   ↑

Remainder Quotient   **Answer: 33 R6**

1. Another way to rename 237 with multiples of 7 is

$$237 = 70 + 70 + 70 + 21 + 6$$

If the example had used this name for 237, what would the partial quotients have been?

_____

2. $6\overline{)166}$

Answer: _____

3. $214 / 5$

Answer: _____

4. $485 \div 15$

Answer: _____

5. $17\overline{)408}$

Answer: _____

| Practice |

6. $3{,}817 + 168 =$ _____

Check: _____ − _____ = _____

7. $52{,}517 - 281 =$ _____

Check: _____ + _____ = _____

LESSON 4·2 Divisibility by the Digits

Ms. Winters asked Vito and Jacob to make answer cards for a division puzzle.
They had to find numbers that met all of the following characteristics.

	Example:
◆ The first digit is divisible by 1.	1
◆ The first two digits are divisible by 2.	12
◆ The first three digits are divisible by 3.	120
◆ The first four digits are divisible by 4.	1,204
◆ The first five digits are divisible by 5.	12,040
◆ The first six digits are divisible by 6.	120,402
◆ The first seven digits are divisible by 7.	1,204,021
◆ The first eight digits are divisible by 8.	12,049,216
◆ The first nine digits are divisible by 9.	120,402,162

1. Jacob knew that with divisibility rules, it should be easy. The boys started with 3-digit numbers and found 123 and 242. Latoya checked their work. What should she tell them?

_____

_____

_____

_____

_____

2. Use the characteristics listed above to find as many puzzle numbers as you can. Record them in the boxes below.

Puzzle Numbers					
4-digit	**5-digit**	**6-digit**	**7-digit**	**8-digit**	**9-digit**

STUDY LINK 4·3 | Distance to School

There are two ways to go from Josephina's house to school. She can take Elm Street and then Washington Avenue. She can also take Snakey Lane.

211 212

Use the map and scale below to answer the questions.

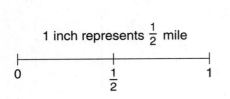

1 inch represents $\frac{1}{2}$ mile

0         $\frac{1}{2}$ 1

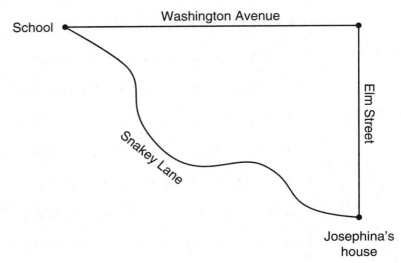

1. Josephina started walking from home to school along Elm Street.

     a. How far would Josephina walk before she
turned onto Washington Avenue?   _____

     b. How far would she be from school when she
turned the corner?   _____

2. Suppose Josephina could take a straight path from her house to school.
Estimate the distance.

     a. Draw and measure a straight line on the map
from Josephina's house to the school.   _____

     b. Use the scale to measure this distance
in miles.   _____

Practice

3. 376 − 188 = _____

     Check: _____ + _____ = _____

4. 3,997 + 151 = _____

     Check: _____ − _____   = _____

LESSON 4·3 | Estimating Curved-Path Distances

Use a ruler, string, compass, paper and pencil, or any other tool.

1. The map below shows the border between Mexico and the United States. Estimate the length of the border. _____ mi

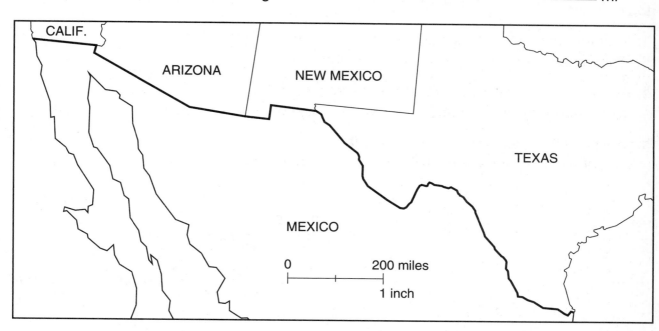

2. a. Estimate the lengths of the following rivers. Use the map on pages 386 and 387 of the *Student Reference Book.*

River	Length (miles)
Arkansas (CO, KS, OK, and AR)	
Missouri (MT, ND, SD, NE, IA, KS, and MO)	
Brazos (NM and TX)	
Chattahoochee (GA, AL, FL)	

b. Explain how you found the length of the Chattahoochee River.

_____

_____

_____

_____

107

LESSON 4·3 | **A Trip through the Panama Canal**

The Panama Canal crosses the country of Panama near its capital city, Panama City. The canal connects the Atlantic Ocean and the Pacific Ocean.

Pretend that you will travel by ship from New York, through the Panama Canal, to Los Angeles.

1. Use the map below to decide on a route your ship will take. Then use a pencil to draw this route on the map.

2. Estimate the length of the route you have chosen. Use a ruler, string, compass, paper and pencil, or any other tool.   _____ mi

3. How much longer is your route than the straight-line distance from New York to Los Angeles?   _____ mi

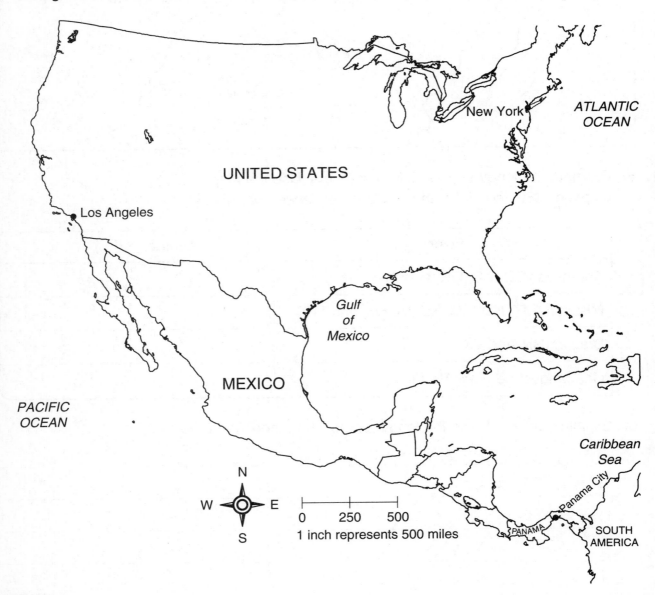

LESSON 4·4 | Easy Multiples

1,000 * _____ = _____

100 * _____ = _____

50 * _____ = _____

20 * _____ = _____

10 * _____ = _____

5 * _____ = _____

1,000 * _____ = _____

100 * _____ = _____

50 * _____ = _____

20 * _____ = _____

10 * _____ = _____

5 * _____ = _____

1,000 * _____ = _____

100 * _____ = _____

50 * _____ = _____

20 * _____ = _____

10 * _____ = _____

5 * _____ = _____

1,000 * _____ = _____

100 * _____ = _____

50 * _____ = _____

20 * _____ = _____

10 * _____ = _____

5 * _____ = _____

1,000 * _____ = _____

100 * _____ = _____

50 * _____ = _____

20 * _____ = _____

10 * _____ = _____

5 * _____ = _____

1,000 * _____ = _____

100 * _____ = _____

50 * _____ = _____

20 * _____ = _____

10 * _____ = _____

5 * _____ = _____

STUDY LINK 4·4 Division

Here is an example of the partial-quotients algorithm using an "at least...not more than" strategy.

```
8)185

  − 80        10      Begin estimating with multiples of 10.
  ─────
   105

  − 80        10
  ─────
    25

  − 24         3
  ─────
     1        23
```

Begin estimating with multiples of 10.

How many 8s are in 185? At least 10.
The first partial quotient. 10 * 8 = 80
Subtract. 105 is left to divide.

How many 8s are in 105? At least 10.
The second partial quotient. 10 * 8 = 80
Subtract. 25 is left to divide.

How many 8s are in 25? At least 3.
The third partial quotient. 3 * 8 = 24
Subtract. 1 is left to divide.

Add the partial quotients: 10 + 10 + 3 = 23

↑ Remainder   ↑ Quotient   **Answer: 23 R1**

Solve.

1. 639 ÷ 9

Answer: _____

2. 954 ÷ 18

Answer: _____

3. 1,990 / 24

Answer: _____

4. 972 / 37

Answer: _____

5. Robert is making a photo album. 6 photos fit on a page. How many pages will he need for 497 photos? _____ pages

---

Practice

6. 2,746 + 68 = _____

Check: _____ − _____ = _____

7. 3,461 − 165 = _____

Check: _____ + _____ = _____

LESSON 4·4 | **Division Practice**

For each division problem, complete the list of multiples of the divisor.
Then divide.

1. _____)_____

Answer: _____

200 * _____ = _____

100 * _____ = _____

50 * _____ = _____

20 * _____ = _____

10 * _____ = _____

5 * _____ = _____

2. _____ ÷ _____

Answer: _____

200 * _____ = _____

100 * _____ = _____

50 * _____ = _____

20 * _____ = _____

10 * _____ = _____

5 * _____ = _____

3. _____ / _____

Answer: _____

200 * _____ = _____

100 * _____ = _____

50 * _____ = _____

20 * _____ = _____

10 * _____ = _____

5 * _____ = _____

4. _____ ÷ _____

Answer: _____

200 * _____ = _____

100 * _____ = _____

50 * _____ = _____

20 * _____ = _____

10 * _____ = _____

5 * _____ = _____

111

LESSON 4·4

Using Expanded Notation

- ◆ Work with a partner. Use a deck with 4 each of cards 1–9.
- ◆ Take turns dealing 4 cards and forming a 4-digit number.
- ◆ Write the number in standard notation and expanded notation.
- ◆ Then write equivalent names for the value of each digit.

1. Write a 4-digit number. _____

2. Write the number in expanded notation.

_____ + _____ + _____ + _____

3. Write equivalent names for the value of each digit.

1st digit	2nd digit	3rd digit	4th digit

4. Write a 4-digit number. _____

5. Write the number in expanded notation.

_____ + _____ + _____ + _____

6. Write equivalent names for the value of each digit.

1st digit	2nd digit	3rd digit	4th digit

STUDY LINK 4·5 Estimate and Calculate Quotients

For each problem:

◆ Make a magnitude estimate of the quotient. Ask yourself:
   Is the answer in the tenths, ones, tens, or hundreds?
◆ Circle a box to show the magnitude of your estimate.
◆ Write a number sentence to show how you estimated.
◆ If there is a decimal point, ignore it. Divide the numbers.
◆ Use your magnitude estimate to place the decimal point in the final answer.
◆ Check that your final answer is reasonable.

1. 6)$\overline{78.6}$

0.1s	1s	10s	100s

How I estimated: _____

Answer: _____

2. 3)$\overline{387}$

0.1s	1s	10s	100s

How I estimated: _____

Answer: _____

3. $29.52 ÷ 8

0.1s	1s	10s	100s

How I estimated: _____

Answer: _____

4. 989 ÷ 43

0.1s	1s	10s	100s

How I estimated: _____

Answer: _____

5. 845 / 5

0.1s	1s	10s	100s

How I estimated: _____

Answer: _____

6. 15.84 / 9

0.1s	1s	10s	100s

How I estimated: _____

Answer: _____

Practice

7. 8.54 + 6.004 = _____

Check: _____ − _____ = _____

LESSON 4·5   Division with Base-10 Blocks

For each problem:

◆ First use ☐ | . to represent the dividend with base-10 blocks.

◆ Then use ☐ | . to show how you would distribute the blocks in equal groups to represent the division.

◆ Record your answer with digits.

Example: 5)‾689‾   ☐☐☐☐☐☐ ‖‖‖‖ ‖‖ ::::.

| ☐ ‖‖ ::... | ☐ ‖‖ ::... | ☐ ‖‖ ::... | ☐ ‖‖ ::... | ☐ ‖‖ ::... | .... |

Answer: *137 R4*
       5)‾689‾

1. 3)‾427‾

◆ Show the dividend:

◆ Show equal groups below.

◆ Write the answer.   3)‾427‾

2. 4)‾555‾

◆ Show the dividend:

◆ Show equal groups below.

◆ Write the answer.   4)‾555‾

114

LESSON 4·5 — A Division Challenge

Judy and two friends bought a raffle ticket at the school fund-raiser.
They agreed that if they won, they would share the winnings equally.
They won $145! They received one $100 bill, four $10 bills, and five $1 bills.
Judy used this division algorithm to calculate how much money
each person should get. Can you figure out how the algorithm works?

(*Hint:* There were 3 people in all. Judy realized that in order to share the
$100 bill, they needed to trade it for ten $10 bills. Then they would have fourteen
$10 bills and five $1 bills.)

	100s	10s	1s	10ths	100ths
		4	8•	3	3
3)	1̸	4̸	5̸	0̸	0̸
		14	25	10	10
		−12	−24	−9	−9
		2	1̸	1̸	1

1. Explain how you think the algorithm works. _____

_____

_____

_____

_____

_____

_____

_____

2. Explain what Judy did when she had $1 left. _____

_____

3. How much money did each person get? _____

4. Use the algorithm to divide: 4)‾51.6‾ _____

STUDY LINK
4·6   **Division Number Stories with Remainders**

For each number story draw a picture or write a number sentence on the back
of this page. Then divide to solve the problem. Decide what to do about
the remainder. Explain what you did.

SRB
226 243

Example:

How many benches?
7 seats per bench

You need to set up benches for a picnic. Each bench
seats 7 people. You expect 25 people to attend. How many
benches do you need?

$$25 \div 7 = b$$

| 7 |
| 7 |
| 7 |
| 4 |

⎫
⎬ 25 people
⎭

Circle what you did with the remainder.   _4_ benches

Ignored it   Reported it as a fraction or decimal   ⟨Rounded the answer up⟩

Why? _3 benches seat 21 people. One more bench is needed._

1. It costs $50.00 to be a member of a soccer team. The team
   plays 8 games during the season. What is the cost per game? $ _____

   Circle what you did with the remainder.

   Ignored it   Reported it as a fraction or decimal   Rounded the answer up

   Why? _____

   _____

2. Lynn is having a party. Pizzas cost $8.00 each.
   How many pizzas can she buy with $60.00?   _____ pizzas

   Circle what you did with the remainder.

   Ignored it   Reported it as a fraction or decimal   Rounded the answer up

   Why? _____

   _____

Practice

3. $31 \div 2 \rightarrow$ _____   4. $629 * 84 =$ _____

LESSON 4·6 | Finding Number Story Information

For each problem, write the number of the sentence that has the information for each part of the situation diagram. Then complete the situation diagram.

SRB
226 243

Problem 1

1. Ms. Haag is rearranging her classroom.

2. There are 32 students.

3. The students sit at tables.

4. Four students can sit at each table.

5. How many tables does she need?

Sentence(s): _____

tables	per _____	total students
?	4	_____

Problem 2

1. Marc needs 3 yards of fabric to make a cape for a costume party.

2. His friends want capes that match his.

3. If Marc has 15 yards of fabric, how many capes can he make?

Sentence(s): _____

_____	_____ per _____	_____ _____ in all
_____		_____

LESSON 4·7

Math Message

Math Message

Name: _____

1st die _____

2nd die _____

Product (*P*) _____

20 * *P* = _____

Math Message

Name: _____

1st die _____

2nd die _____

Product (*P*) _____

20 * *P* = _____

Math Message

Name: _____

1st die _____

2nd die _____

Product (*P*) _____

20 * *P* = _____

Math Message

Name: _____

1st die _____

2nd die _____

Product (*P*) _____

20 * *P* = _____

Math Message

Name: _____

1st die _____

2nd die _____

Product (*P*) _____

20 * *P* = _____

Math Message

Name: _____

1st die _____

2nd die _____

Product (*P*) _____

20 * *P* = _____

STUDY LINK 4·7 Variables

For Problems 1–3:

◆ Find the value of x in the first number sentence.

◆ Use this value to complete the second number sentence.

1. x = number of days in a week

   $x^2 =$ _____

2. $x = \frac{1}{10}$ of 100

   $x * 78 =$ _____

3. x = largest sum possible with 2 six-sided dice

   $598 + x =$ _____

4. Count the number of letters in your first name and in your last name.

   a. My first name has _____ letters.

   b. My last name has _____ letters.

   c. Find the product of these 2 numbers. Product = _____

Answer the questions in Problems 5–11 by replacing x with the product you found in Problem 4.

5. Is x a prime or a composite number? _____

6. Is $\frac{x}{30}$ less than 1? _____

7. Which is larger, $3 * x$, or $x + 100$? _____

8. What is the median and the range for
   this set of 3 weights: 30 pounds, 52 pounds, x pounds? _____

9. There are 200 students at Henry Clissold School.
   x% speak Spanish. How many students speak Spanish? _____

10. $(3x + 5) - 7 =$ _____

11. True or false: $x^2 > 30 * x$ _____

Practice

12. $3{,}817 + 168 =$ _____

13. $52{,}517 - 281 =$ _____

Solving for Unknown Quantities

For each number story:

◆ Draw a situation diagram.

◆ Fill in the numbers. Write a ? for the unknown quantity.

◆ Write a number sentence with ☐ for the unknown.

◆ Solve the problem.

Example:

Fran bought a bag of 14 marbles from a game store. She added them to her collection. She now has 47 marbles. How many marbles did she have before she bought more?

Number sentence: $14 + \boxed{} = 47$

Solution: $\boxed{} = 33$

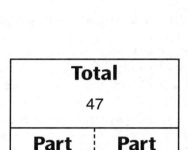

Total	
47	
Part	**Part**
14	?

Diagram

1. It was 68° when Nadine left for school. By lunchtime, it was 75°. By how many degrees had the temperature gone up?

   Number sentence: _____

   Solution: _____

2. Michael wants to buy a milkshake. With tax, it costs \$3.92, and he has \$3.43. How much more money does he need?

   Number sentence: _____

   Solution: _____

3. Lora bought 5 packages of pencils. Each package had 12 pencils in it. How many pencils did she buy in all?

   Number sentence: _____

   Solution: _____

4. Make up a problem of your own on the back of this page.

STUDY LINK 4·8

Unit 5: Family Letter

Fractions, Decimals, and Percents

Unit 5 focuses on naming numbers as fractions, decimals, and percents. Your child will use pattern blocks to review basic fraction and mixed-number concepts as well as notations. Your child will also formulate rules for finding equivalent fractions.

In *Fourth Grade Everyday Mathematics,* your child learned to convert easy fractions, such as $\frac{1}{2}$, $\frac{1}{4}$, $\frac{1}{10}$, and $\frac{3}{4}$, to equivalent decimals and percents. For example, $\frac{1}{2}$ can be renamed as 0.5 or 50%. Your child will now learn (with the use of a calculator) how to rename any fraction as a decimal and as a percent.

Unit 5 also introduces two new games: *Estimation Squeeze,* to practice estimating products; and *Frac-Tac-Toe,* to practice converting fractions to decimals and percents. These games, like others introduced earlier, are used to reinforce arithmetic skills. Both games use simple materials (calculator, number cards, and pennies or other counters) so you can play them at home.

Your child will study data about the past and compare it with current information as the American Tour continues.

Please keep this Family Letter for reference as your child works through Unit 5.

Vocabulary

Important terms in Unit 5:

bar graph A graph that uses horizontal or vertical bars to represent data.

circle graph A graph in which a circle and its interior are divided through its center into parts to show the parts of a set of data. The whole circle represents the whole set of data.

denominator The number below the line in a fraction. In a fraction representing a whole, or ONE, divided into equal parts, the denominator is the total number of equal parts. In the fraction $\frac{a}{b}$, b is the denominator.

equivalent fractions Fractions that have different denominators but name the same amount. For example, $\frac{1}{2}$ and $\frac{4}{8}$ are equivalent fractions.

improper fraction A fraction whose numerator is greater than or equal to its denominator. For example, $\frac{4}{3}$, $\frac{5}{2}$, $\frac{4}{4}$, and $\frac{24}{12}$ are improper fractions. In *Everyday Mathematics,* improper fractions are sometimes called "top-heavy" fractions.

mixed number A number that is written using both a whole number and a fraction. For example, $2\frac{1}{2}$ is a mixed number equal to $2 + \frac{1}{4}$.

numerator The number above the line in a fraction. In a fraction representing a whole, or ONE, divided into equal parts, the numerator is the number of equal parts that are being considered. In the fraction $\frac{a}{b}$, a is the numerator.

percent (%) Per hundred, or out of a hundred. For example, *48% of the students in the school are boys* means that, on average, 48 out of every 100 students in the school are boys.

Percent Circle A tool on the Geometry Template that is used to measure or draw figures that involve percents, such as *circle graphs.*

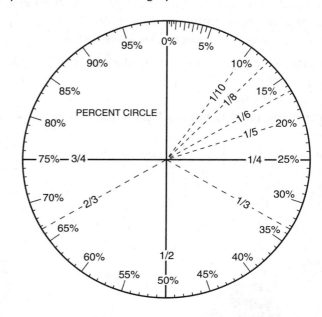

repeating decimal A decimal in which one digit or a group of digits is repeated without end. For example, 0.333... and $0.\overline{147}$ are repeating decimals.

Do-Anytime Activities

To work with your child on the concepts taught in this unit and in previous units, try these interesting and rewarding activities.

1. Help your child find fractions, decimals, and percents in the everyday world—in newspaper advertisements, on measuring tools, in recipes, in the sports section of the newspaper, and so on.

2. Over a period of time, have your child record daily temperatures in the morning and in the evening. Keep track of the temperatures in a chart. Then have your child make a graph from the data. Ask questions about the data. For example, have your child find the differences in temperatures from morning to evening or from one day to the next.

3. Practice using percents in the context of tips. For example, have your child calculate $\frac{1}{10}$ or 10% of amounts of money. Invite your child to find the tip the next time the family goes out for dinner.

4. Ask your child to identify 2-dimensional and 3-dimensional shapes around the house.

Building Skills through Games

In Unit 5, your child will practice operations and computation skills by playing the following games. For detailed instructions, see the *Student Reference Book*.

Estimation Squeeze See *Student Reference Book,* page 304.
This is a game for two players who use a single calculator. The game provides practice in estimating products.

Frac-Tac-Toe See *Student Reference Book,* pages 309–311.
This is a game for two players. Game materials include 4 each of the number cards 0–10, pennies or counters of two colors, a calculator, and a gameboard. The gameboard is a 5-by-5 number grid that resembles a bingo card. Several versions of the gameboard are shown in the *Student Reference Book.* *Frac-Tac-Toe* helps students practice converting fractions to decimals and percents.

Fraction Of See *Student Reference Book,* pages 313 and 314.
This is a game for two players. Game materials include 1 deck each of *Fraction Of* Fraction Cards and Set Cards, the *Fraction Of* Gameboard, and a record sheet. This game provides practice with multiplication of fractions and whole numbers.

Fraction/Percent Concentration See *Student Reference Book,* page 315.
This game helps students memorize some of the easy fraction/percent equivalencies. Two or three players use 1 set of *Fraction/Percent Concentration* tiles and a calculator to play.

Fraction Top–It See *Student Reference Book,* page 316.
This game is for 2–4 players. Game materials include 1 deck of 32 Fraction Cards. This game provides practice with comparing fractions.

As You Help Your Child with Homework

As your child brings assignments home, you might want to go over the instructions together, clarifying them as necessary. The answers listed below will guide you through this unit's Study Links.

Study Link 5·1

1. 9   **2.** 14   **3.** $\frac{16}{20}$, or $\frac{4}{5}$

4. $\frac{45}{50}$, or $\frac{9}{10}$ **5.** 70   **6.** 16

7. 9   **8. a.** $12   **b.** $20

c. Jen paid. $\frac{2}{5}$ of the bill: $8 \div 2 = 4$. So that means each fifth of the total was $4. Then $\frac{3}{5}$ must be $12. And $12 + $8 = $20.

9. 14   **10.** 140   **11.** 14   **12.** 140

Study Link 5·2

1. $2\frac{1}{2}$; $\frac{5}{2}$ **2.** $2\frac{4}{6}$, or $2\frac{2}{3}$; $\frac{16}{6}$, or $\frac{8}{3}$

3. $1\frac{2}{3}$; $\frac{5}{3}$ **4.** $2\frac{1}{6}$; $\frac{13}{6}$ **5.** $2\frac{5}{6}$; $\frac{17}{6}$

7. 262   **8.** 32 R4   **9.** 123   **10.** 72 R3

Study Link 5·3

1. 4   **2.** 12   **3.** 1; 4

4. $\frac{4}{4} = 1$ **5.** $\frac{6}{8} = \frac{3}{4}$ **6.** $\frac{5}{4} = 1\frac{1}{4}$

7. $\frac{9}{8}$, or $1\frac{1}{8}$ cups   **9.** 297

10. 148 R3   **11.** 74 R3   **12.** 37 R3

Study Link 5·4

1. =   **2.** ≠   **3.** ≠   **4.** =   **5.** =

6. =   **7.** =   **8.** =   **9.** 6   **10.** 21

11. 4   **12.** 40   **13.** 12   **14.** 80   **15.** 27

16. 56   **17.** 150   **18.** 70   **19.** $7.04

20. $20.03   **21.** 17 R10   **22.** 80 R4

Study Link 5·5

2. 0.4; 1.9; 20.7; 24.0; 60.9; 160.6; 181.3; 297.4; 297.9; 316.0

Study Link 5·6

1. $7\frac{79}{100}$; $7\frac{78}{100}$, or $7\frac{39}{50}$; $6\frac{21}{100}$; $4\frac{7}{10}$; $3\frac{6}{10}$, or $3\frac{3}{5}$

2. a. $\frac{15}{45}$, or $\frac{1}{3}$ **b.** $\frac{9}{45}$, or $\frac{1}{5}$ **c.** $\frac{3}{45}$, or $\frac{1}{15}$

3. $0.\overline{3}$; 0.2; $0.0\overline{6}$ **4.** 714 R6

5. 8 R4   **6.** 67 R5

Study Link 5·7

Sample answers given for Problem 1–5.

1. 0.25; 0.5; 0.75   **2.** 2.25; 2.5; 2.75

3. 0.65; 0.7; 0.775   **4.** 0.325; 0.35; 0.375

5. 0.051; 0.055; 0.059   **6.** 0.53

7. 0.2   **8.** 0.77   **9.** $0.\overline{8}$ **10.** 0.051

11. 0.043; 0.05; 0.1; 0.12; 0.2; 0.6; 0.78

12. $7.06   **13.** 6 R17   **14.** 81   **15.** 694 R3

Study Link 5·8

1. $\frac{3}{4} = 0.75 = 75\%$; $\frac{14}{16} = 0.875 = 88\%$;

$\frac{15}{25} = 0.6 = 60\%$; $\frac{17}{20} = 0.85 = 85\%$;

$\frac{3}{8} = 0.375 = 38\%$

3. $\frac{3}{8}$; $\frac{15}{25}$; $\frac{3}{4}$; $\frac{17}{20}$; $\frac{14}{16}$ **4.** $130   **5.** 10 questions

6. 97 R5   **7.** 48 R15   **8.** 32 R15   **9.** 24 R15

Study Link 5·9

2. Bar graph

3. Line graph; Temperature went up and down.

Study Link 5·10

1. a. 50%   **b.** 15%   **c.** 35%

3. 25% of the students in my class have skateboards. 25% have in-line skates. 50% have bicycles.

4. 633   **5.** 1.1636   **6.** 10 R1   **7.** 100 R4

Study Link 5·11

Check your child's circle graph.

2. 17   **3.** 23   **4.** 9   **5.** 7

Study Link 5·12

1. Mona ate 1 more cookie than Tomas. $\frac{3}{8}$ of 24 is 9; but $\frac{2}{5}$ of 25 is 10.

2. 12 students were sick. If $\frac{2}{3}$ is 24, that means $\frac{1}{3}$ is 12 students. So that means the rest of the class, or $\frac{1}{3}$ of the class, or 12 students, is sick.

4. 3   **5.** 24   **6.** 22   **7.** 24

Parts-and-Whole Fraction Practice

SRB
74 75
243

For the following problems, use counters or draw pictures to help you.

1. If 15 counters are the whole set, how many are $\frac{3}{5}$ of the set?

   _____ counters

2. If 18 counters are the whole set, how many are $\frac{7}{9}$ of the set? _____ counters

3. If 20 counters are the whole set, what fraction of the set is 16 counters? _____

4. If 50 counters are the whole set, what fraction of the set is 45 counters? _____

5. If 35 counters are half of a set, what is the whole set? _____ counters

6. If 12 counters are $\frac{3}{4}$ of a set, what is the whole set? _____ counters

7. Gerald and Michelle went on a 24-mile bike ride.
   By lunchtime, they had ridden $\frac{5}{8}$ of the total distance.

   How many miles did they have left to ride after lunch? _____ miles

8. Jen and Heather went to lunch. When the bill came, Jen discovered that she had
   only $8. Luckily, Heather had enough money to pay the other part, or $\frac{3}{5}$, of the bill.

   a. How much did Heather pay? _____   b. How much was the total bill? _____

   c. Explain how you figured out Heather's portion of the bill.

   _____

   _____

   _____

Practice

9. 3)‾42‾ _____

10. 3)‾420‾ _____

11. 30)‾420‾ _____

12. 30)‾4,200‾ _____

125

LESSON 5·1   Birthday Box

Use only numbers from one data bank below to fill in the missing values for this number story.

Reminder: oz means ounce

For her birthday, Alisha got a box containing _____ pieces of candy that weighed

_____ oz. Each piece of candy weighed _____ oz. She ate

_____ pieces of candy. The remaining _____ pieces of candy and

the box weighed _____ oz. The weight of the box is _____ oz.

1. Read the problem.

2. Think about how the missing values need to relate to each other. Which values should be greater than other values? Which should be less than other values? Are there multiples that can help you?

3. Fill in the missing values.

4. Read the problem again. Make sure the number relationships make sense.

Data Bank: Whole Numbers						
1	2	6	30	36	61	73

Data Bank: Fractions and Mixed Numbers						
$\frac{1}{3}$	$\frac{3}{4}$	$5\frac{3}{4}$	$8\frac{3}{4}$	9	15	24

STUDY LINK 5·2

Fraction and Mixed-Number Practice

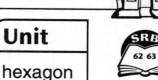

For the problems below, the hexagon is worth 1.
Write the mixed-number name and the fraction name
shown by each diagram.

Unit
hexagon

1.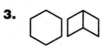

Mixed number _____

Fraction _____

2.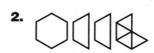

Mixed number _____

Fraction _____

3.

Mixed number _____

Fraction _____

4.

Mixed number _____

Fraction _____

5.

Mixed number _____

Fraction _____

6. Make up a mixed-number problem of your own in the space below.

Practice

7. 7)1,834 _____

8. 6)196 → _____

9. 8)984 _____

10. 9)651 → _____

LESSON 5·2   Pattern Block Fractions

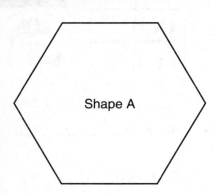

Shape A

1. Cover Shape A with trapezoid blocks.

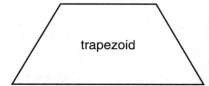

trapezoid

   a. How many trapezoid blocks
does it take to cover Shape A? _____

   b. Write a fraction for this amount. _____

   c. What fraction of Shape A is
covered by one trapezoid block? _____

2. Cover Shape A with rhombus blocks.

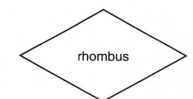

rhombus

   a. How many rhombus blocks
does it take to cover Shape A? _____

   b. Write a fraction for this amount. _____

   c. What fraction of Shape A is
covered by one rhombus block? _____

3. Cover Shape A with triangle blocks.

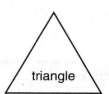

triangle

   a. How many triangle blocks
does it take to cover Shape A? _____

   b. Write a fraction for this amount. _____

   c. What fraction of Shape A is
covered by one triangle block? _____

LESSON 5·2

Pattern Blocks and Fractions

Use your △, ▱, and ⬭ pattern blocks to solve these problems.

1. Choose one pattern block and give it a value. The block can be worth ONE or a fraction of ONE. Draw the block and record its value.

The _____ is worth _____.

Use the figure you chose in Problem 1 to answer Problems 2–5.

2.

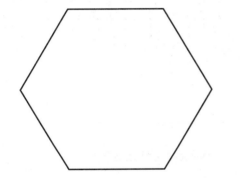

A hexagon is worth _____.

3.

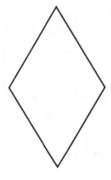

A rhombus is worth _____.

4.

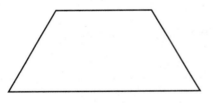

A trapezoid is worth _____.

5.

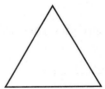

A triangle is worth _____.

6. In the space below or on another piece of paper, make a design with about 10 pattern blocks. Trace the outline of each block. (Or use the pattern-block shapes on the Geometry Template.)

7. Label each part of your design with a fraction. How much is the design worth? _____

8. Write a number model to show how you calculated the value of the design.

LESSON 5·3

Fraction-Stick Chart

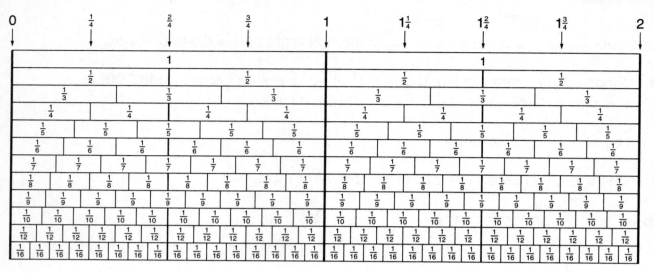

1. Using the Fraction-Stick Chart, list all the
   fractions that are equivalent to $\frac{1}{2}$. _____

   a. What pattern do you notice in the numerators for these fractions?

   _____

   _____

   b. What pattern do you notice in the denominators for these fractions?

   _____

   _____

   c. Are the patterns complete? _____

   d. What fraction is missing that would make the pattern complete? _____

2. Using the Fraction-Stick Chart, list all the fractions that are equivalent to $\frac{1}{3}$.

   _____

   a. What pattern do you notice in these fractions?

   _____

   _____

   b. Use this pattern to find the next 3 fractions that are equivalent to $\frac{1}{3}$. _____

130

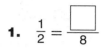

Fraction-Stick Problems

Shade the fraction sticks to help you find equivalent fractions.

1. $\dfrac{1}{2} = \dfrac{\boxed{}}{8}$

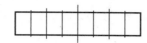

2. $\dfrac{3}{4} = \dfrac{\boxed{}}{16}$

3. $\dfrac{\boxed{}}{4} = \dfrac{2}{8} = \dfrac{\boxed{}}{16}$

Shade the fraction sticks to help you solve the addition problems.

4. $\dfrac{1}{4} + \dfrac{3}{4} =$ _____

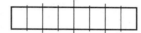

5. $\dfrac{1}{2} + \dfrac{2}{8} =$ _____

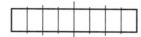

6. $\dfrac{1}{2} + \dfrac{3}{4} =$ _____

Shade the fraction sticks to help you solve the fraction number stories.

7. Joe was baking a cake. He added $\dfrac{3}{4}$ cup of white sugar and $\dfrac{3}{8}$ cup of brown sugar. How much sugar did he use in all?

_____
(unit)

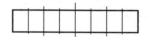

8. On the back of this page, write a number story using fractions. Then write a number model to show how you solved it.

Practice

9. $3\overline{)891}$ _____

10. $6\overline{)891} \rightarrow$ _____

11. $12\overline{)891} \rightarrow$ _____

12. $24\overline{)891} \rightarrow$ _____

STUDY LINK 5·4   Equivalent Fractions

If the fractions are equivalent, write = in the answer blank.

If the fractions are not equivalent, write ≠ (not equal to) in the answer blank.

1. $\frac{3}{4}$ _____ $\frac{9}{12}$

2. $\frac{3}{10}$ _____ $\frac{1}{5}$

3. $\frac{7}{14}$ _____ $\frac{8}{15}$

4. $\frac{10}{12}$ _____ $\frac{5}{6}$

5. $\frac{16}{100}$ _____ $\frac{8}{50}$

6. $\frac{36}{72}$ _____ $\frac{1}{2}$

7. $\frac{7}{12}$ _____ $\frac{21}{36}$

8. $\frac{8}{3}$ _____ $\frac{16}{6}$

Fill in the boxes to complete and match the equivalent fractions.

Example: $\frac{\boxed{2}}{15} = \frac{6}{45}$

9. $\frac{3}{5} = \frac{\boxed{}}{10}$

10. $\frac{2}{3} = \frac{14}{\boxed{}}$

11. $\frac{44}{55} = \frac{\boxed{}}{5}$

12. $\frac{12}{\boxed{}} = \frac{3}{10}$

13. $\frac{35}{60} = \frac{7}{\boxed{}}$

14. $\frac{9}{16} = \frac{45}{\boxed{}}$

15. $\frac{9}{36} = \frac{\boxed{}}{108}$

16. $\frac{7}{\boxed{}} = \frac{1}{8}$

17. $\frac{30}{135} = \frac{\boxed{}}{27}$

18. $\frac{10}{16} = \frac{\boxed{}}{112}$

Practice

19. $7\overline{)\$49.28}$ _____

20. $15\overline{)\$300.45}$ _____

21. $21\overline{)367} \rightarrow$ _____

22. $8\overline{)644} \rightarrow$ _____

132

LESSON 5·4 | Exploring Simplest Form

A fraction is in simplest form if no other equivalent fraction can be found by dividing the numerator and the denominator by a whole number. For example, $\frac{1}{2}$ is in simplest form.

1. Use the division rule to find equivalent fractions.

a. $\frac{4}{10}$ = _____

b. $\frac{3}{15}$ = _____

c. $\frac{4}{20}$ = _____

d. $\frac{5}{25}$ = _____

e. $\frac{6}{30}$ = _____

f. $\frac{30}{36}$ = _____

g. $\frac{35}{42}$ = _____

h. $\frac{40}{48}$ = _____

i. $\frac{45}{54}$ = _____

j. $\frac{20}{32}$ = _____

2. List the fractions from your answers in Problem 1 that are in simplest form.

_____

3. Find and list the simplest form for the remaining fractions.

_____

4. Jamie wants to be able to find the simplest form for any fraction by using the division rule and dividing only once. What should she do?

_____

_____

_____

_____

_____

_____

_____

_____

STUDY LINK 5·5 Decimal Numbers

1. Mark each number on the number line. The first one is done for you.

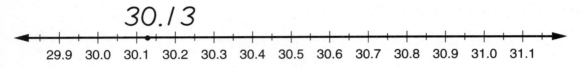

30.13　　30.72　　31.05　　29.94　　30.38

$$30.13$$

29.9　30.0　30.1　30.2　30.3　30.4　30.5　30.6　30.7　30.8　30.9　31.0　31.1

2. Round the area of each country to the nearest tenth of a square kilometer.

	Ten Smallest Countries	Area in Square Kilometers	Area Rounded to the Nearest Tenth of a Square Kilometer
1	Vatican City	0.44 km²	_____ km²
2	Monaco	1.89 km²	_____ km²
3	Nauru	20.72 km²	_____ km²
4	Tuvalu	23.96 km²	_____ km²
5	San Marino	60.87 km²	_____ km²
6	Liechtenstein	160.58 km²	_____ km²
7	Marshall Islands	181.30 km²	_____ km²
8	St. Kitts and Nevis	296.37 km²	_____ km²
9	Maldives	297.85 km²	_____ km²
10	Malta	315.98 km²	_____ km²

Source: *The Top 10 of Everything 2005*

Practice

Solve and write the fact family number sentences.

3. $32\overline{)768}$

_____ ÷ _____ = _____　　　　_____ ÷ _____ = _____

_____ * _____ = _____　　　　_____ * _____ = _____

LESSON 5·5 **Renaming Fractions as Decimals**

1. Fill in the missing numbers and shade the squares.
   Each large square is worth 1.

Whole
large square

Shade $\frac{4}{5}$ of the square.

Shade $\frac{1}{4}$ of the square.

Shade $\frac{5}{25}$ of the square.

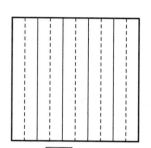

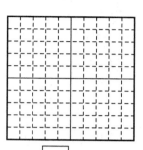

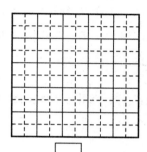

a. $\frac{4}{5} = \frac{\boxed{}}{10} = 0.\rule{1cm}{0.4pt}$

b. $\frac{1}{4} = \frac{\boxed{}}{100} = 0.\rule{1cm}{0.4pt}$

c. $\frac{5}{25} = \frac{\boxed{}}{100} = 0.\rule{1cm}{0.4pt}$

Shade $\frac{1}{25}$ of the square. Shade $\frac{4}{50}$ of the square.

Write the shaded part as a fraction and as a decimal.

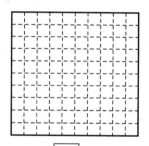

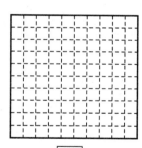

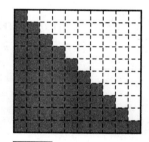

d. $\frac{1}{25} = \frac{\boxed{}}{100} = 0.\rule{1cm}{0.4pt}$

e. $\frac{4}{50} = \frac{\boxed{}}{100} = 0.\rule{1cm}{0.4pt}$

f. $\frac{\boxed{}}{\boxed{}} = 0.\rule{1cm}{0.4pt}$

2. Write each number below as a decimal. Then use the letters to mark
   the decimals on the number line.

a. $\frac{3}{4} = \rule{0.6cm}{0.4pt}.\rule{0.8cm}{0.4pt}$

b. $\frac{3}{10} = \rule{0.6cm}{0.4pt}.\rule{0.8cm}{0.4pt}$

c. $\frac{2}{5} = \rule{0.6cm}{0.4pt}.\rule{0.8cm}{0.4pt}$

d. $\frac{27}{100} = \rule{0.6cm}{0.4pt}.\rule{0.8cm}{0.4pt}$

e. $\frac{11}{25} = \rule{0.6cm}{0.4pt}.\rule{0.8cm}{0.4pt}$

f. $\frac{17}{50} = \rule{0.6cm}{0.4pt}.\rule{0.8cm}{0.4pt}$

g. $\frac{6}{5} = \rule{0.6cm}{0.4pt}.\rule{0.8cm}{0.4pt}$

h. $1\frac{5}{50} = \rule{0.6cm}{0.4pt}.\rule{0.8cm}{0.4pt}$

```
|__|__|__|__|__|__|__|__|__|__|__|__|__|__|__|__|__|__|__|__|__|__|__|__|__|__|__|__|__|__|
0   0.1  0.2  0.3  0.4  0.5  0.6  0.7  0.8  0.9  1.0  1.1  1.2  1.3  1.4  1.5
```

LESSON 5·5 Rounding Whole Numbers and Decimals

Draw number lines to help you round the numbers below.

Example: Round 37 to the nearest ten.

◆ Draw and label a number line from the first multiple of 10 less than 37 (that is, 30) to the first multiple of 10 greater than 37 (that is, 40). Mark and label the point halfway between these endpoints (35).

◆ Find 37 on the number line. Mark and label it.

◆ Since 37 is closer to 40, round 37 up to 40.

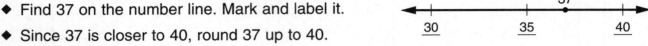

1. Round 26 to the nearest ten.

_____

2. Round 1,256 to the nearest hundred.

_____

3. Round 1,256 to the nearest thousand.

_____

4. Round 2.6 to the nearest whole number.

_____

5. Round 182.73 to the nearest ten.

_____

6. Round 1,009 to the nearest hundred.

_____

LESSON 5·6 · Fraction-Stick Chart and Decimal Number Line

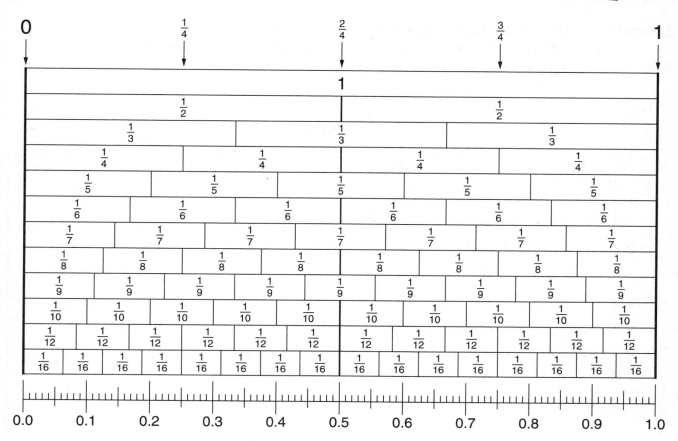

LESSON 5·6

Table of Decimal Equivalents for Fractions

Example: To find the decimal equivalent for $\frac{1}{4}$, use the row for the denominator 4. Go to the column for the numerator 1. The box where the row and the column meet shows the decimal 0.25.

Numerator

Denominator	1	2	3	4	5	6	7	8	9	10
1	1.0	2.0	3.0							
2	0.5	1.0	1.5							
3							$2.\overline{3}$			
4	0.25				1.25					
5	0.2				1.0					
6										$1.\overline{6}$
7	$0.\overline{142857}$									
8					0.625					
9								$0.\overline{8}$		
10	0.1									

STUDY LINK 5·6 Decimals, Fractions, and Mixed Numbers

1. Convert each decimal measurement to a mixed number.

Longest Road and Rail Tunnels in the U.S.	Decimal Length	Mixed-Number Length
Cascade Tunnel (Washington)	7.79 miles	_____ miles
Flathead Tunnel (Montana)	7.78 miles	_____ miles
Moffat Tunnel (Colorado)	6.21 miles	_____ miles
Hoosac Tunnel (Massachusetts)	4.7 miles	_____ miles
BART Transbay Tubes (San Francisco, CA)	3.6 miles	_____ miles

Source: *The Top 10 of Everything 2005*

2. The longest one-word name of any place in America is Chargoggagoggmanchauggagoggchaubunagungamaugg.

   This name for a lake near Webster, Massachusetts, is 45 letters long. It is a Native American name that means "You fish on your side, I'll fish on mine, and no one fishes in the middle." Use this word to answer the problems below.

   a. What fraction of the word is made up of the letter *g*? _____ $=$ _____

   b. What fraction of the word is made up of the letter *a*? _____ $=$ _____

   c. What fraction of the word is made up of the letter *c*? _____ $=$ _____

3. In the space above, write the decimal equivalents for the fractions in Problem 2.

Practice

4. $10\overline{)7{,}146}$ → _____   5. $10\overline{)84}$ → _____   6. $10\overline{)675}$ → _____

LESSON 5·6
Fractions and Decimals

Write the fraction name and decimal name for the shaded portion of each square. Use your transparent 100-grid to check your answer. For Problem 9, color the grid to show a fraction and then write the fraction and decimal name for the shaded portion of the square.

1.

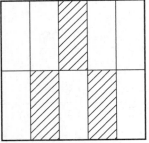

$$\frac{3}{10} = 0.\underline{3}$$

2.

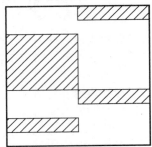

$$\frac{}{} = 0.\underline{}$$

3.

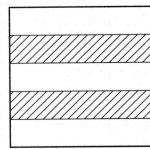

$$\frac{}{} = 0.\underline{}$$

4.

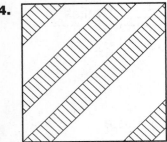

$$\frac{}{} = 0.\underline{}$$

5.

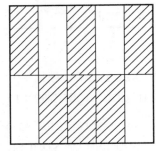

$$\frac{}{} = 0.\underline{}$$

6.

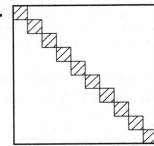

$$\frac{}{} = 0.\underline{}$$

7.

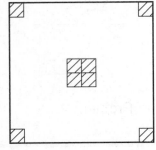

$$\frac{}{} = 0.\underline{}$$

8.

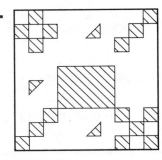

$$\frac{}{} = 0.\underline{}$$

9.

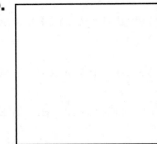

$$\frac{}{} = 0.\underline{}$$

LESSON 5·6 | 100-Grids

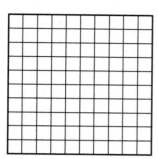

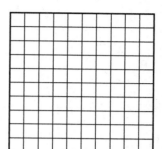

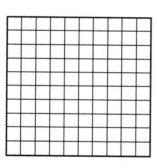

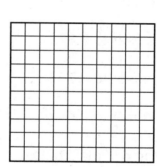

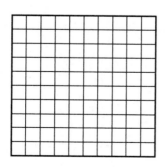

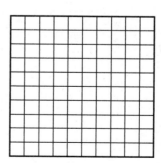

STUDY LINK 5·7   Decimal Comparisons

Write three numbers between each pair of numbers.

1. 0 and 1   ———————— , ———————— , ————————

2. 2 and 3   ———————— , ———————— , ————————

3. 0.6 and 0.8   ———————— , ———————— , ————————

4. 0.3 and 0.4   ———————— , ———————— , ————————

5. 0.06 and 0.05   ———————— , ———————— , ————————

Circle the correct answer to each question.

6. Which is closer to 0.6?   0.5   or   0.53

7. Which is closer to 0.3?   0.02   or   0.2

8. Which is closer to 0.8?   0.77   or   0.85

9. Which is closer to 0.75?   0.6   or $0.\overline{8}$

10. Which is closer to 0.04?   0.3   or   0.051

11. Arrange the decimals below in order from least to greatest.

    0.12   0.05   0.2   0.78   0.6   0.043   0.1

    ————   ————   ————   ————   ————   ————   ————

Practice

12. $9\overline{)\$63.54}$ ————————

13. $45\overline{)287} \rightarrow$ ————————

14. $7\overline{)567}$ ————————

15. $7\overline{)4,861} \rightarrow$ ————————

STUDY LINK 5·8 — Percent Problems

1. Convert the following fractions to decimals and percents. Round to the nearest whole percent.

Fraction	Decimal	Percent
$\frac{3}{4}$		
$\frac{14}{16}$		
$\frac{15}{25}$		
$\frac{17}{20}$		
$\frac{3}{8}$		

2. On the back of this page, explain how you could find the percent equivalent to $\frac{17}{20}$ without using a calculator.

3. Write the five fractions from Problem 1 in order from least to greatest.

   _____   _____   _____   _____   _____

4. Katie spent 50% of her money on shoes for soccer. The shoes cost $65. How much money did Katie start with? _____

5. Tom got 70% of the questions correct on a music test. If he got 7 questions correct, how many questions were on the test? _____

Practice

6. $10\overline{)975}$ → _____

7. $20\overline{)972}$ → _____

8. $30\overline{)975}$ → _____

9. $40\overline{)975}$ → _____

LESSON 5·8 | Solving Percent Number Stories

Solve.

1. Paul has 150 marbles in his collection. How many marbles are about 25% of the collection?

   _____

   About how many marbles are 66%? _____

2. Beatrice decided to sell some of her doll collection. She sold 20 dolls. This was 40% of her collection. How many dolls did she have left?

   _____

3. Each day, the bakery makes pastries: 25% are chocolate donuts, 37.5% are butter cookies, 25% are breakfast buns, and the rest are the daily special. There are 90 breakfast buns.

   How many pastries are made each day? _____

   What percent of each day's pastries are the daily special? _____

   How many of the daily special pastries are made? _____

4. After the first 85 days of school, a fifth-grade class had perfect attendance for 80% of that time. How many days did the class have perfect attendance?

   _____

5. Write a percent of story problem for your partner to solve. Remember that you must provide either the whole, or an amount and the percent of the whole that it represents.

   _____

   _____

   _____

   _____

STUDY LINK
5·9 | **Graphs**

Brenda;s class made a list of their favorite colors. Here are the results.

Blue 8   Red 7   Yellow 3   Green 2   Other 4

1. Circle each graph that correctly represents the data above. (There may be more than one.)

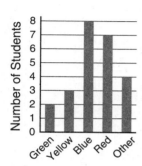   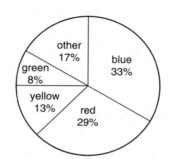   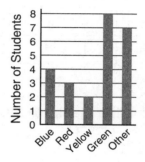

Marsha kept track of low temperatures. Here are the results for the end of May:

May 17	50°F	May 18	63°F	May 19	58°F	May 20	60°F
May 21	65°F	May 22	57°F	May 23	58°F	May 24	65°F
May 25	68°F	May 26	70°F	May 27	66°F	May 28	65°F
May 29	64°F	May 30	68°F	May 31	74°F		

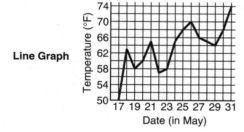   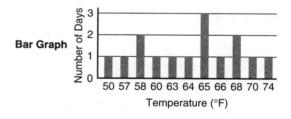

2. Which graph do you think is more helpful for answering the question, "On how many days was the low temperature 65°F?" _____

3. Which graph do you think is more helpful for showing trends in the temperature for the last two weeks of May? _____

4. On the back of this page, explain your choices for Problems 2 and 3.

145

LESSON 5·9 | **Finding Equivalent Fractions**

1. Fill in the blanks to show how the multiplication rule or the division rule is used to find equivalent fractions.

a. $\dfrac{6\ \boxed{}}{8\ \boxed{}} = \dfrac{42}{56}$

b. $\dfrac{72\ \boxed{}}{81\ \boxed{}} = \dfrac{8}{9}$

c. $\dfrac{56\ \boxed{}}{63\ \boxed{}} = \dfrac{8}{9}$

d. $\dfrac{3\ \boxed{}}{4\ \boxed{}} = \dfrac{9\ \boxed{}}{12\ \boxed{}} = \dfrac{27\ \boxed{}}{36\ \boxed{}} = \dfrac{54\ \boxed{}}{72\ \boxed{}} = \dfrac{6\ \boxed{}}{8\ \boxed{}} = \dfrac{3}{4}$

2. Fill in the blanks to make equivalent fractions.

a. $\dfrac{2}{6} = \dfrac{\boxed{}}{42}$

b. $\dfrac{8}{56} = \dfrac{1}{\boxed{}}$

c. $\dfrac{\boxed{}}{33} = \dfrac{1}{3}$

d. $\dfrac{3}{\boxed{}} = \dfrac{9}{27}$

e. $\dfrac{9}{4} = \dfrac{\boxed{}}{8}$

f. $\dfrac{\boxed{}}{110} = \dfrac{12}{11}$

3. Circle T or F.

a. $\dfrac{54}{72} > \dfrac{3}{4}$ T   F

b. $\dfrac{9}{12} = \dfrac{3}{4}$ T   F

c. $\dfrac{9}{8} < \dfrac{8}{9}$ T   F

d. $\dfrac{2}{6} = \dfrac{200}{600}$ T   F

e. $\dfrac{3}{4} = \dfrac{1}{4} + \dfrac{1}{2}$ T   F

f. $\dfrac{10}{4} = \dfrac{4}{4} + \dfrac{4}{4} + \dfrac{1}{2}$ T   F

LESSON 5·10 **Circle Graph**

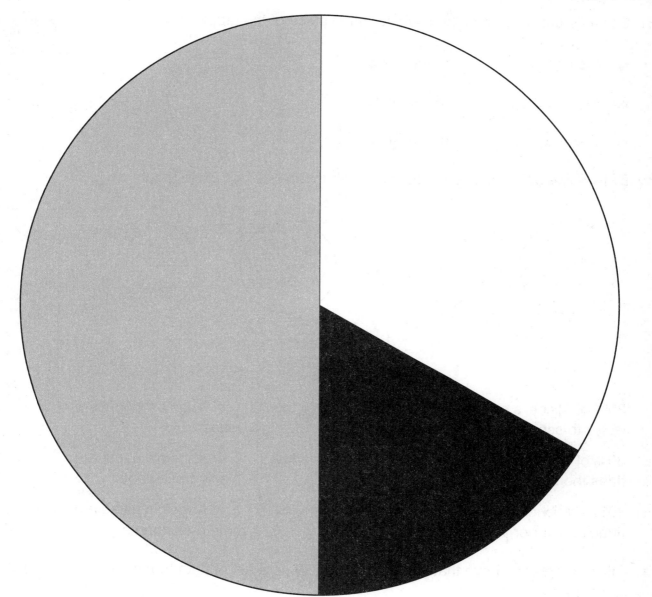

STUDY LINK 5·10 | Circle Graphs and Collecting Data

1. Estimate the percent of the circle for each piece of the graph at the right.

   SRB 125 126

   a. A is about _____ of the circle.

   b. B is about _____ of the circle.

   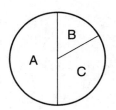

   c. C is about _____ of the circle.

2. Draw a line connecting each data set with the most likely circle graph.

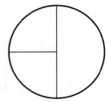 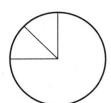 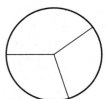 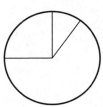

30% of Michel's class walks to school.	25% of Jeannene's toy cars are blue.	$\frac{1}{8}$ of Angelo's pants are jeans.
30% of Michel's class rides the bus.	10% of Jeannene's toy cars are striped.	$\frac{1}{8}$ of Angelo's pants are black dress pants.
40% of Michel's class rides in a car or van.	65% of Jeannene's toy cars are red.	$\frac{3}{4}$ of Angelo's pants are blue dress pants.

3. Circle the graph above that you did not use. Write a set of data to match that circle graph.

   _____

   _____

Practice

4. $6\overline{)3,798}$ _____

5. $7\overline{)8.145}$ _____

6. $2\overline{)21} \rightarrow$ _____

7. $8\overline{)804} \rightarrow$ _____

148

STUDY LINK 5·10

Circle Graphs and Collecting Data *cont.*

The Number of States We've Been In

8. Talk with an adult at home and think of all the states you have visited. (Be sure to include the state you're living in.) Look at the map below to help you remember.

   Use a pencil or crayon to mark each state you have visited.

   Don't count any state that you have flown over in an airplane unless the plane landed, and you left the airport.

9. Count the number of states you have marked.

   I have been in _____ states in my lifetime.

10. Now ask the adult to mark the map to show the states he or she has been in, using a different color or mark from yours.

    Keep a tally as states are marked.

    The adult I interviewed has visited _____ states.

Note: Alaska and Hawaii are not shown to scale.

Student and adult: This data is important for an upcoming lesson on data organization. Please bring this completed Study Link back to school tomorrow.

STUDY LINK 5·11 — What's in a Landfill?

People who study landfills have estimated the percent of landfill space
(volume) taken up by paper, food, plastic, and so on.

Space in landfills taken up by:

Paper. 50%

Food and yard waste. 13%

Plastic 10%

Metal 6%

Glass 1%

Other waste. 20%

Think of it this way:
For every 100 boxes of garbage
hauled to the dump, expect that
about 50 boxes could be filled with
paper, 6 with metal, 1 with glass,
and so on.

1. Cut out the Percent Circle. Use it to make a circle graph for the data in the
   table. (Remember to label the graph and give it a title.)

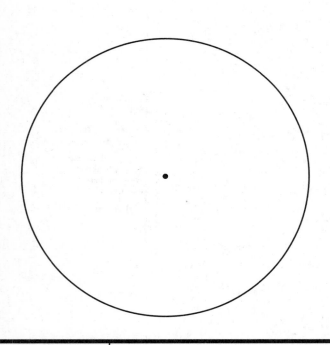

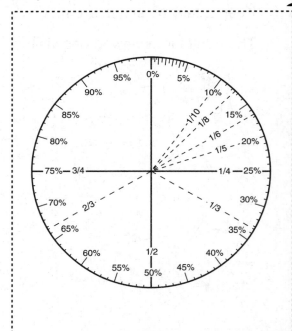

Practice

2. 23)391 _____

3. 17)391 _____

4. 43)387 _____

5. 37)259 _____

STUDY LINK 5·12 | **Finding "Fractions of"**

Solve.

1. Tomas ate $\frac{3}{8}$ of a bag of 24 cookies. Mona ate $\frac{2}{5}$ of a bag of 25 cookies. Who ate more cookies? Explain your answer.

_____

_____

_____

_____

_____

2. On Thursday, 24 fifth-grade students came to school. That was only $\frac{2}{3}$ of the total class. The rest were home sick. How many students were sick? Explain your answer.

_____

_____

_____

_____

_____

3. Mario was on a 21-mile hiking trail. He walked $\frac{3}{7}$ of the trail before stopping for lunch. How far did he walk before lunch? Explain your answer.

_____

_____

_____

_____

_____

Practice

4. $52\overline{)156}$ _____

5. $24\overline{)576}$ _____

6. $13\overline{)286}$ _____

7. $22\overline{)528}$ _____

151

LESSON 5·12 | Mathematics Instruction in History

Throughout our nation's history, students have learned mathematics in different ways and have spent their time working on different kinds of problems. This is because people's views of what students can and should learn are constantly changing.

1. *1840s* It was discovered that children could be very good at mental arithmetic, and students began to solve mental arithmetic problems as early as age 4. A school in Connecticut reported that its arithmetic champion could mentally multiply 314,521,325 by 231,452,153 in $5\frac{1}{2}$ minutes.

   After studying arithmetic two hours per day for 7 to 9 years, 94% of eighth graders in Boston in 1845 could solve the following problem. Try to solve it.

   What is $\frac{1}{2}$ of $\frac{1}{3}$ of 9 hours and 18 minutes?

   _____
   (unit)

   Explain your solution: _____

   _____

   _____

   _____

2. *1870s* Many textbooks were step-by-step guides on how to solve various problems. Students were given problems and answers. They had to show how the rules in the textbook could be used to produce the given answers.

   Here is a problem from around 1870 (without the answer) given to students at the end of 6 to 8 years of elementary arithmetic study. Try to solve it.

   I was married at the age of 21. If I live 19 years longer,
   I will have been married 60 years. What is my age now? _____
   (unit)

   Explain your solution: _____

   _____

   _____

   _____

   _____

STUDY LINK 5·13 | **Unit 6: Family Letter**

Using Data; Addition and Subtraction of Fractions

The authors of *Everyday Mathematics* believe that students should work substantially with data. Unit 6 is designed to present and teach relevant data skills and concepts, allowing your child ample opportunities to practice organizing and analyzing the data that he or she collects.

The data that your child collects at first will usually be an unorganized set of numbers. After organizing the data using a variety of methods, he or she will study the **landmarks** of the data. The following terms are called landmarks because they show important features of the data.

- ◆ The **maximum** is the largest data value observed.

- ◆ The **minimum** is the smallest data value observed.

- ◆ The **range** is the difference between the maximum and the minimum.

- ◆ The **mode** is the most popular data value—the value observed most often.

- ◆ The **median** is the middle data value observed.

- ◆ The **mean,** commonly known as the average, is a central value for a set of data.

At the end of the unit, students will demonstrate their skills by conducting a survey of their peers, gathering and organizing the data, analyzing their results, and writing a summary report.

Your child will continue the American Tour by studying Native American measurements for length and distance, based on parts of the body. Students will convert these body measures to personal measures by measuring their fingers, hands, and arms in both metric and U.S. customary units. In addition, your child will learn how to read a variety of contour-type maps, such as climate, precipitation, and growing-seasons maps.

Finally, students will explore addition and subtraction of fractions by using a clock face and fraction sticks. They will learn to find common denominators and apply this skill to add and subtract fractions with unlike denominators.

Please keep this Family Letter for reference as your child works through Unit 6.

Vocabulary

Important terms in Unit 6:

angle of separation In *Everyday Mathematics,* the angle measure between spread fingers. The figure shows the angle of separation between a person's thumb and first finger.

Angle of separation

common denominator Any number except zero that is a multiple of the denominators of two or more fractions. For example, the fractions $\frac{1}{2}$ and $\frac{2}{3}$ have common denominators 6, 12, 18, and so on.

contour line A curve on a map through places where a certain measurement (such as temperature or elevation) is the same. Often, contour lines separate regions that have been colored differently to show a range of conditions.

cubit An ancient unit of length, measured from the point of the elbow to the end of the middle finger. A cubit is about 18 inches.

decennial Occurring every 10 years.

fair game A game in which each player has the same chance of winning. If any player has an advantage or disadvantage, then the game is not fair.

fathom A unit used by people who work with boats and ships to measure depths underwater and lengths of cables. A fathom is now defined as 6 feet.

great span The distance from the tip of the thumb to the tip of the little finger (pinkie), when the hand is stretched as far as possible.

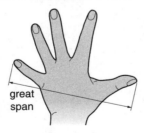

great span

landmark A notable feature of a data set. Landmarks include the *median, mode, maximum, minimum,* and *range.*

line plot A sketch of data in which check marks, Xs, or other marks above a labeled line show the frequency of each value.

map legend (map key) A diagram that explains the symbols, markings, and colors on a map.

mode The value or values that occur most often in a set of data.

normal span The distance from the tip of the thumb to the tip of the first (index) finger of an outstretched hand. Also called *span.*

normal span

population In data collection, the group of people or objects that is the focus of the study.

range The difference between the *maximum* and *minimum* in a set of data.

sample A part of a population chosen to represent the whole population.

simplest form A fraction less than 1 is in simplest form if there is no number other than 1 that divides its numerator and denominator evenly. A mixed number is in simplest form if its fractional part is in simplest form.

stem-and-leaf plot A display of data in which digits with larger place values are "stems" and digits with smaller place values are "leaves."
Data list: 24, 24, 25, 26, 27, 27, 28, 31, 31, 32, 32, 36, 36, 36, 41, 41, 43, 45, 48, 50, 52

Stem-and-leaf plot

Stems (10s)	Leaves (1s)
2	4 4 5 6 7 7 8
3	1 1 2 2 6 6 6
4	1 1 3 5 8
5	0 2

survey A study that collects data.

Do-Anytime Activities

To work with your child on the concepts taught in this unit and in previous units, try these interesting and rewarding activities.

1. Have your child design and conduct an informal survey. Help him or her collect and organize the data, and then describe the data using data landmarks. Challenge your child to create different ways to present the data.

2. Encourage your child to develop his or her own set of personal measures for both metric and U.S. customary units.

Building Skills through Games

In this unit, your child will work on his or her understanding of angles and the addition and subtraction of fractions by playing the following games. For detailed instructions, see the *Student Reference Book.*

Divisibility Dash See *Student Reference Book,* page 302. This is a game for two or three players. Game materials include 4 each of the number cards 0–9 as well as 2 each of the number cards 2, 3, 5, 6, 9, and 10. This game provides practice in recognizing multiples and using divisibility rules in a context that also develops speed.

Frac-Tac-Toe See *Student Reference Book,* pages 309–311. This is a game for two players. Game materials include 4 each of the number cards 0–10, pennies or counters of two colors, a calculator, and a gameboard. The gameboard is a 5-by-5 number grid that resembles a bingo card. Several versions of the gameboard are shown in the *Student Reference Book. Frac-Tac-Toe* helps students practice converting fractions to decimals and percents. In Unit 6, students practice fraction/decimal conversions.

Fraction Capture See *Math Journal,* page 198. This is a game for two players and requires 2 six-sided dice and a gameboard. Partners roll dice to form fractions and then attempt to capture squares on a *Fraction Capture* gameboard. This game provides practice in finding equivalent fractions and in adding fractions.

As You Help Your Child with Homework

As your child brings assignments home, you might want to go over the instructions together, clarifying them as necessary. The answers listed below will guide you through this unit's Study Links.

Study Link 6·1

3. a. 59 **b.** 24 **c.** 33

d. 36 **e.** 39.5

5. 18.43 **6.** 16

Study Link 6·2

2. a. cm; ft **b.** ounces; gal; liters

c. m; miles **d.** cm; ft; mm

e. kg; lb; grams

3. 2,686 **6.** 141.63

Study Link 6·3

1. 73; maximum **2.** 19 **3.** 53

4. Sample answer: Cross off the highest and lowest values—31 and 73. Continue by crossing off the highest and lowest values remaining, so that only one number, 53, remains.

5. 3,286 **8.** 65,250

Study Link 6·4

1. Tapes and CDs **2.** Books and magazines

3. Movie tickets **4.** 5,593

5. 16,539 **6.** 582 R3 **7.** 75,896

Study Link 6·5

Sample answers given for Problems 1–3.

1. 5, 7, 7, 8, 8, 9, 10, 13, 14, 15, 15, 15, 20

2.
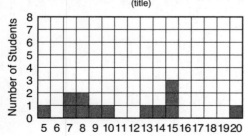
Minutes Needed to Get Ready for Bed (title)

3. The number of minutes it takes to get ready for bed

5. 443 **7.** 1,839

Study Link 6·6

1. Sample answer: Ages of the oldest people we know
Title: The Oldest People Our Class Knows
Unit: Years

4. a. 32 **b.** 99 **c.** 66 **d.** 78.5

5. 12,495 **7.** 8,484

Study Link 6·7

1. California; Arizona **2.** Montana; Washington

4. 2,086 **6.** 81

Study Link 6·8

1. 2 **2.** 0 **3.** less than 1

4. Sample answer:

 less than $\frac{3}{4}$

5. Answers vary.

Study Link 6·9

1. $\frac{22}{15}$, or $1\frac{7}{15}$ **2.** $\frac{1}{18}$

3. $\frac{9}{4}$, or $2\frac{1}{4}$ **4.** 4; $7\frac{3}{4}$

5. $5\frac{5}{6}$

Study Link 6·10

1. $\frac{18}{22} - \frac{11}{22} = \frac{7}{22}$ **2.** $\frac{20}{36} - \frac{9}{36} = \frac{11}{36}$

3. $\frac{21}{30} + \frac{8}{30} = \frac{29}{30}$ **4.** $\frac{21}{30} - \frac{8}{30} = \frac{13}{30}$

5. $\frac{19}{18}$, or $1\frac{1}{18}$ **6.** $\frac{59}{42}$, or $1\frac{17}{42}$

7. $\frac{1}{6}$ **8.** $\frac{3}{4}$

9. $\frac{2}{12}$, or $\frac{1}{6}$ **10.** $\frac{1}{2}$

11. $\frac{1}{3}$ **12.** $\frac{23}{12}$, or $1\frac{11}{12}$

13. $\frac{23}{12}$, or $1\frac{11}{12}$ **14.** $\frac{19}{12}$, or $1\frac{7}{12}$

The Standing Long Jump

Ms. Perez's physical education class participated in the standing long jump. Following are the results rounded to the nearest inch.

| 24 | 35 | 33 | 48 | 33 | 48 | 27 | 35 | 27 | 55 | 43 | 24 |
| 55 | 33 | 52 | 33 | 29 | 59 | 26 | 59 | 48 | 37 | 42 | 42 |

1. Organize these data on the line plot below.

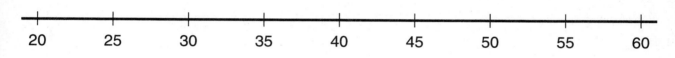

```
+     +     +     +     +     +     +     +     +
20    25    30    35    40    45    50    55    60
```

2. Make a bar graph for these data.

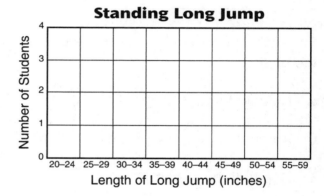

Standing Long Jump

Number of Students

4
3
2
1
0

20–24 25–29 30–34 35–39 40–44 45–49 50–54 55–59

Length of Long Jump (inches)

3. Find the following landmarks for the standing long jump data:

a. Maximum: _____ in.   **b.** Minimum: _____ in.

c. Mode: _____ in.   **d.** Median: _____ in.

e. Mean (average): _____ in. (Use a calculator. Add the distances and divide the sum by the number of jumps. Round to the nearest tenth.)

Practice

4. $48 * 29 =$ _____

5. 98.25
   $- 79.82$

6. $24\overline{)384}$

7. $767.5 + 30.82 =$ _____

157

STUDY LINK 6·2 Standard and Nonstandard Units

1. Use your body measures to find three objects that are about the size of each measurement below.

SRB
397

a. 1 cubit

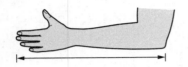

b. 1 great span

great
span

c. 1 finger width

_____   _____   _____

_____   _____   _____

_____   _____   _____

2. For each problem below, mark the unit or units you *could* use to measure the object.

a. Height of your ceiling	○ cm	○ ft	○ lb	○ miles
b. Amount of milk in a pitcher	○ cm	○ ounces	○ gal	○ liters
c. Depth of the ocean	○ m	○ ounces	○ gal	○ miles
d. Length of a bee	○ cm	○ ft	○ mm	○ liters
e. Weight of a nickel	○ in.	○ kg	○ lb	○ grams

Practice

3. $34 * 79 =$ _____

4. $\begin{array}{r} 8{,}201 \\ -2{,}190 \\ \hline \end{array}$

5. $6\overline{)4{,}152}$

6. $59.46 + 82.17 =$ _____

LESSON 6·2 · Metric Measures and Conversions

On metric rulers, centimeters (cm) are divided into 10 equal parts. Each part is called a millimeter (mm).

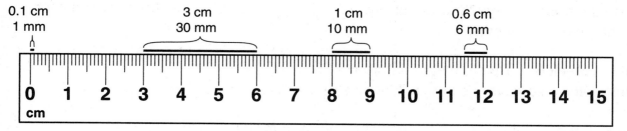

1. Measure each line segment to the nearest tenth of a centimeter and then to the nearest millimeter.

   a. _____   _____   _____

   b. _____   _____   _____

   c. _____   _____   _____

2. Draw a line segment that is 6.5 cm long. What is its length in millimeters?

   _____

3. Describe a pattern you see when you measure the same line segment in centimeters and in millimeters.

   _____

   _____

   _____

4. If you know that a line segment is 32 mm long, explain how to find its length in centimeters without measuring.

   _____

   _____

   _____

LESSON 6·2

Another Look at Personal Measures

Different people have different body measures, but is there a relationship between an individual's personal measures? For example, does knowing a person's arm span help predict that person's height? In this activity, you will compare the class measurements for palm width and joint length.

1. Make a prediction: Do students with greater palm widths also have greater joint lengths? _____

2. Collect the data for palm widths and joint lengths in millimeters that you and your classmates recorded on journal page 168.

3. Make a table on the back of this page to organize the data.

Example:

Student	Palm Width	Joint Length
1	70 mm	30 mm
2		

4. What are the landmarks for this data?

Palm Width

Minimum _____	Maximum _____	Mode _____
Median _____	Mean _____	Range _____

Joint Length

Minimum _____	Maximum _____	Mode _____
Median _____	Mean _____	Range _____

5. What relationships exist between the Palm Width and Joint Length data?

_____

6. Explain why the data does or does not support your prediction.

_____

_____

160

STUDY LINK 6·3 **Reading a Stem-and-Leaf Plot**

Use the information below to answer the questions.

Jamal was growing sunflowers. After eight weeks, he measured the height of his sunflowers in inches. He recorded the heights in the stem-and-leaf plot below.

1. How tall is the tallest sunflower? _____ in.

Which landmark is the height of the tallest flower? Circle its name.

minimum   mode

maximum   mean

2. How many sunflowers did Jamal measure? _____ sunflowers.

3. What is the mode for his measurements? _____ in.

4. Explain how to find the median for his measurements.

_____

_____

_____

_____

_____

Height of Sunflowers (inches)

Stems (10s)	Leaves (1s)
3	9 1
4	7 6 9 2 9
5	2 3 3 5 2 8 7 3
6	5 3 4
7	3

Practice

5. 62 * 53 = _____

6. 6,711
     − 4,140
     _____

7. 22)‾398‾ → _____

8. 725 * 90 = _____

LESSON 6·3 | **Using a Half-Circle Protractor**

Example: To measure angle *PQR* with a half-circle protractor:

Step 1 Lay the baseline of the protractor on $\overrightarrow{QR}$.

Step 2 Slide the protractor so the center of the baseline is over the vertex of the angle, point *Q*.

Step 3 Read the degree measure where $\overrightarrow{QP}$ crosses the edge of the protractor. There are two scales on the protractor. Use the scale that makes sense for the size of the angle you are measuring.

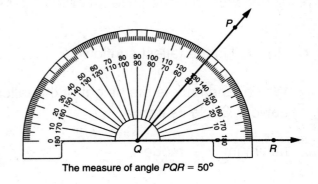

The measure of angle *PQR* = 50°

Use your half-circle protractor to find the measures of the angles below.

1. The measure of angle *GET* is _____.

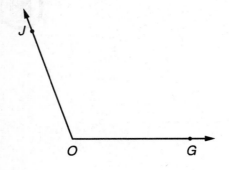

2. The measure of angle *TOP* is _____.

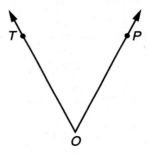

3. The measure of angle *JOG* is _____.

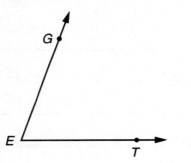

4. The measure of obtuse angle *LID* is _____.

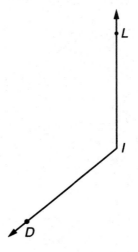

LESSON 6·4 | Math Message

Find the minimum, maximum, range, mode, and median for this stem-and-leaf plot.

Unit: inches

Stems (10s)	Leaves (1s)
4	4 7
5	0 8 6 0
6	1 5 3

minimum _____

maximum _____

range _____

mode _____

median _____

✂ -

Name _____ Date _____ Time _____

LESSON 6·4 | Math Message

Find the minimum, maximum, range, mode, and median for this stem-and-leaf plot.

Unit: inches

Stems (10s)	Leaves (1s)
4	4 7
5	0 8 6 0
6	1 5 3

minimum _____

maximum _____

range _____

mode _____

median _____

How Much Do Students Spend?

A fifth-grade class collected data about class spending per month on various items. Below are some of the results.

◆ A median amount of $6 per month was spent for books and magazines.

◆ A median amount of $10 per month was spent for tapes and CDs.

◆ A median amount of $8 per month was spent for movie tickets.

The number-line plots below display the data. Match the plots with the items: books and magazines, tapes and CDs, and movie tickets.

1. _____

```
                                  X   X
                                  X   X
                              X   X   X
                    X   X     X   X   X   X               X
   ────────────────────────────────────────────────────────────
     1   2   3   4   5   6   7   8   9  10  11  12  13  14  15  16
```

2. _____

```
                                  X
          X       X       X       X
          X       X   X   X   X   X       X
   ────────────────────────────────────────────────────────────
     1   2   3   4   5   6   7   8   9  10  11  12  13  14  15  16
```

3. _____

```
                          X           X
                          X           X
                  X   X   X   X   X   X
                  X   X   X   X   X   X   X
   ────────────────────────────────────────────────────────────
     1   2   3   4   5   6   7   8   9  10  11  12  13  14  15  16
```

Practice

4. 119 * 47 = _____

5. 9,402
     + 7,137

6. 9)5,241 → _____

7. 9,487 * 8 = _____

164

LESSON 6·4 | More Mystery Plots

Match each of the following data set descriptions with the appropriate line plot. Then fill in the unit for each plot.

1. The number of days students were tardy in the first 2 weeks of school.

2. The ages of students participating in organized sports at a community center.

3. The number of books read by each of Ms. Wong's fifth-grade students in 1 month.

4. The number of minutes it takes each fifth-grade student to get ready for school.

Plot A

Unit: _____

```
        X   X
        X   X           X
        X   X   X   X   X
        X   X   X   X   X
        X   X   X   X   X   X
        X   X   X   X   X   X
    X   X   X   X   X   X   X
+---+---+---+---+---+---+---+---+--
0   5  10  15  20  25  30  35  40
```

Plot B

Unit: _____

```
            X
            X
            X
            X
            X
            X
            X   X
    X   X   X   X
    X   X   X   X   X
    X   X   X   X   X
    X   X   X   X   X
+---+---+---+---+---+---+---+---+--
0   2   4   6   8  10  12  14  16
```

Plot C

Unit: _____

```
X           X
X   X   X
X   X   X
X   X   X
X   X   X
X   X   X   X
X   X   X   X               X
X   X   X   X   X   X   X   X
+--+--+--+--+--+--+--+--+--+--+--+--+--+--+--
0  1  2  3  4  5  6  7  8  9 10 11 12 13 14
```

Plot D

Unit: _____

```
                                        X
                                        X
                                    X   X
                                    X   X   X           X
                                X   X   X   X   X   X   X
                            X   X   X   X   X   X   X   X
                            X   X   X   X   X   X   X   X
                        X   X   X   X   X   X   X   X   X
                    X   X   X   X   X   X   X   X   X   X
                    X   X   X   X   X   X   X   X   X   X
+--+--+--+--+--+--+--+--+--+--+--+--+
3  4  5  6  7  8  9 10 11 12 13 14
```

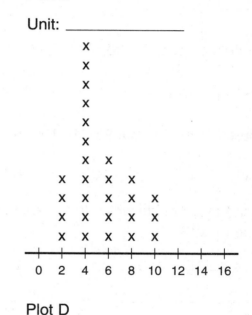

165

LESSON 6·4 Making the Grade

Ms. Hallaran has her students collect their spelling test scores for 9 weeks. She asks students if they want her to record the median or mean of their scores. For each set of scores below, which landmark should they choose?

After finding the landmarks for each student, circle the better score.

1. Eliezer's scores: 0, 70, 95, 85, 90, 70, 95, 100, 80

median _____   mean _____

2. Miles' scores: 100, 80, 80, 80, 95, 80, 95, 100, 80

median _____   mean _____

3. Charlene's scores: 80, 80, 70, 65, 60, 80, 60, 80, 80

median _____   mean _____

4. Kiyada's scores: 75, 80, 95, 80, 100, 80, 95, 100, 80

median _____   mean _____

5. How can they decide which landmark to choose without finding the median and the mean?

_____

_____

_____

_____

_____

_____

6. An *outlier* is a data point that is located far from the rest of the data. What score is the outlier in the spelling score data?

_____

Constructing a Graph from Landmarks

1. Make up a list of data with the following landmarks:

mode: 15   minimum: 5   median: 10   maximum: 20

Use at least 10 numbers.

_____

2. Draw and label a bar graph to represent your data.

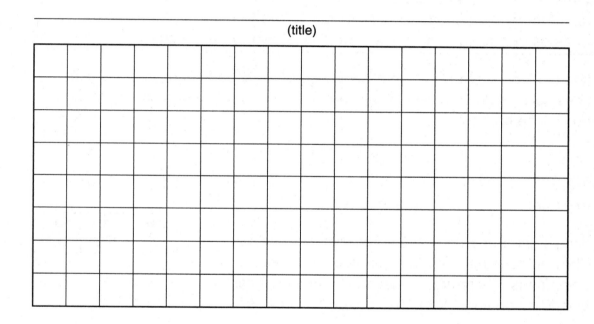

(title)

3. Describe a situation in which these data might actually occur.

_____

_____

Practice

4. 305 ∗ 29 = _____   **5.** 524 − 81 = _____

6. 671 ∗ 132 = _____   **7.** 7,356 ÷ 4 = _____

LESSON 6·5 | **Identify the Whole**

In the following number stories, find the whole using parts-and-total diagram. Write the fraction for the given part, and rename the fraction as a percent.

Example: Two girls each have 5 hats. Three of their hats are purple. What percent of the hats are purple?

Solution: $2 * 5 = 10$ hats; 3 out of $10 = \frac{3}{10}$; Rename $\frac{3}{10}$ as a fraction with 100 as the denominator $\frac{10 * 3}{10 * 10} = \frac{30}{100}$; $\frac{30}{100} = 0.30$, or 30%.

> **Reminder:** To use a calculator to convert a fraction to a percent, divide the numerator by the denominator. Use your fix key to round to the nearest hundredth, or multiply the decimal by 100 to display the percent.

1. Lamont, Jose, and Kenji are recycling soda cans. Lamont collects 13 cans. Jose collects 20 cans, and Kenji collects 17 cans. What percent of the cans does Jose collect?

   Unit: _____   Whole: _____

   Fraction: _____   Percent: _____

Total		
?		
Part	**Part**	**Part**
13	20	17

2. Jacqui and Edna decide to share their hot lunches. They put together their fried potatoes and their onion rings. There are 33 pieces of fried potatoes and 17 onion rings. What percent of the lunches are the onion rings?

   Unit: _____   Whole: _____

   Fraction: _____   Percent: _____

Total	
?	
Part	**Part**
33	17

3. The boy's club is having a popcorn sale. Each of the 10 members of the club is given 5 boxes of popcorn, but Edward sells only 3. What percent of the 5 boxes remain for Edward to sell?

   Unit: _____   Whole: _____

   Fraction: _____   Percent: _____

Total	
5	
Part	**Part**
3	?

168

LESSON 6·5

Investigating Sample Size

1. Choose a specific outcome or event for one of the following actions.

   ◆ Flipping a coin

   Example: The coin will land heads up. _____

   ◆ Rolling a die

   Example: The die will land with a 4 on the top. _____

2. Predict the results of 10 trials and 100 trials. Report your predictions as the fraction of the total you think will result in a favorable outcome, or favorable event. For example, the coin will land heads up about $\frac{1}{2}$ of the time, or the die will land with a 4 on the top about $\frac{1}{6}$ of the time.

Event	10 trials		100 trials		1,000 trials
	Prediction	**Result**	**Prediction**	**Result**	**Prediction**

3. Perform 10 trials. Record the results first with tally marks on a separate piece of paper and then in the table as a fraction.

4. Repeat for 100 trials. Record the results first with tally marks on a separate piece of paper and then in the table as a fraction.

5. How do your predictions compare with the actual results?

   _____

   _____

6. Predict the results for 1,000 trials, and explain your prediction.

   _____

   _____

   _____

7. On the back of this page, name two ways you and your partner could get data on the actual results for 1,000 trials.

169

STUDY LINK 6·6 Data Analysis

1. Describe a situation in which the data in the line plot below might occur. Then give the plot a title and a unit.

SRB
117–119

_____

_____ _____
(title)   (unit)

```
                              X
                          X   X                    X
          X       X       X X X X        X         X
   X      X       X X X X X X X X     X   X         X   X
   +---+---+---+---+---+---+---+---+---+---+---+---+---+---+---+---+---+
   77  78  79  80  81  82  83  84  85  86  87  88  89  90  91  92  93  94
```

2. Find the following landmarks for the data in the line plot.

   a. minimum: _____   b. maximum: _____   c. mode: _____   d. median: _____

3. Describe a situation in which the data in the stem-and-leaf plot shown below might occur. Then give the plot a title and a unit.

_____
(title)

_____
(unit)

   _____

   _____

4. Find the following landmarks for the data in the stem-and-leaf plot.

   a. minimum: _____   b. maximum: _____

   c. mode: _____   d. median: _____

Stems (10s)	Leaves (1s)
3	2
4	0
5	1 3 7
6	0 4 5 6 6 6 7 9
7	1 3 8 8 9
8	0 2 2 5 5 8 8 9
9	0 2 2 5 5 8 9 9

Practice

5. 245 * 51 = _____

6. 764 + 37 = _____

7. 2,121 * 4 = _____

8. 1,976 ÷ 38 = _____

170

LESSON 6·6 Stem-and-Leaf Plots

List the data sets for each stem-and-leaf plot on the lines below.

1. Candy bars sold by art club members (Bars)

Stem 10s	Leaves 1s
1	0 1 3
2	5 7 7 8
3	2 4

_____

_____

How many people are in the art club? _____

2. Rainy days in April for 10 cities (Days)

Stem 10s	Leaves 1s
0	3 4 5 5
1	0 1 2 3 3
2	1

_____

_____

3. Number of people visiting the reptile display at the zoo in one week (People)

Stem 100s and 10s	Leaves 1s
23	3 4 5 9
31	1 3
40	0

_____

_____

4. Seed sprouting time science experiment (Days)

Stem 10s	Leaves 1s
1	0 0 1 2
2	0 1 4 6
3	2 3 4

_____

_____

What was the maximum seed sprouting time? _____

LESSON 6·6 **Making Stem-and-Leaf Plots**

1. Make a stem-and-leaf plot for the following data:

74, 86, 68, 90, 98, 60, 94, 74, 84, 72, 90, 96, 88, 92, 88, 70, 80, 90, 98, 88, 68, 76, 88, 62, 90, 82, 90, 72, 74, 98

_____   _____
(title)   (unit)

Stem	Leaves
10s	1s

2. Find the following landmarks for this set of data.

a. minimum: _____

b. maximum: _____

c. mode: _____

d. median: _____

3. Describe a situation in which the data in the stem-and-leaf plot might occur. Then give the plot a title and a unit.

_____

_____

_____

STUDY LINK 6·7 | **Contour Map**

Study the map below to answer the questions.

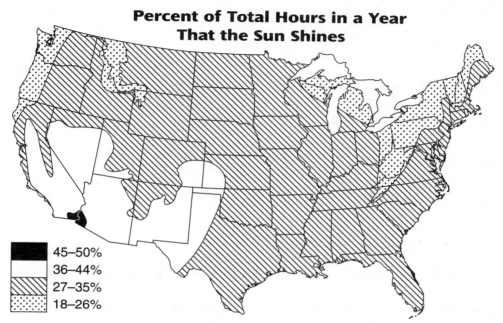

Percent of Total Hours in a Year That the Sun Shines

- ■ 45–50%
- ☐ 36–44%
- ▨ 27–35%
- ⣿ 18–26%

1. States where at least part of the state has sunny days more than 45% of the time.

○ Washington   ○ California   ○ Arizona   ○ New York

2. States that border Canada where at least some part of the state has days that are NOT sunny at least 31% of the time.

○ California   ○ Montana   ○ Nebraska   ○ Washington

3. Make up your own question about the map. Answer your question.

_____

_____

Practice

4. $149 * 14 =$ _____

5. $134 * 29 =$ _____

6. $2,997 \div 37 =$ _____

7. $3,682$
      $-1,590$
      _____

STUDY LINK
6·8 | **Estimating with Fractions**

Circle the best estimate for each situation described below.

1. The sum of $\frac{3}{4}$ and $\frac{18}{19}$ is closest to

      0   1   2

2. The sum of $\frac{1}{11}$ and $\frac{1}{15}$ is closest to

      0   1   2

3. The sum of $\frac{9}{10}$ and $\frac{1}{32}$ is

      less than 1   greater than 1

4. Use the circle below to draw a spinner as follows:

  ◆ Shade a red sector that is more than $\frac{1}{8}$ of the circle, but less than $\frac{1}{4}$ of the circle.

  ◆ Shade a blue sector that is more than $\frac{1}{4}$ of the circle, but less than $\frac{1}{2}$ the circle.

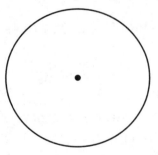

The total amount of the circle that is shaded is

      less than $\frac{3}{4}$ equal to $\frac{3}{4}$ greater than $\frac{3}{4}$

5. The number line below shows an estimate for the sum of $\frac{6}{13}$ and $\frac{1}{8}$. Explain why the sum is greater than $\frac{1}{2}$.

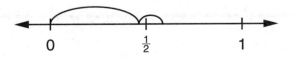

_____

_____

174

LESSON 6·8 — Comparing Fractions with $\frac{1}{2}$

Use the Fraction Cards from *Math Journal 2*, Activity Sheets 5–7.
Sort the cards into three piles.

◆ Fractions less than $\frac{1}{2}$

◆ Fractions equal to $\frac{1}{2}$

◆ Fractions greater than $\frac{1}{2}$

Place the cards next to one another to check your work. When you are finished, write the fractions in each pile in the correct box below.

Less than $\frac{1}{2}$	Equal to $\frac{1}{2}$	Greater than $\frac{1}{2}$

LESSON 6·8   Math Log

LESSON 6·9   Number Strips

Cut out each of the strips below.

| 10 | 20 | 30 | 40 | 50 | 60 | 70 | 80 | 90 | 100 |

| 4 | 8 | 12 | 16 | 20 | 24 | 28 | 32 | 36 | 40 |

| 7 | 14 | 21 | 28 | 35 | 42 | 49 | 56 | 63 | 70 |

| 9 | 18 | 27 | 36 | 45 | 54 | 63 | 72 | 81 | 90 |

| 6 | 12 | 18 | 24 | 30 | 36 | 42 | 48 | 54 | 60 |

| 8 | 16 | 24 | 32 | 40 | 48 | 56 | 64 | 72 | 80 |

| 3 | 6 | 9 | 12 | 15 | 18 | 21 | 24 | 27 | 30 |

| 1 | 2 | 3 | 4 | 5 | 6 | 7 | 8 | 9 | 10 |

| 5 | 10 | 15 | 20 | 25 | 30 | 35 | 40 | 45 | 50 |

| 2 | 4 | 6 | 8 | 10 | 12 | 14 | 16 | 18 | 20 |

STUDY LINK 6·9 | **Adding and Subtracting Fractions**

Multiplication Rule

To find a fraction equivalent to a given fraction, multiply the numerator and the denominator of the fraction by the same number.

$$\frac{a}{b} = \frac{a * n}{b * n}$$

Example 1: $\frac{4}{9} - \frac{1}{3} = ?$

$\frac{1}{3} = \frac{2}{6} = \boxed{\frac{3}{9}} = \frac{4}{12} = \frac{5}{15} = \frac{6}{18} = \dots$

9 is a common denominator.

$\frac{4}{9} - \frac{1}{3} = \frac{4}{9} - \frac{3}{9} = \frac{1}{9}$

Example 2: $\frac{5}{8} + \frac{2}{5} = ?$

$\frac{5}{8} = \frac{10}{16} = \frac{15}{24} = \frac{20}{32} = \boxed{\frac{25}{40}} = \frac{30}{48} = \dots$

$\frac{2}{5} = \frac{4}{10} = \frac{6}{15} = \frac{8}{20} = \frac{10}{25} = \frac{12}{30} = \frac{14}{35} = \boxed{\frac{16}{40}} = \frac{18}{45} = \dots$

Both fractions can be rewritten with the common denominator 40.

$\frac{5}{8} + \frac{2}{5} = \frac{25}{40} + \frac{16}{40} = \frac{41}{40}$, or $1\frac{1}{40}$

Find a common denominator. Then add or subtract.

1. $\frac{2}{3} + \frac{4}{5} =$ _____

2. $\frac{8}{9} - \frac{5}{6} =$ _____

3. $\frac{3}{4} + 1\frac{1}{2} =$ _____

4. Lisa was 4 feet $10\frac{1}{2}$ inches tall at the end of fifth grade. During the year, she had grown $2\frac{3}{4}$ inches. How tall was Lisa at the start of fifth grade?

_____ feet _____ in.

5. Bill was baking two different kinds of bread. One recipe called for $3\frac{1}{2}$ cups of flour. The other called for $2\frac{1}{3}$ cups of flour. How much flour did Bill need in all?

_____ cups

178

LESSON 6·9 **Fractions in Military Time**

Whole
day

On a military clock, the whole is 1 day or 24 hours. $\frac{1}{24}$ is one hour. The time shown on this clock face is 08:14:42 (8 hours, 14 minutes, and 42 seconds).

Using the clock face, write the fractions as days, hours, and minutes. The first one has been done for you.

1. $\frac{2}{24} = \frac{1}{12}$ of a day = 2 hours = ☐ 120 ☐ minutes

2. $\frac{18}{24} = \frac{}{}$ of a day = ☐ hours = ☐ minutes

3. $\frac{10}{24} = \frac{}{}$ of a day = ☐ hours = ☐ minutes

4. $\frac{1}{2}$ hour = $\frac{}{}$ of a day

5. Explain how you found your answer for Problem 4.

_____

_____

_____

179

Writing Elapsed-Time Number Stories

LESSON 6·9

The numbers on a clock face divide one hour into twelfths. Each $\frac{1}{12}$ of an hour is 5 minutes.

Whole
hour

Use fractions to represent amounts of elapsed time and write a number story for a partner to solve.

Example:

Maria started her piano practice at 3:15. She practiced for $\frac{8}{12}$ of an hour. At what time did she finish practicing?

Think: $\frac{1}{12}$ hour = 5 minutes; $\frac{8}{12}$ hour is 8 * 5, or 40 minutes; 40 minutes more than 3:15 is 3:55.

Maria finished practicing at 3:55.

Your Elapsed-Time Number Story:

_____

_____

_____

_____

_____

Your Partner's Solution:

_____

_____

Explain your answer.

_____

_____

_____

_____

STUDY LINK 6·10 | Fractions

Find a common denominator. Then add or subtract.

1. $\frac{9}{11} - \frac{1}{2} =$ _____

2. $\frac{5}{9} - \frac{1}{4} =$ _____

3. $\frac{7}{10} + \frac{4}{15} =$ _____

4. $\frac{7}{10} - \frac{4}{15} =$ _____

5.
$$\begin{array}{r} \frac{3}{2} \\ \frac{4}{9} \\ \hline - \end{array}$$

6.
$$\begin{array}{r} \frac{5}{6} \\ \frac{4}{9} \\ \hline + \end{array}$$

Write the fraction represented by the shaded part of each fraction stick.

7. 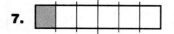 _____

8. 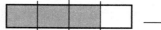 _____

9.  _____

10.  _____

11. 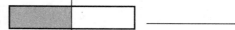 _____

12. The sum of the five fractions in Problems 7–11 is _____.

Use the information on Kwame's shopping list to fill in the blanks below.

13. He plans to buy _____ pounds of meat.

14. He plans to buy _____ pounds of cheese.

> **Kwame's Shopping List**
> $\frac{1}{2}$ pound ham
> $\frac{3}{4}$ pound roast beef
> $\frac{2}{3}$ pound turkey
> $\frac{2}{3}$ pound Swiss cheese
> $\frac{1}{4}$ pound Parmesan cheese
> $\frac{2}{3}$ pound cheddar cheese

LESSON 6·10 | **Common Denominators**

1. For each pair of fractions below:

   ◆ Find a common denominator.

   ◆ Rewrite the fractions with this common denominator.

   ◆ Add the fractions.

Original Fractions	Fractions with a Common Denominator	Sum
$\frac{1}{2}$ and $\frac{3}{4}$		
$\frac{2}{9}$ and $\frac{7}{3}$		
$\frac{3}{8}$ and $\frac{5}{16}$		
$\frac{3}{5}$ and $\frac{9}{20}$		
$\frac{7}{14}$ and $\frac{6}{8}$		
$\frac{8}{10}$ and $\frac{15}{25}$		
$\frac{6}{9}$ and $\frac{8}{12}$		
$\frac{2}{3}$ and $\frac{3}{4}$		
$\frac{1}{5}$ and $\frac{3}{8}$		
$\frac{3}{10}$ and $\frac{6}{7}$		

2. Explain how you found a common denominator for one of the fraction pairs above.

_____

_____

Unit 7: Family Letter

Exponents and Negative Numbers

In Unit 7, your child will learn to write exponential and scientific notation for naming very large and very small numbers. These topics become increasingly important later on when your child begins algebra. If you have enjoyed playing math games in the past, you might want to play *Exponent Ball* during these lessons.

Your child will also review how parentheses make expressions unambiguous and will learn rules that determine the order for performing operations in a mathematical expression.

Finally, your child will learn to work with positive and negative numbers, using a variety of tools. For example, your child will use number lines and red and black "counters" to model addition and subtraction problems.

The counter activities are especially helpful. Students use counters to represent an account balance. The red counters (−$1) represent a debit, and the black counters (+$1) represent a credit. If there are more red counters than black ones, the account is "in the red," that is, the balance is negative. On the other hand, if there are more black counters than red ones, the account is "in the black," that is, the balance is positive. By adding or subtracting red and black counters from an account, your child can model addition and subtraction of positive and negative numbers. To assist your child, you might want to explain how a checking or savings account works. Students will practice their new skills in the *Credits/Debits Game*.

Please keep this Family Letter for reference as your child works through Unit 7.

183

Vocabulary

Important terms in Unit 7:

account balance An amount of money that you have or that you owe.

exponential notation A way to show repeated multiplication by the same factor. For example, 2^3 is exponential notation for $2 * 2 * 2$.

expression A mathematical phrase made up of numbers, variables, operation symbols, and/or grouping symbols. An expression does not contain symbols such as $=$, $>$, and $<$.

in the black Having a positive balance; having more money than is owed.

in the red Having a negative balance; owing more money than is available.

negative number A number less than zero.

nested parentheses Parentheses within parentheses in an *expression*. Expressions are evaluated from within the innermost parentheses outward following the *order of operations*.

Example:

$$((6 * 4) - 2) / 2$$
$$(24 - 2) / 2$$
$$22 / 2 = 11$$

number-and-word notation A way of writing a large number using a combination of numbers and words. For example, 27 *billion* is number-and-word notation for 27,000,000,000.

opposite of a number A number that is the same distance from 0 on the number line as a given number but on the opposite side of 0. For example, the opposite of $+3$ is -3; the opposite of -5 is $+5$.

order of operations Rules that tell the order in which operations in an *expression* should be carried out. The order of operations is:

1. Do operations inside grouping symbols first. (Use rules 2–4 inside the grouping symbols.)
2. Calculate all the expressions with exponents.
3. Multiply and divide in order from left to right.
4. Add and subtract in order from left to right.

parentheses ( ) Grouping symbols used to indicate which operations in an expression should be done first.

scientific notation A system for writing numbers in which a number is written as the product of a power of 10 and a number that is at least 1 and less than 10. Scientific notation allows you to write big and small numbers with only a few symbols. For example, $4 * 10^{12}$ is scientific notation for 4,000,000,000,000.

standard notation Our most common way of representing whole numbers, integers, and decimals. Standard notation is base-ten, place-value numeration. For example, standard notation for three hundred fifty-six is 356.

Do-Anytime Activities

To work with your child on the concepts taught in this unit and in previous units, try these interesting and rewarding activities:

1. Have your child pick out a stock from the stock-market pages of a newspaper. Encourage your child to watch the stock over a period of time and to report the change in stock prices daily, using positive and negative numbers.

2. Using the same stock in Activity 1, have your child write the high and low of that stock for each day. After your child has watched the stock over a period of time, have him or her find. . .

- ◆ the *maximum* value observed.
- ◆ the *minimum* value observed.
- ◆ the *range* in values.
- ◆ the *mode,* if there is one.
- ◆ the *median* value observed.

3. Review tessellations with your child. Encourage your child to name the regular tessellations and to draw and name the 8 semiregular tessellations. Challenge your child to create Escher-type translation tessellations. You might want to go to the library first and show your child examples of Escher's work.

4. Practice finding perimeters of objects and circumferences of circular objects around your home.

Building Skills through Games

In Unit 7, your child will practice operations and computation skills by playing the following games. For detailed instructions, see the *Student Reference Book.*

Credits/Debits Game See *Student Reference Book,* page 301. Two players use a complete deck of number cards, cash and debt cards, and a record sheet to tally a balance. This game helps students add and subtract signed numbers.

Exponent Ball See *Student Reference Book,* page 305. This game involves two players and requires a gameboard, 1 six-sided die, a penny or counter, and a calculator. This game develops skills dealing with forming and comparing exponential values.

Name That Number See *Student Reference Book,* page 325. This is a game for two or three players using the Everything Math Deck or a complete deck of number cards. Playing *Name That Number* helps students review operations with whole numbers.

Scientific-Notation Toss See *Student Reference Book,* page 329. Two players will need 2 six-sided dice to play this game. This game develops skill in converting numbers from scientific notation to standard notation.

As You Help Your Child with Homework

As your child brings assignments home, you might want to go over the instructions together, clarifying them as necessary. The answers listed below will guide you through this unit's Study Links.

Study Link 7·1

2. Should be $6^3 = 6 * 6 * 6$; 216

3. Should be $2^9 = 2 * 2 * 2 * 2 * 2 * 2 * 2 * 2 * 2$; 512

4. Should be $4^7 = 4 * 4 * 4 * 4 * 4 * 4 * 4$; 16,384

5. 14.7   6. 0.48   7. $\frac{15}{7}$, or $2\frac{1}{7}$

Study Link 7·2

1. billion   2. 10^3 3. trillion

4. 10^6 5. thousand; 10^3 6. million; 10^6

7. $2^4 * 3$ 8. $2^2 * 3 * 5$

9. $3,000 + 200 + 60 + 4$

Study Link 7·3

1. 600; 3   2. 6   3. 500 million

4. 260 million   5. 10 million   6. 125

Study Link 7·4

1. $2 = (3 * 2) - (4 / 1)$ 2. $3 = (4 + 3 - 1) / 2$

3. $4 = (3 - 1) + (4 / 2)$ 5. $1 = ((4 + 1) - 3) / 2$

6. $6 = (1 + (4 * 2)) - 3$

7. $(4^2 - ((3 * 3)) + 1((2 + 1)^4 \div 9) - 1$

8. $a = 1\frac{4}{12}$, or $1\frac{1}{3}$ 9. $p = 1\frac{1}{2}$

10. $d = 2\frac{2}{8}$, or $2\frac{1}{4}$ 11. $y = 0$

Study Link 7·5

1. 34   2. 25   3. 28   4. 30

5. 21   6. 28   7. false   8. true

9. true   10. true   11. false   12. true

13. false   14. true   15. $z = 9,204$

16. $r = 78,002$ 17. $s = 1.25$

Study Link 7·6

1. Sales were at their highest in 1930. Sales dropped by 60 million from 1940 to 1970.

3. Before TV sets were common, more people went to the movies.

Study Link 7·7

1. 2.6   2. 1.58   3. −5.5

4. −9.8   5. −1.2, −1, 3.8, $5\frac{1}{4}$, $5\frac{3}{8}$

7. F   8. F   9. T

10. T   11. −1 < 1; T   13. $f = 12.53$

15. $n = \frac{3}{4}$

Study Link 7·8

1. <   2. >   3. >   4. >

5. 2 debt   6. 5 cash   7. −9   9. −88

11. 3   15. $a = 30$ 17. $p = 5$

Study Link 7·9

1. −41   2. 43   3. 0   4. −8

5. 40   6. 20   7. −85   8. −0.5

9. 2   10. (−10)   12. $u = 65, 664$

13. $e = 3$ 14. $w = 30.841$ 15. $m = 5.46$

Study Link 7·10

1. $\frac{1}{8}$ 2. $1\frac{1}{4}$ 3. $1\frac{1}{8}$ 4. $\frac{1}{8}$ 5. $\frac{1}{4}$

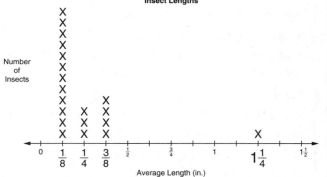

Study Link 7·11

1. $-5 - (-58) = 53$ 3. 10^4

7. 20,000   13. $7 * 10^9$ 19. $b = 0.46$

21. $a = 1,571$ 23. $137\frac{4}{7}$, or 137 R4

LESSON 6·1   Arm Circumference Data

Sometimes measurements need to be very precise. When a blood pressure reading is taken, it is important that the proper cuff size is used. Blood pressure cuffs come in different sizes and are adjustable. Using a blood pressure cuff that is too small or too large can lead to inaccurate results. Before doing a blood pressure screening of the members of the fifth-grade running club, the school nurse measured the circumference of each student's upper arm to the nearest $\frac{1}{8}$ inch. Measurements are shown in the table below.

Student	Upper Arm Circumference (to the nearest $\frac{1}{8}$ in.)	Student	Upper Arm Circumference (to the nearest $\frac{1}{8}$ in.)
Jason	$5\frac{1}{4}$	Robin	$6\frac{3}{8}$
Mike	$6\frac{1}{8}$	Javon	6
Kylie	$6\frac{1}{2}$	Beatrice	$5\frac{1}{4}$
Peter	$6\frac{1}{8}$	Charlie	$6\frac{1}{8}$
Diego	5	Shawn	$6\frac{3}{8}$
Juan Carlos	6	India	6
Lisa	$5\frac{1}{2}$	Katy	$6\frac{3}{8}$
Pamela	7		

Make a line plot in the grid below to display the arm circumference measurements. Begin by completing the labeling of the x-axis. Use these data and the completed line plot to answer the questions on the next page.

Upper Arm Circumference

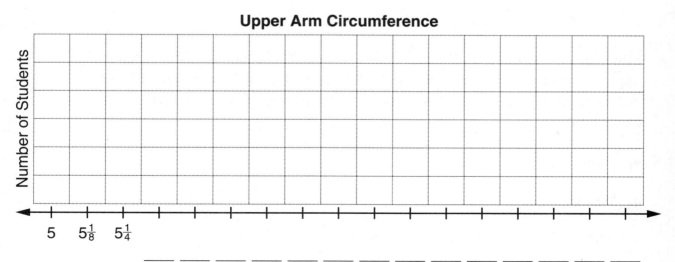

Circumference (inches)

LESSON
6·1 | **Arm Circumference Data** *continued*

Use the line plot on *Math Masters,* page 186A to answer the questions.

1. What is the minimum arm circumference of the students in the fifth-grade

   running club? _____ in.

2. How much smaller is Kylie's upper arm circumference than the club's

   maximum? _____ in.

3. What is the range in arm circumference of the members of the fifth-grade

   running club? _____ in.

4. **a.** What is the median of the data set? _____ in.

   b. How much greater is the median arm circumference than the minimum arm

   circumference? _____ in.

5. What is the mode (or modes) for the data set?

   _____

6. What is the mean arm circumference measurement? _____ in.

7. On the day of the blood pressure screening, the nurse brought a cuff that is
   made for people with arm circumferences between $5\frac{1}{8}$ in. and $6\frac{3}{4}$ in. What
   fraction of the fifth-grade running club was able to use that cuff?

   _____

8. Suppose a new member, Denise, joins the club. The circumference of her
   upper arm is $6\frac{1}{2}$ in. Tell whether each of these club's landmarks will increase,
   decrease, or stay the same. Determine your answers without doing any
   calculations.

   a. Mean: _____

   b. Median: _____

   c. Mode: _____

186B

Exponents

In exponential notation, the **exponent** tells how many times the **base** is used as a factor. For example, $6^4 = 6 * 6 * 6 * 6 = 1,296$. The base is 6, and the exponent is 4. The product is written as 1,296 in standard notation.

1. Complete the table.

Exponential Notation	Base	Exponent	Repeated Factors	Standard Notation
9^3	9	3	$9 * 9 * 9$	729
	4	5		
			$7 * 7 * 7 * 7$	
			$10 * 10 * 10 * 10 * 10 * 10$	
				262,144

Describe the mistake. Then find the correct solution.

2. $6^3 = 6 + 3 = 9$

   Mistake: _____

   Correct solution: _____

3. $2^9 = 9 + 9 = 18$

   Mistake: _____

   Correct solution: _____

4. $4^7 = 4 * 7 = 28$

   Mistake: _____

   Correct solution: _____

Practice

5. $351.82 + n = 366.52$ 6. $100 - r = 99.52$ 7. $\frac{4}{7} + u = \frac{19}{7}$

   $n =$ _____ $r =$ _____ $u =$ _____

187

LESSON 7·1 Exploring Exponents

The number sentences below contain **exponents.** Find the pattern, and
complete the number sentences.

1. $3 * 3 = 3^2$ $3 * 3 * 3 = 3^3$ $3 * 3 * 3 * 3 = 3^4$

2. $5 * 5 = 5^2$ $5 * 5 * 5 = 5^3$ $5 * 5 * 5 * 5 = 5^4$

3. $18 * 18 = 18^2$ $18 * 18 * 18 = 18^3$ $18 * 18 * 18 * 18 = 18^4$

4. $7 * 7 =$ _____   _____ $= 7^3$ $7 * 7 * 7 * 7 =$ _____

5. $4 * 4 * 4 * 4 * 4 * 4 * 4 =$ _____

6. $2^6 =$ _____

7. If you were going to explain to someone how to use exponents to write a
number, what would you say?

_____

_____

_____

_____

_____

_____

_____

Try This

Write the repeated-factor expression or the exponential notation.

8. $28^6 =$ _____

9. $309 * 309 * 309 * 309 * 309 =$ _____

10. $2^3 * 2^3 =$ _____

LESSON 7·1 Patterns with Fibonacci Numbers

1. The sequence of numbers 1, 1, 2, 3, 5, 8, 13, ... is called the **Fibonacci sequence.** In the Fibonacci sequence, every number, starting with the third number, is equal to the sum of the two numbers that come before it.

   Examples:

   Third number: $1 + 1 = 2$ Fourth number: $1 + 2 = 3$

   Fill in the next three Fibonacci numbers. 1, 1, 2, 3, 5, 8, 13, _____, _____, _____

2. Study the following pattern:
$$1^2 + 1^2 = 1 * 2$$
$$1^2 + 1^2 + 2^2 = 2 * 3$$
$$1^2 + 1^2 + 2^2 + 3^2 = 3 * 5$$
$$1^2 + 1^2 + 2^2 + 3^2 + 5^2 = 5 * 8$$

   a. Write the next two number sentences in the pattern.

   _____

   _____

   b. Describe the pattern in words.

   _____

   _____

   _____

3. **a.** Solve the following problems: $2^2 - (1 * 3) =$ _____ $3^2 - (2 * 5) =$ _____

                        $5^2 - (3 * 8) =$ _____ $8^2 - (5 * 13) =$ _____

   b. Write the next two number sentences in the pattern.

   _____

   c. Describe the pattern in words.

   _____

   _____

   _____

189

LESSON 7·1   Counting Computer Passwords

The computer at a local library provides a different computer password
for every library card. The passwords can include letters, numbers,
or a combination of letters and numbers. Both lower-case and upper-case
letters can be used. This results in 62 choices for each character
in the password.

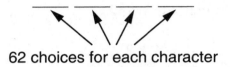

62 choices for each character

A	a	B	b	C	c	D	d	E	e	F	f
G	g	H	h	I	i	J	j	K	k	L	l
M	m	N	n	O	o	P	p	Q	q	R	r
S	s	T	t	U	u	V	v	W	w	X	x
Y	y	Z	z	0	1	2	3	4	5	6	7
8	9										

1. List three possible 4-character passwords.

a. _____   _____   _____   _____

b. _____   _____   _____   _____

c. _____   _____   _____   _____

2. The total number of possible passwords can be found by using 62 as a factor 4 times.

$$62 * 62 * 62 * 62, \text{ or } 62^4$$

Use your calculator to find the number of
different possible 4-character computer passwords. _____

STUDY LINK 7·2   Guides for Powers of 10

There are prefixes that name powers of 10. You know some of them from the metric system. For example, *kilo-* in kilometer (1,000 meters). It's helpful to memorize the prefixes for every third power of 10 through one trillion.

Memorize the table below. Have a friend quiz you. Then cover the table, and try to complete the statements below.

Standard Notation	Number-and-Word Notation	Exponential Notation	Prefix
1,000	1 thousand	10^3	kilo-
1,000,000	1 million	10^6	mega-
1,000,000,000	1 billion	10^9	giga-
1,000,000,000,000	1 trillion	10^{12}	tera-

1. More than 10^9, or one _____, people live in China.

2. One thousand, or $10^{\boxed{}}$, feet is a little less than $\frac{1}{5}$ of a mile.

3. Astronomers estimate that there are more than 10^{12}, or one _____, stars in the universe.

4. More than one million, or $10^{\boxed{}}$, copies of *The New York Times* are sold every day.

5. A kiloton equals one _____, or $10^{\boxed{}}$, metric tons.

6. A megaton equals one _____, or $10^{\boxed{}}$, metric tons.

Practice

Find the prime factorization of each number, and write it using exponents.

7. 48 = _____   8. 60 = _____

Write each number in expanded notation.

9. 3,264 = _____

10. 675,511 = _____

LESSON 7·2   Powers of 10

Find the patterns and complete the table below. Do not use your *Student Reference Book*.

1,000,000	100,000	10,000				1
				one hundred		one
			10 * 10 * 10			$10 * \frac{1}{10}$
					10^1	10^0

1. Describe at least one pattern you used to complete the table.

2. Describe what happens to the decimal point in the standard notation as you move one column to the right in the table.

3. Describe what happens to the value of the digit 1 when you move one column to the left.

4. Describe what happens to the value of the digit 1 when you move one column to the right.

5. Describe a pattern in the number of zeros used in the standard notation that you used to complete the table.

LESSON 7·2   Negative Powers of 10

Our base-ten place-value system works for decimals as well as for whole numbers.

Tens	Ones	.	Tenths	Hundredths	Thousandths
10s	1s	.	0.1s	0.01s	0.001s

Negative powers of 10 can be used to name decimal places.

Example: $10^{-2} = \frac{1}{10^2} = \frac{1}{10 * 10} = \frac{1}{10} * \frac{1}{10} = 0.1 * 0.1 = 0.01$

Very small decimals can be hard to read in standard notation, so people often use number-and-word notation, exponential notation, or prefixes instead.

Guides for Small Numbers			
Number-and-Word Notation	**Exponential Notation**	**Standard Notation**	**Prefix**
1 tenth	$10^{-1} = \frac{1}{10}$	0.1	deci-
1 hundredth	$10^{-2} = \frac{1}{10 * 10}$	0.01	centi-
1 thousandth	$10^{-3} = \frac{1}{10 * 10 * 10}$	0.001	milli-
1 millionth	$10^{-6} = \frac{1}{10 * 10 * 10 * 10 * 10 * 10}$	0.000001	micro-
1 billionth	$10^{-9} = \frac{1}{10 * 10 * 10 * 10 * 10 * 10 * 10 * 10 * 10}$	0.000000001	nano-
1 trillionth	$10^{-12} = \frac{1}{10*10*10*10*10*10*10*10*10*10*10*10}$	0.000000000001	pico-

Use the table above to complete the following statements.

1. A fly can beat its wings once every 10^{-3} seconds, or once every one thousandth

of a second. This is one _____ second.

2. Earth travels around the sun at a speed of about one inch per microsecond.

This is $10^{\boxed{}}$ second, or a _____ of a second.

3. Electricity can travel one foot in a nanosecond, or one _____ of a second.

This is $10^{\boxed{}}$ second.

4. In $10^{\boxed{}}$ second, or one picosecond, an air molecule can spin once.

This is one _____ of a second.

193

Interpreting Scientific Notation

Scientific notation is a short way to represent large and small numbers. In scientific notation, a number is written as the product of two factors. One factor is a number greater than or equal to 1 and less than 10. The other factor is a power of 10.

Scientific notation: $4 * 10^4$

    Meaning: Multiply 10^4 (10,000) by 4.

                 $4 * 10^4 = 4 * 10{,}000 = 40{,}000$

Number-and-word notation: 40 thousand

Scientific notation: $6 * 10^6$

    Meaning: Multiply 10^6 (1,000,000) by 6.

                 $6 * 10^6 = 6 * 1{,}000{,}000 = 6{,}000{,}000$

Number-and-word notation: 6 million

Guides for Powers of 10	
10^3	one thousand
10^6	one million
10^9	one billion
10^{12}	one trillion

Complete the following statements.

1. The area of Alaska is about $6 * 10^5$, or _____ thousand, square miles.

    The area of the lower 48 states is about $3 * 10^6$, or _____ million, square miles.

2. There are about $6 * 10^9$, or _____ billion, people in the world.

3. It is estimated that about $5 * 10^8$, or _____, people speak English as their first or second language.

4. In Bengal, India, and Bangladesh there are about $2.6 * 10^8$, or _____, people who speak Bengali.

5. At least 1 person in each of $1 * 10^7$ households, or _____, watches the most popular TV shows.

Source: *The World Almanac and Book of Facts, 2000*

---

6. $5 * (3^2 + 4^2) =$ _____

7. $3 * (9 + 16) =$ _____

8. $2 * (9 + h) = 20$ _____

9. $g = (7^2 - 2^2)$ _____

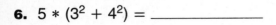

LESSON 7·3 | Using Place Value to Rename Numbers

Write the numbers from the name-collection box tag in the place-value chart.
Then follow the pattern in Problem 1 to complete each name-collection box.

	Billions			Millions			Thousands			Ones		
	100	10	1	100	10	1	100	10	1	100	10	1
1.									1	3	0	0
2.												
3.												
4.												

1. Example:

1,300
1,000 + 300
1 thousand 3 hundred
13 hundred
$1\frac{300}{1,000}$ thousands
$1\frac{3}{10}$ thousands
1.3 thousands

2.

1,800

3.

1,400,000

4.

1,600,000

LESSON 7·3   **Writing in Expanded Notation**

A   Standard Notation: 325

B   Expanded Notation as an addition expression: $300 + 20 + 5$

C   Expanded Notation as the sum of multiplication expressions:
$(3 * 100) + (2 * 10) + (5 * 1)$

D   Expanded Notation as the sum of multiplication expressions
using powers of 10: $(3 * 10^2) + (2 * 10^1) + (5 * 10^0)$

Write each number below in the other three possible ways, as shown above.

1. a.   5,314

   b. _____

   c. _____

   d. _____

2. a. _____

   b. $2,000 + 700 + 50 + 6$

   c. _____

   d. _____

3. a. _____

   b. _____

   c. $(9 * 100) + (8 * 10) + (3 * 1)$

   d. _____

4. a. _____

   b. _____

   c. _____

   d. $(7 * 10^3) + (4 * 10^2) + (5 * 10^1) + (2 * 10^0)$

STUDY LINK 7·4 | **Using Parentheses**

Make each sentence true by inserting parentheses.

1. $2 = 3 * 2 - 4 / 1$ **2.** $3 = 4 + 3 - 1 / 2$ **3.** $4 = 3 - 1 + 4 / 2$

4. Write seven names for 8. Use only numbers less than 10, and use at least three different operations in each name. Use parentheses. Follow the directions in Problem 7 to fill in the last two rows.

8

Make each sentence true by inserting parentheses.

> **Reminder:** When you have a pair of parentheses inside another pair, the parentheses are called **nested parentheses.**
>
> **Example:** $8 = ((5 * 6) + 2) / 4$

5. $1 = 4 + 1 - 3 / 2$ **6.** $7 = 4 * 3 / 2 + 1$

7. Add two names to your name-collection box in Problem 4. Use nested parentheses.

Practice

Find the number that each variable represents.

8. $2\frac{5}{12} = (1\frac{1}{12} + a)$ _____

9. $(1\frac{1}{2} + p) * 2^2 = 12$ _____

10. $6\frac{5}{8} + d = 7\frac{15}{8}$ _____

11. $6.4 - y = 6\frac{2}{5}$ _____

LESSON 7·4

Reviewing Parentheses

1. Read the following sentence. Mary Grace the lizard ate three crickets.

This sentence could have multiple meanings.

1. The speaker is telling someone named Mary Grace that the lizard ate three crickets.

2. The lizard, named Mary Grace, ate three crickets.

3. The speaker is telling someone named Mary that the lizard, named Grace, ate three crickets.

Without commas, it's hard to tell which meaning was intended. Write the number of the meaning next to each sentence below.

    a. _____ Mary Grace, the lizard, ate three crickets.

    b. _____ Mary Grace, the lizard ate three crickets.

    c. _____ Mary, Grace the lizard, ate three crickets.

By adding commas, the meaning of a sentence becomes clear. In number sentences, parentheses are used to indicate what to calculate first.

2. Insert parentheses in each sentence to make the sentence true.

    a. $3 * 4 + 7 = 33$ _____

    b. $6 + 9 * 5 = 51$ _____

    c. $27 / 4 + 5 + 6 = 9$ _____

3. Insert parentheses in the expressions below, and find their solutions.

    a. $7 * 5 - 4 =$ _____

    b. $6 + 9 \div 3 =$ _____

LESSON 7·4   Describing Dot Patterns

The total dots in this dot array can be found by using patterns.

Here is one way to find the total:

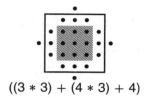

$$((3 * 3) + (4 * 3) + 4)$$

Use shape outlines or colors to identify a pattern on this dot array. Write a number model for your pattern. Then write a number story that matches your number model.

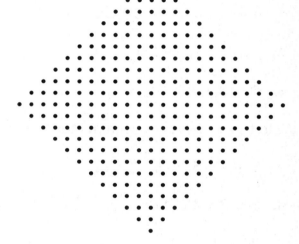

Number model: _____

Number story: _____

_____

_____

_____

_____

_____

_____

STUDY LINK 7·5 Order of Operations

SRB
223

Rules for Order of Operations

① Do operations inside **parentheses**.

② Calculate all expressions with **exponents**.

③ **Multiply** and **divide** in order, from left to right.

④ **Add** and **Subtract** in order, from left to right.

Solve.

1. $4 + 5 * 6 =$ _____

2. $(2 + 3)^2 =$ _____

3. $12 * 2 + 8 ÷ 2 =$ _____

4. $115 - 10^2 + 3 * 5 =$ _____

5. $6 * (3 + 2^2) ÷ 2 =$ _____

6. $7 + 9 * 7 ÷ 3 =$ _____

Write true or false for each number sentence. Follow the rules for order of operations.

7. $3 + 4 * 5 = 35$ _____

8. $(3 + 4) * 5 = 35$ _____

9. $0 = 3 * 4 - 12$ _____

10. $0 = (3 * 4) - 12$ _____

11. $36 = 12 - 3 * 4$ _____

12. $36 = (12 - 3) * 4$ _____

13. $8 ÷ 2 + 6 = 1$ _____

14. $8 ÷ (2 + 6) = 1$ _____

Practice

Find the number that each variable represents.

15. $354 * 26 = z$ _____

16. $907 * 86 = r$ _____

17. $3.000 - 1.75 = s$ _____

18. $0.006 + 3.2 + 0.75 + 4 = h$ _____

200

LESSON 7·5 | **Evaluating Expressions**

Janet and Alisha are using their calculators to evaluate expressions. Janet has a four-function calculator, and Alisha has a scientific calculator. They both enter the same key sequence, but their calculator displays are different.

1. Study the key sequence and calculator displays below.

Key Sequence	Janet's Display	Alisha's Display
③ ⊞ ⑤ ☒ ② ⊟	16	13

2. Decide the order that each calculator used to perform the operations. Use parentheses to write a number sentence that models each order.

  a. Number model for Janet's calculator: _____

  b. Number model for Alisha's calculator: _____

3. Use your number models in Problem 2 to evaluate the following key sequence. Then complete the table for each calculator.

Key Sequence	Janet's Display	Alisha's Display
⑤ ☒ ③ ⊞ ⑦ ⊖ ⑧ ÷ ② ⊟		

Try This

4. Write number models that show what each calculator did in Problem 3.

  a. Number model for Janet's calculator:

  _____

  b. Number model for Alisha's calculator:

  _____

LESSON 7·5 Discovering Exponent Patterns

Look for a pattern in the number sentences below. Then use the pattern to solve Problems 1–3.

$$7^2 * 7^3 = 7^5$$

$$12^7 * 12^3 = 12^{10}$$

$$34^6 * 34^6 = 34^{12}$$

1. $2^2 * 2^3 =$ _____

Explain how you can prove your answer to Problem 1 is correct.

_____

_____

_____

2. $5^5 * 5^7 =$ _____   **3.** $94^8 * 94^2 =$ _____

Describe the pattern you are using to solve the problems.

_____

_____

4. Circle the problem below for which the pattern does *not* work.

$28^5 * 5^3$ $14^8 * 14^9$ $22^5 * 22^2$

Try This

5. What do you think happens when two numbers with the same base are divided?

_____

_____

_____

6. Solve this problem to check your prediction.

$2^5 / 2^3 =$ _____

STUDY LINK
7·6

Making Line Graphs

Bar graphs, circle graphs, and line graphs display information in a way that
makes it easy to show comparisons, but line graphs can also show trends.

1. Use the information in the line
   graph to write two true statements
   about movie ticket sales.

   _____

   _____

   _____

   _____

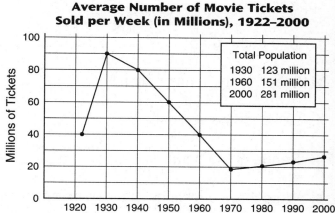

**Average Number of Movie Tickets
Sold per Week (in Millions), 1922–2000**

Total Population
1930   123 million
1960   151 million
2000   281 million

2. The table data lists the estimated percent of households with television sets
   from 1940 to 2000. Plot the data on the line graph below.

Estimated Percent of Households with Television Sets, 1940–2000						
Year	1940	1950	1960	1970	1980	1990	2000
Percentage	0%	12%	88%	96%	98%	98%	98%

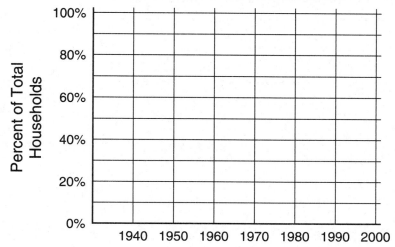

**Estimated Percent of Households with
Television Sets, 1940–2000**

3. Compare the information in the line graphs from Problems 1 and 2. What
   relationships do you see?

   _____

   _____

203

LESSON 7·6 | Looking at Line Graphs

Look closely at the graph you have. List each of the following features for your graph. If any of the features are missing from your graph, make up one that is appropriate.

1. Title of the graph: _____

2. Label for the horizontal axis: _____

3. Label for the vertical axis: _____

4. Range of the data: _____

5. Write three questions that can be answered by looking at your graph.

_____

_____

_____

_____

6. Line graphs are often used to show trends—how things change over time. If your graph shows a trend, describe what it shows. If not, explain what you think the graph tells you.

_____

_____

_____

_____

_____

LESSON 7·6   Graphing Sets of Data on a Line Graph

The following table shows the average high and low temperatures (°F) of a city in the Midwest United States.

Average Temperatures (°F)												
Month	Jan	Feb	Mar	Apr	May	Jun	Jul	Aug	Sep	Oct	Nov	Dec
High	33	36	46	59	72	80	85	82	75	62	49	38
Low	20	22	29	39	51	60	65	64	56	45	36	25

Make a line graph for this data using the grid below. Use a different colored pencil to connect the points for each data set.

1. Choose and write a title for the graph.   **2.** Label each axis.

3. Plot all the points for the high temperatures. Connect the data points. Write the words *High Temperature* above the line formed.

4. Plot all the points for the low temperatures. Connect the data points. Write the words *Low Temperature* under the line formed.

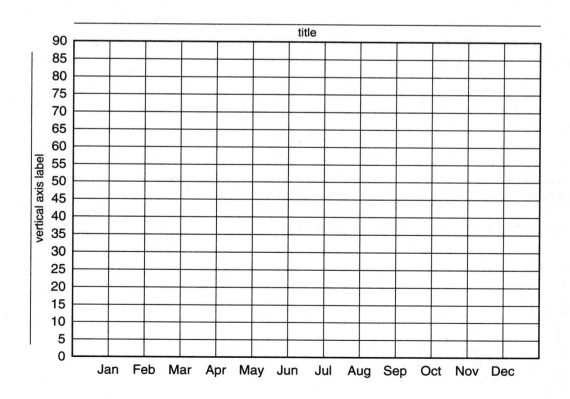

STUDY LINK 7·7 | Greater Than or Less Than?

Name a number between each pair of numbers.

1. 2 and 3 _____

2. 1.5 and 2 _____

3. −5 and −6 _____

4. −9.5 and −10 _____

Order each set of numbers from *least* to *greatest*.

5. $5\frac{1}{4}$, 3.8, −1.2, −1, $5\frac{3}{8}$ _____

6. −6, $-4\frac{1}{2}$, −0.5, −7, 0 _____

True or false? Write T for true and F for false.

7. −6 > 5 _____

8. $5\frac{1}{2} < 5\frac{3}{6}$ _____

9. −2.5 > −3.5 _____

10. −4 is less than 0 _____

Write one true and one false number sentence. In each sentence,
use at least one negative number and one of the >, <, or = symbols.
Label each sentence T or F.

11. _____   _____

12. _____   _____

Practice

Find the number that each variable represents.

13. 92.47 + f = 105 _____

14. 32 + 15 + 25 + 8 + s = 10^2 _____

15. $4\frac{3}{12} + n = 5$ _____

16. $4\frac{3}{12} - r = 3\frac{6}{12}$ _____

LESSON 7·7 | **Change in Price**

A local store is changing the price of some popular items. Listed below are the items with the new changes. Complete the table.

Item	Original Price	Change in Price (Fraction)	Change in Price (Dollars)	Price After Change
Gloves	$5.00	$-\frac{1}{5}$	$-$1.00	$4.00
Hats	$7.50	$-\frac{1}{10}$		$6.75
Belts	$10.00	$+\frac{1}{4}$		
Socks	$1.50	$+\frac{1}{2}$		
Pants	$12.00	$-\frac{1}{20}$		
Shirts	$8.50	$+\frac{3}{10}$		

1. Which item has the largest price increase? _____

2. Which item has the largest price decrease? _____

3. Which item has a 20% change? _____

4. If you were to purchase a hat and belt after the price
change, would you pay more or less than the original price? _____

How much more or less? _____

5. If you purchased one each of the items before the price changes and one of each item after the price changes, what would be the total change in cost? State your answer as a positive or negative number. Explain your solution.

_____

_____

_____

_____

207

STUDY LINK 7·8 Positive and Negative Numbers

Write < or >.

1. -7 _____ 6

2. 0.01 _____ -32

3. 8.5 _____ -10^3

4. $-\frac{3}{4}$ _____ -1.6

Find the account balance. $\boxed{+}$ = $1 cash. $\boxed{-}$ = $1 debt.

5. Balance = $ _____

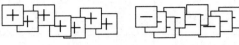

6. Balance = $ _____

Solve these addition problems.

7. $-15 + 6 =$ _____

8. $17 + (-5) =$ _____

9. $-56 + (-32) =$ _____

10. $90 + (-20) =$ _____

11. $18 + (-15) =$ _____

12. $-987 + 987 =$ _____

13. Use the rule to complete the table.

-200
in ↓

Rule

out = $-25 +$ in

↓ out
-225

in	out
25	
50	
-25	
-100	
100	
0	

Practice

Find the number that each variable represents.

14. $3\frac{2}{3} = \frac{j}{3}$ _____

15. $7\frac{9}{3} = \frac{a}{3}$ _____

16. $\frac{19}{25} * \frac{y}{y} = \frac{57}{75}$ _____

17. $\frac{75}{100} \div \frac{p}{p} = \frac{15}{20}$ _____

STUDY LINK 7·9   Addition and Subtraction Problems

Solve each problem. Be careful. Some problems involve addition, and some involve subtraction.

Reminder:
To subtract a number, you can add the opposite of that number.

1. $-25 + (-16) =$ _____

2. $0 - (-43) =$ _____

3. $-4 - (-4) =$ _____

4. $-4 - 4 =$ _____

5. $29 - (-11) =$ _____

6. $9 - (-11) =$ _____

7. $-100 + 15 =$ _____

8. $10 - 10.5 =$ _____

9. $4\frac{1}{2} + (-2\frac{1}{2}) =$ _____

10. $10 -$ _____ $= 20$

11. For each temperature change in the table, two number models are shown in the Temperature after Change column. Only one of the number models is correct. Cross out the incorrect number model. Then complete the correct number model.

Temperature before Change	Temperature Change	Temperature after Change	
40°	up 7°	$40 + 7 =$ _____	$40 + (-7) =$ _____
10°	down 8°	$10 - (-8) =$ _____	$10 - 8 =$ _____
−15° (15° below zero)	up 10°	$-15 + 10 =$ _____	$15 + 10 =$ _____
−20° (20° below zero)	down 10°	$-20 - 10 =$ _____	$20 - (-10) =$ _____

Practice

Find the number that each variable represents.

12. $684 * 96 = u$ _____

13. $69 \div e = 23$ _____

14. $32.486 - 1.645 = w$ _____

15. $9.45 - m = 3.99$ _____

LESSON 7·9   Comparing Elevations

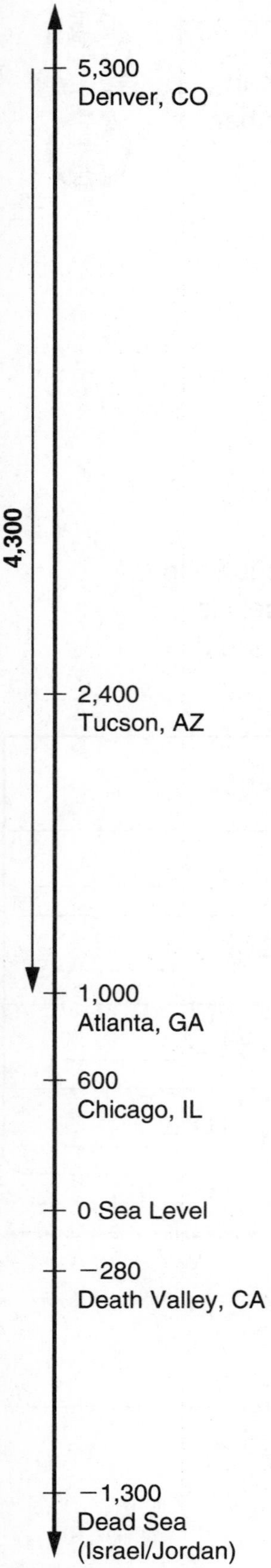

This number line shows the elevation of several places. Elevation measures how far above or below sea level a location is. For example, an elevation of 5,300 for Denver means that Denver is 5,300 feet above sea level. An elevation of −280 for Death Valley means that some point in Death Valley is 280 feet below sea level.

Fill in the table below. Use the example as a guide.

Example:

If you start at Denver and travel to Atlanta, what is your change in elevation?

Solution:

Draw an arrow next to the number line. Start it at the elevation for Denver (5,300 feet). End it at the elevation for Atlanta (1,000 feet). Use the number line to find the length of the arrow (4,300 feet). Your final elevation is lower, so report the change in elevation as *4,300 feet down.* Write a number model for the problem: 5,300 − 1,000 = 4,300.

Number line (left margin):

- 5,300   Denver, CO
- 4,300
- 2,400   Tucson, AZ
- 1,000   Atlanta, GA
- 600   Chicago, IL
- 0 Sea Level
- −280   Death Valley, CA
- −1,300   Dead Sea (Israel/Jordan)

Start at	Travel to	Change in Elevation / Number Model
Denver	Atlanta	*4,300 feet down* 5,300 − 1,000 = 4,300
Chicago	Tucson	_____ feet _____
Death Valley	Dead Sea	_____ feet _____
Dead Sea	Death Valley	_____ feet _____
Tucson	Death Valley	_____ feet _____
Dead Sea	Atlanta	_____ feet _____

210

LESSON
7·10 | **Identifying Fractions on a Number Line**

Label each number line with the correct fractions.

1.

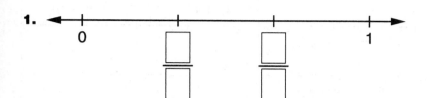

2.

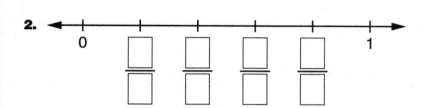

3.

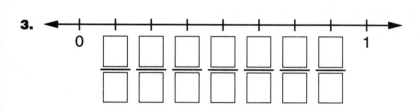

4. Draw and label the following points on this number line. The first one is done for you.

$A: 1\frac{2}{4}$ $B: \frac{1}{4}$ $C: \frac{4}{4}$ $D: \frac{8}{4}$ $E: 2\frac{3}{4}$

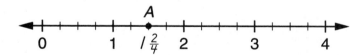

5. Jay, Kay, and Mae are in a 3-mile walk-a-thon. So far, Jay has walked $\frac{3}{4}$ mi, Kay has walked $1\frac{1}{2}$ mi, and Mae has walked $\frac{5}{2}$ mi. Draw and label points on the number line below to show their approximate locations.

211

Scouting for Insects

Some insects are harmful to farmers' crops. The insects listed in this table are harmful to alfalfa crops. Farmers scout their crops and randomly collect sample plants. They regularly observe the plants and gather data to determine if the insect population is growing or remaining stable.

The table shows the result of one farmer's insect scouting.

Type of Insect	Average Length of Insect (in.)	Number of Insects
Alfalfa Weevil Larvae	$\frac{3}{8}$	4
Fall Armyworm	$1\frac{1}{4}$	1
Meadow Spittlebug	$\frac{1}{4}$	3
Pea Aphid	$\frac{1}{8}$	6
Potato Leafhopper	$\frac{1}{8}$	6

Plot and label the lengths of the insects from the scouting sample on the line plot below. Use the line plot to find the following data landmarks:

1. Minimum insect length _____ in.

2. Maximum insect length _____ in.

3. Range of insect lengths _____ in.

4. Median insect length _____ in.

5. Mean insect length _____ in.

Insect Lengths

Number
of
Insects

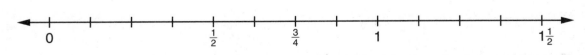

Average Length (in.)

LESSON 7·10 Plotting Rain Gauge Data

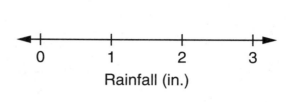

Rainfall (in.)

Example: Read the rain gauge pictured above and place an X on the line plot to show how much rain has been collected.

1. Read each rain gauge to find out how much rain fell each day. Write the amount of rain on the line below the gauge.

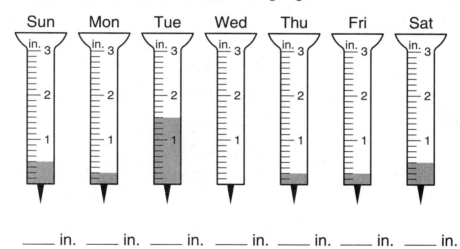

Sun   Mon   Tue   Wed   Thu   Fri   Sat

_____ in. _____ in. _____ in. _____ in. _____ in. _____ in. _____ in.

2. Use the number line to make a line plot recording daily rainfall for 1 week. Label the tick marks on the number line. Place an X to represent each rain amount.

Daily Rainfall

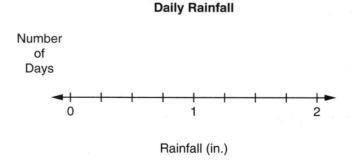

Number of Days

Rainfall (in.)

3. Analyze the rain gauge data to answer the questions below.

   a. What is the mode amount of rain that fell each day? _____ in.

   b. What is the range of the rainfall during the week? _____ in.

213

STUDY LINK 7·11

Unit 7 Review

1. Circle the number sentences that are true.

$$25 + (-6) < -32 \qquad 4^2 < 2^4 \qquad 15 * 15 * 15 < 15^3$$

$$21 * 21 = 21^3 \qquad -5 - (-58) = 53 \qquad 25 > 5^2 - (-2)$$

Write each number as a power of 10.

2. 1,000,000 _____

3. 10,000 _____

4. 1 hundred-thousand _____

5. 1 billion _____

Match the number written in number-and-word notation with its standard notation. Fill in the oval next to the correct answer.

6. 3 million
- ○ 300,000
- ○ 30,000,000
- ○ 3,000,000
- ○ 30,000

7. 20 thousand
- ○ 200,000
- ○ 20,000
- ○ 2,000,000
- ○ 20,000,000

8. 640 thousand
- ○ 6,400,000
- ○ 64,000,000
- ○ 640,000,000
- ○ 640,000

9. 2.6 million
- ○ 26,000,000
- ○ 2,060,000
- ○ 20,600,000
- ○ 2,600,000

Write the following numbers in expanded notation.

10. 8,759 _____

11. 87.59 _____

214

STUDY LINK
7·11

Unit 7 Review *continued*

SRB
5–9

Write each number in scientific notation.

12. 8 million _____

13. 7 billion _____

14. 3 thousand _____

15. 17 billion _____

16. Louise bought three 6-pack containers of yogurt. She ate 5 individual containers of yogurt in one week. How many containers did she have left?

Number model: _____   Answer: _____

17. The water in Leroy's and Jerod's fish tank had evaporated so it was about $\frac{5}{8}$ inch below the level it should be. They added water and the water level went up about $\frac{3}{4}$ inch. Did the water level end up above or below where it should be?

_____

How much above or below?

Number model: _____   Answer: _____

Find the number that each variable represents.

18. $2.4 + 62.8 + 3.752 = f$ _____

19. $86.54 + b = 87$ _____

20. $33\frac{1}{3}\% + p = 100\%$ _____

21. $6,284 \div 4 = a$ _____

22. $8,463 \div 8 = v$ _____

23. $963 \div 7 = k$ _____

Broken Calculator Problems

Change the display in the calculator without using the broken key. *You may only add and subtract negative numbers to reach the ending number.* The first one is done for you.

Starting Number	Ending Number	Broken Key	Keystrokes
38	48	0	38 ⊖ ⊟ 5 ⊖ ⊟ 5 **Enter**
24	70	6	
200	89	1	
351	251	0	
1,447	1,750	3	

Make up five problems of your own. When you have finished, trade papers with your partner, and solve each other's problems. *You may only add and subtract negative numbers to reach the ending number.*

Starting Number	Ending Number	Broken Key	Keystrokes

216

STUDY LINK 7·12   # Unit 8: Family Letter

Fractions and Ratios

In Unit 4, your child reviewed equivalent fractions. In this unit, we will apply this knowledge to compute with fractions and mixed numbers. Students will learn that the key to fraction computation with unlike denominators is to find common denominators.

Unit 8 also introduces fraction multiplication. Students will use folded paper to represent fractions of a whole. Then the class will study fraction multiplication using area models, which are diagrams that show a *whole* divided into parts. This concept building will lead to a rule for multiplying fractions:

$$\frac{a}{b} * \frac{c}{d} = \frac{a * c}{b * d}$$

Example: $\frac{2}{5} * \frac{3}{4} = \frac{2 * 3}{5 * 4} = \frac{6}{20}$, or $\frac{3}{10}$

For mixed-number multiplication, students will rename the mixed numbers as fractions, then use the rule to multiply. Finally they rename the product as a mixed number.

Example: $2\frac{1}{2} * 1\frac{2}{3} = \frac{5}{2} * \frac{5}{3} = \frac{5 * 5}{2 * 3} = \frac{25}{6} = 4\frac{1}{6}$

Your child might want to use partial products to solve this problem:

$2\frac{1}{2} * 1\frac{2}{3}$ can be thought of as $(2 + \frac{1}{2}) * (1 + \frac{2}{3})$. There are 4 partial products, as shown below.

$(2+\frac{1}{2}) * (1+\frac{2}{3})$

$2 * 1 = 2$

$2 * \frac{2}{3} = \frac{4}{3}$

$\frac{1}{2} * 1 = \frac{1}{2}$

$\frac{1}{2} * \frac{2}{3} = \frac{2}{6}$

Add the partial products: $2 + \frac{4}{3} + \frac{1}{2} + \frac{2}{6} = 2 + \frac{8}{6} + \frac{3}{6} + \frac{2}{6} = 2 + \frac{13}{6} = 4\frac{1}{6}$

Your child will play several games such as, *Build-It* and *Fraction Action, Fraction Friction,* to practice sorting fractions and adding fractions with unlike denominators.

Finally, as part of the American Tour, students will explore data related to population distribution and household sizes.

Please keep this Family Letter for reference as your child works through Unit 8.

Vocabulary

Important terms in Unit 8:

area model A model for multiplication problems in which the length and width of a rectangle represent the factors and the area represents the product.

discount The amount by which a price of an item is reduced in a sale, usually given as a fraction or percent of the original price, or as a "percent off." For example, a $4 item on sale for $3 is discounted to 75% or $\frac{3}{4}$ of its original price. A $10.00 item at 10% off costs $9.00, or $\frac{1}{10}$ less than the usual price.

majority A number or amount that is more than half of a total number or amount.

quick common denominator The product of the denominators of two or more fractions. For example, the quick common denominator of $\frac{3}{4}$ and $\frac{5}{6}$ is $4 * 6 = 24$. In general, the quick common denominator of $\frac{a}{b}$ and $\frac{c}{d}$ is $b * d$.

unit fraction A fraction whose numerator is 1. For example, $\frac{1}{2}$, $\frac{1}{3}$, $\frac{1}{8}$, and $\frac{1}{20}$ are unit fractions. Unit fractions are especially useful in converting between measurement systems. For example, because 1 foot = 12 inches you can multiply a number of inches by $\frac{1}{12}$ to convert to feet.

unit percent One percent (1%).

Building Skills through Games

In Unit 8, your child will practice skills with fractions and other numbers by playing the following games. For detailed instructions of most games, see the *Student Reference Book*.

Build-It See *Student Reference Book,* p. 300. This game for partners requires a deck of 16 *Build-It* fraction cards. This game provides practice in comparing and ordering fractions.

Factor Captor See *Student Reference Book,* p. 306. Partners play this game with a calculator and paper and pencil. This game provides practice finding factors of a number.

Mixed-Number Spin See *Student Reference Book,* p. 322. Partners use a spinner to randomly select fractions and mixed numbers, used to complete number sentences. This game provides practice in adding and subtracting fractions and mixed numbers.

Frac-Tac-Toe See *Student Reference Book,* p. 309–311. This game for partners requires a deck of number cards 0–10 and a gameboard similar to a bingo card. The game provides practice converting between fractions, decimals, and percents.

Fraction Action, Fraction Friction See *Student Reference Book,* p. 312. This game for partners requires a set of 16 *Fraction Action, Fraction Friction* cards. The game provides practice adding fractions with unlike denominators.

Name That Number See *Student Reference Book,* p. 325. Partners play a card game. This game provides practice in using order of operations to write number sentences.

Do-Anytime Activities

To work with your child on the key concepts, try these rewarding activities.

1. Ask your child to measure the lengths of two objects using a ruler. Then ask him or her to calculate the sum and difference of their lengths.

2. Ask your child to explain how to use the fraction operation keys on his or her calculator. For example, ask your child to show you how to enter fractions and mixed numbers, simplify fractions, and convert between fractions and decimals.

3. Help your child identify advertisements in signs, newspapers, and magazines that use percents. Help your child find the sale price of an item that is discounted by a certain percent. For example, a $40 shirt reduced by 25% costs $30.

As You Help Your Child with Homework

As your child brings assignments home, you might want to go over the instructions together, clarifying them as necessary. The answers listed below will guide you through this unit's Study Links.

Study Link 8·1

1. $\frac{3}{6}$ 2. $\frac{2}{3}$ 3. $\frac{5}{6}$

4. $\frac{19}{20}$ 5. $\frac{9}{17}$ 6. $\frac{4}{7}$

7. Sample answer: The quick common denominator is 21 * 17, or 357. $\frac{11}{21} =$ $\frac{11 * 17}{21 * 17} = \frac{187}{357}$, and $\frac{9}{17} = \frac{9 * 21}{17 * 21} = \frac{189}{357}$. So $\frac{9}{17}$ is greater.

8. 0.75   9. $0.\overline{6}$ 10. 0.625

11. 0.7   12. 0.55   13. 0.84

14. Sample answer: $\frac{1}{8}$ is half of $\frac{1}{4}$ $\left(\frac{0.25}{2} = 0.125\right)$. $\frac{5}{8} = \frac{4}{8} + \frac{1}{8} = 0.5 + 0.125$, or 0.625.

15. >   16. =   17. >

18. >   19. >   20. >

21. Sample answer: $\frac{6}{7} + \frac{1}{7} = 1$. $\frac{1}{8}$ is less than $\frac{1}{7}$, so $\frac{6}{7} + \frac{1}{8}$ is less than 1.

Study Link 8·2

2. 2   3. $10\frac{2}{3}$ 5. $5\frac{1}{2}$

7. 6   9. 14   11. $5\frac{1}{4}$

13. $9\frac{3}{8}$ 15. $8\frac{1}{4}$

Study Link 8·3

1. 11   3. 10   6. $6\frac{5}{3}$

7. $2\frac{1}{2}$ 9. $2\frac{1}{5}$ 11. $5\frac{4}{9}$

13. $2\frac{1}{4}$ 15. $\frac{1}{2}$

Study Link 8·4

1. $\frac{4}{5}$; $\frac{155}{200}$ 2. $< \frac{1}{2}$ 3. $> \frac{1}{2}$

4. $= \frac{1}{2}$ 5. $< \frac{1}{2}$

6. $\dfrac{\boxed{6}}{\boxed{1}} + \dfrac{\langle 5 \rangle}{\boxed{6}} = \frac{41}{6} = 6\frac{5}{6}$

Study Link 8·5

1. $\frac{3}{12}$, or $\frac{1}{4}$ 2. $\frac{6}{15}$, or $\frac{2}{5}$

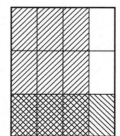

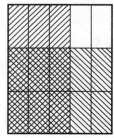

5. Nina: $\frac{1}{2}$; Phillip: $\frac{1}{6}$; Ezra: $\frac{1}{6}$; Benjamin: $\frac{1}{6}$

Study Link 8·6

1. $\frac{1}{3} * \frac{2}{5} = \frac{2}{15}$

3. $\frac{7}{8} * \frac{1}{3} = \frac{7}{24}$

5. $\frac{10}{18}$, or $\frac{5}{9}$

7. $\frac{12}{25}$

9. $\frac{5}{63}$

11. 9; 3

Study Link 8·7

7.

Rule	in (□)	out (△)
$\triangle = \square * 4$	$\frac{2}{3}$	$\frac{8}{3}$ or $2\frac{2}{3}$
	$\frac{4}{5}$	$\frac{16}{5}$, or $3\frac{1}{5}$
	$\frac{8}{9}$	$\frac{32}{9}$, or $3\frac{5}{9}$
	$\frac{5}{4}$	$\frac{20}{4}$, or 5
	$\frac{7}{3}$	$\frac{28}{3}$, or $9\frac{1}{3}$

8.

Rule	in (□)	out (△)
$\triangle = \square * \frac{1}{4}$	2	$\frac{1}{2}$
	3	$\frac{3}{4}$
	$\frac{5}{6}$	$\frac{5}{24}$
	$\frac{2}{3}$	$\frac{1}{6}$

Study Link 8·8

1. a. $\frac{46}{24}$, or $1\frac{11}{12}$ **b.** $\frac{10}{40}$, or $\frac{1}{4}$

c. $\frac{85}{24}$, or $3\frac{13}{24}$ **d.** $\frac{174}{24}$, or $7\frac{7}{24}$

e. $\frac{296}{60}$, or $4\frac{14}{15}$ **f.** $\frac{364}{40}$, or $9\frac{1}{10}$

2. a. $8\frac{5}{9}$ **b.** $5\frac{1}{2}$ **c.** $2\frac{1}{12}$

3. a. 5   **b.** $5\frac{5}{8}$

Study Link 8·9

1. $\frac{45}{100}$; 0.45; 45%; $\frac{3}{10}$; 0.3; 30%

$\frac{2}{10}$; 0.2; 20%; $\frac{15}{100}$; 0.15; 15%

2. Calculated discounts: $100.00; $1,600.00; $7.84; $0.75; $8.70; $5.28; $810.00; $385.00

Study Link 8·10

1. 4;20   **3.** 1,200 miles

5. 16 min.   **6.** yes

Study Link 8·11

Sample answers for Problems 1–4:

1. $\frac{14}{16}, \frac{28}{32}, \frac{35}{40}$ **2.** $\frac{6}{8}, \frac{9}{12}, \frac{12}{16}$ **3.** $\frac{1}{2}, \frac{2}{4}, \frac{3}{6}$

4. $\frac{4}{6}, \frac{6}{9}, \frac{8}{12}$ **5.** $\frac{3}{8}$ **6.** $\frac{5}{9}$

7. $\frac{7}{9}$ **8.** $\frac{7}{12}$

9. Sample answer: I changed $\frac{4}{10}$ and $\frac{7}{12}$ to fractions with a common denominator.

$\frac{4}{10} = \frac{24}{60}$ and $\frac{7}{12} = \frac{35}{60}$. Because $\frac{1}{2} = \frac{30}{60}$, $\frac{7}{12}$ is $\frac{5}{60}$ away from $\frac{1}{2}$, and $\frac{4}{10}$ is $\frac{6}{60}$ away from $\frac{1}{2}$. So, $\frac{7}{12}$ is closer to $\frac{1}{2}$.

11. $\frac{11}{18}$ **13.** $\frac{17}{24}$ **14.** $\frac{3}{10}$ **15.** $3\frac{1}{3}$

Study Link 8·12

1. a.   **2. a.**

b. 32, 32   **b.** $\frac{1}{6}, \frac{1}{6}$

3. $\frac{15}{2}$, or $7\frac{1}{2}$ **4.** $\frac{20}{21}$ **5.** $\frac{11}{2}$, or $5\frac{1}{2}$

6. $\frac{60}{7}$, or $8\frac{4}{7}$ **7.** 5   **8.** 22

9. $3\frac{4}{5}$ **10.** $1\frac{6}{8}$, or $1\frac{3}{4}$ **11.** $1\frac{5}{9}$

12. $4\frac{38}{35}$, or $5\frac{3}{35}$ **13.** $7\frac{17}{12}$, or $8\frac{5}{12}$ **14.** $2\frac{1}{4}$

15. $9\frac{9}{4}$, or $11\frac{1}{4}$ **16.** $\frac{28}{7}$, or 4

Comparing Fractions

SRB
66–68
83–88

Circle the greater fraction for each pair.

1. $\frac{3}{8}$ or $\frac{3}{6}$ **2.** $\frac{2}{3}$ or $\frac{2}{9}$ **3.** $\frac{4}{7}$ or $\frac{5}{6}$

4. $\frac{19}{20}$ or $\frac{4}{8}$ **5.** $\frac{11}{21}$ or $\frac{9}{17}$ **6.** $\frac{4}{7}$ or $\frac{6}{11}$

7. Explain how you got your answer for Problem 5.

_____

_____

_____

Write the decimal equivalent for each fraction.

8. $\frac{3}{4}$ = _____   **9.** $\frac{2}{3}$ = _____   **10.** $\frac{5}{8}$ = _____

11. $\frac{7}{10}$ = _____   **12.** $\frac{11}{20}$ = _____   **13.** $\frac{21}{25}$ = _____

14. Explain how you can do Problem 10 without using a calculator.

_____

_____

Use >, <, or = to make each number sentence true.

15. $\frac{1}{2} + \frac{5}{8}$ _____ 1   **16.** $\frac{2}{3} + \frac{2}{6}$ _____ 1   **17.** $\frac{7}{9} + \frac{3}{5}$ _____ 1

18. 1 _____ $\frac{6}{10} + \frac{5}{20}$ **19.** 1 _____ $\frac{3}{8} + \frac{4}{9}$ **20.** 1 _____ $\frac{6}{7} + \frac{1}{8}$

21. Explain how you found the answer to Problem 20.

_____

_____

Practice

22. 675 * 42 = _____   **23.** 28,350 ÷ 675 = _____

24. 67.5 − 0.42 = _____   **25.** 28,350 + 42 + 67.08 = _____

LESSON 8·1 | Exploring Least Common Multiples

One way to find a common denominator is to use the least common multiple. The LCM is the smallest number that is a multiple of the given denominators.

You can find the least common multiple by making lists of multiples.

Find the least common multiple for $\frac{4}{9}$, $\frac{5}{6}$, and $\frac{1}{4}$. List the multiples of each denominator.

◆ Multiples of 9: _____

◆ Multiples of 6: _____

◆ Multiples of 4: _____

◆ Least common multiple: _____

Another way to find the least common multiple is to use prime factorization.

Find the least common multiple for 8 and 6.

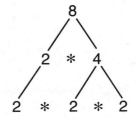

Step 1 Use factor trees to find the prime factorization.

Step 2 Count the appearance of each different prime number. Note only the largest counts.

◆ 2 appears 3 times in the prime factorization of 8.

◆ 3 appears once in the prime factorization of 6.

Step 3 Write a multiplication expression using these counts.

◆ 2 * 2 * 2 * 3 = 24 so 24 is the least common multiple of 8 and 6.

Use the prime factorization method to find the LCM.

1. 9, 6, and 4   **2.** 20 and 90   **3.** 15 and 49   **4.** 12, 15, and 25

LCM: _____   LCM: _____   LCM: _____   LCM: _____

5. What might be an advantage or disadvantage to using the prime factorization method to find the least common multiple?

_____

_____

STUDY LINK 8·2   Adding Mixed Numbers

Rename each mixed number in simplest form.

1. $3\frac{6}{5} = $ ___$4\frac{1}{5}$___

2. $\frac{16}{8} = $ _____

3. $9\frac{5}{3} = $ _____

4. $1\frac{7}{5} = $ _____

5. $4\frac{6}{4} = $ _____

6. $5\frac{10}{6} = $ _____

Add. Write each sum as a whole number or mixed number in simplest form.

7. $3\frac{1}{4} + 2\frac{3}{4} = $ _____

8. $4\frac{1}{5} + 3\frac{4}{5} = $ _____

9. $9\frac{1}{3} + 4\frac{2}{3} = $ _____

10. $3\frac{5}{7} + 8\frac{6}{7} = $ _____

11. $\frac{15}{8} + 3\frac{3}{8} = $ _____

12. $4\frac{2}{9} + 5\frac{5}{9} = $ _____

Add.

13. $2\frac{5}{8}$ **14.** $7\frac{1}{2}$ **15.** $4\frac{6}{9}$ **16.** $5\frac{3}{4}$

   $+\ 6\frac{3}{4}$ $+\ 3\frac{2}{3}$ $+\ 3\frac{7}{12}$ $+\ 2\frac{4}{5}$

| **Practice** |

17. $3{,}540 \div 6 = $ _____

18. $1{,}770 \div 3 = $ _____

19. $7{,}080\ /\ 12 = $ _____

20. $(590 * 5) \div 2 = $ _____

STUDY LINK 8·3 | # Subtracting Mixed Numbers

Fill in the missing numbers.

1. $3\frac{3}{8} = 2\frac{\square}{8}$

2. $4\frac{5}{6} = \square\frac{11}{6}$

3. $2\frac{1}{9} = 1\frac{\square}{9}$

4. $6\frac{3}{7} = \square\frac{10}{7}$

5. $4\frac{3}{5} = 3\frac{\square}{5}$

6. $7\frac{2}{3} = \square\frac{\square}{3}$

Subtract. Write your answers in simplest form.

7. $\quad 5\frac{3}{4}$
   $\underline{-\ 3\frac{1}{4}}$

8. $\quad 6\frac{2}{3}$
   $\underline{-\ 4\frac{1}{3}}$

9. $\quad 5\frac{4}{5}$
   $\underline{-\ 3\frac{3}{5}}$

10. $4 - \frac{3}{8} =$ _____

11. $6 - \frac{5}{9} =$ _____

12. $5 - 2\frac{3}{10} =$ _____

13. $7 - 4\frac{3}{4} =$ _____

14. $3\frac{2}{5} - 1\frac{3}{5} =$ _____

15. $4\frac{3}{8} - 3\frac{7}{8} =$ _____

| **Practice** |

16. $654 * 205 =$ _____

17. $654 * 502 =$ _____

18. $654 * 250 =$ _____

19. $654 * 520 =$ _____

224

LESSON 8·3 | **Addition and Subtraction Patterns**

Add.

1. a. $\frac{1}{1} + \frac{1}{2} =$ _____   **b.** $\frac{1}{2} + \frac{1}{3} =$ _____   **c.** $\frac{1}{3} + \frac{1}{4} =$ _____

d. $\frac{1}{4} + \frac{1}{5} =$ _____   **e.** $\frac{1}{5} + \frac{1}{6} =$ _____

2. What pattern do you notice in Problems 1a–1e? _____

_____

_____

3. Use the pattern above to solve these problems.

a. $\frac{1}{6} + \frac{1}{7} =$ _____   **b.** $\frac{1}{10} + \frac{1}{11} =$ _____   **c.** $\frac{1}{99} + \frac{1}{100} =$ _____

4. Do you think this pattern also works for problems like $\frac{1}{8} + \frac{1}{3}$? Explain.

_____

_____

5. The plus signs in Problem 1 have been replaced with minus signs. Find each answer.

a. $\frac{1}{1} - \frac{1}{2} =$ _____   **b.** $\frac{1}{2} - \frac{1}{3} =$ _____   **c.** $\frac{1}{3} - \frac{1}{4} =$ _____

d. $\frac{1}{4} - \frac{1}{5} =$ _____   **e.** $\frac{1}{5} - \frac{1}{6} =$ _____

f. Describe the pattern. _____

_____

_____

STUDY LINK 8·4 More Fraction Problems

1. Circle all the fractions below that are greater than $\frac{3}{4}$.

$\frac{4}{5}$ $\frac{13}{20}$ $\frac{1}{2}$ $\frac{18}{25}$ $\frac{9}{12}$ $\frac{155}{200}$ $\frac{7}{11}$

Rewrite each expression by renaming the fractions with a common denominator.
Then decide whether the sum or difference is greater than $\frac{1}{2}$, less than $\frac{1}{2}$, or equal to $\frac{1}{2}$.
Circle your answer.

2. $\frac{1}{10} + \frac{2}{7}$ _____ $> \frac{1}{2}$ $< \frac{1}{2}$ $= \frac{1}{2}$

3. $\frac{5}{6} - \frac{1}{4}$ _____ $> \frac{1}{2}$ $< \frac{1}{2}$ $= \frac{1}{2}$

4. $\frac{18}{20} - \frac{2}{5}$ _____ $> \frac{1}{2}$ $< \frac{1}{2}$ $= \frac{1}{2}$

5. $\frac{3}{4} - \frac{1}{3}$ _____ $> \frac{1}{2}$ $< \frac{1}{2}$ $= \frac{1}{2}$

Fraction Puzzle

6. Select and place three different numbers so the sum is as large as possible.

Procedure: Select three different numbers from this list: 1, 2, 3, 4, 5, 6.

◆ Write the same number in each square.
◆ Write a different number in the circle.
◆ Write a third number in the hexagon.
◆ Add the two fractions.

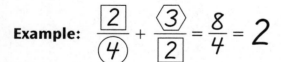

Example: $\frac{\boxed{2}}{\bigcirc\!4} + \frac{\langle 3 \rangle}{\boxed{2}} = \frac{8}{4} = 2$

Practice

7. $3 - 2.564 =$ _____   8. $3 * 2.564 =$ _____

9. $16 - 5.438 =$ _____   10. $3{,}049 / 15 =$ _____

LESSON 8·4 | Charting Common Denominators

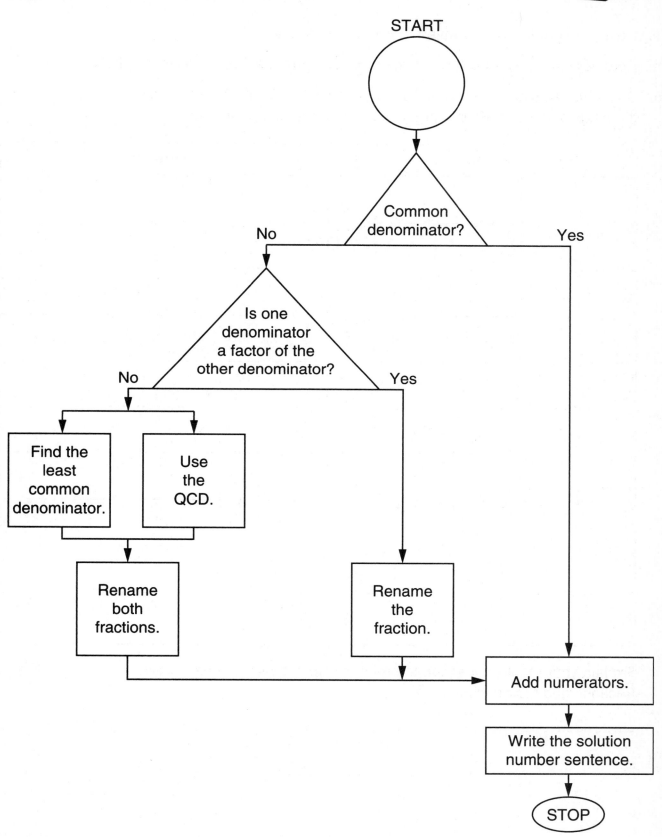

START

Common denominator?
No — Yes

Is one denominator a factor of the other denominator?
No — Yes

Find the least common denominator.

Use the QCD.

Rename both fractions.

Rename the fraction.

Add numerators.

Write the solution number sentence.

STOP

**LESSON
8·4** | **Exploring Equivalent Fractions**

1. Do equivalent fractions convert to the same decimal? _____

2. Complete the fraction column in the table so there are 10 equivalent fractions.

3. Use your calculator to convert each fraction to a decimal. Write the display in the decimal column. (Don't forget to use a repeat bar, if necessary.)

Fractions	Decimals

4. Explain your results. Describe the relationship between the equivalent fractions and their decimal form.

_____

_____

_____

Fractions of a Fraction

Example:

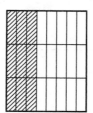

The whole rectangle represents ONE.

Shade $\frac{3}{8}$ of the interior.

Shade $\frac{1}{3}$ of the interior in a different way.

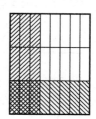

The double shading shows that $\frac{1}{3}$ of $\frac{3}{8}$ is $\frac{3}{24}$, or $\frac{1}{8}$.

In each of the following problems, the whole rectangle represents ONE.

1. Shade $\frac{3}{4}$ of the interior.

   Shade $\frac{1}{3}$ of the interior in a different way.

   The double shading shows that

   $\frac{1}{3}$ of $\frac{3}{4}$ is _____.

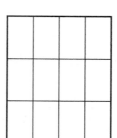

2. Shade $\frac{3}{5}$ of the interior.

   Shade $\frac{2}{3}$ of the interior in a different way.

   The double shading shows that

   $\frac{2}{3}$ of $\frac{3}{5}$ is _____.

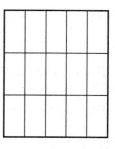

3. Shade $\frac{4}{5}$.

   Shade $\frac{3}{4}$ of the interior in a different way.

   The double shading shows that

   $\frac{3}{4}$ of $\frac{4}{5}$ is _____.

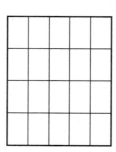

4. Shade $\frac{5}{8}$.

   Shade $\frac{3}{5}$ of the interior in a different way.

   The double shading shows that

   $\frac{3}{5}$ of $\frac{5}{8}$ is _____.

5. Nina and Phillip cut Mr. Ferguson's lawn. Nina worked alone on her half, but Phillip shared his half equally with his friends, Ezra and Benjamin. What fraction of the earnings should each person get?

LESSON 8·5 | Equivalent Fractions

Use the fraction stick to find equivalent fractions. A whole stick is worth 1.

1. Divide the fraction stick into 4 equal parts.

   Find the equivalent fraction.

   $\frac{1}{2} = \frac{\square}{4}$

2. Divide the fraction stick into 8 equal parts.

   Find the equivalent fractions.

   $\frac{1}{2} = \frac{\square}{4} = \frac{\square}{8}$

3. Divide the fraction stick into 16 equal parts.

   Find the equivalent fractions.

   $\frac{1}{2} = \frac{\square}{4} = \frac{\square}{8} = \frac{\square}{16}$

LESSON 8·6 | **An Area Model for Fraction Multiplication**

1. Use the rectangle at the right to find $\frac{2}{3} * \frac{3}{4}$.

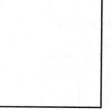

$\frac{2}{3} * \frac{3}{4} =$ _____

Your completed drawing in Problem 1 is called an **area model.**

Use area models to complete the following.

2.

$\frac{2}{3} * \frac{1}{5} =$ _____

3.

$\frac{3}{4} * \frac{2}{5} =$ _____

4.

$\frac{1}{4} * \frac{5}{6} =$ _____

5.

$\frac{3}{8} * \frac{3}{5} =$ _____

6.

$\frac{1}{2} * \frac{5}{8} =$ _____

7.

$\frac{5}{6} * \frac{4}{5} =$ _____

8. Explain how you sketched and shaded the rectangle to solve Problem 7.

_____

_____

_____

_____

_____

_____

STUDY LINK
8·6

Multiplying Fractions

Write a number model for each area model.

Example:

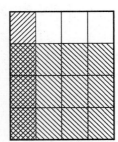

$$\frac{1}{4} * \frac{2}{5} = \frac{2}{20}, \text{ or } \frac{1}{10}$$

1.

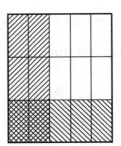

_____

2.

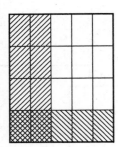

_____

3.

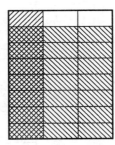

_____

Reminder: $\frac{a}{b} * \frac{c}{d} = \frac{a * c}{b * d}$

Multiply.

4. $\frac{3}{7} * \frac{2}{10} =$ _____

5. $\frac{5}{6} * \frac{2}{3} =$ _____

6. $\frac{1}{2} * \frac{1}{4} =$ _____

7. $\frac{4}{5} * \frac{3}{5} =$ _____

8. $\frac{2}{3} * \frac{3}{8} =$ _____

9. $\frac{1}{7} * \frac{5}{9} =$ _____

10. Matt is making cookies for the school fund-raiser. The recipe calls for $\frac{2}{3}$ cup of chocolate chips. He decides to triple the recipe. How many cups of chocolate chips does he need? _____ cups

11. The total number of goals scored by both teams in the field-hockey game was 15. Julie's team scored $\frac{3}{5}$ of the goals. Julie scored $\frac{1}{3}$ of her team's goals. How many goals did Julie's team score? _____ goals

How many goals did Julie score? _____ goals

LESSON 8·6 | Fraction Multiplication

Problem 1

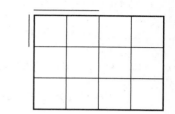

a. How many squares are in this grid? _____

b. How many squares represent $\frac{1}{3}$ of $\frac{1}{2}$ of the grid.

_____ Shade these squares.

c. Think of the total number of squares in the grid as the denominator and the shaded squares as the numerator, and write the fraction. $\frac{1}{3}$ of $\frac{1}{2}$ = _____

d. Write the number model you would use to find the area of this rectangle.
Reminder: Area = length * width

Area = _____

e. The number model to find the fractional part of the rectangle is the same as the number model to find the area of the rectangle. Write the number model you would use to find the fractional part of the rectangle.

_____

Problem 2

Linda bakes a peach pie. She serves $\frac{1}{2}$ of the pie for dessert. She saves $\frac{1}{3}$ of what is left for her mom.

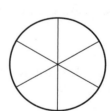

a. Shade the circle to represent the piece of the pie that should be saved.

b. Think of the total number of pie pieces as the denominator and the shaded piece as the numerator, and write the fraction. _____

c. Write a number sentence to show how you could find the fractional part of the pie that was saved without counting pie pieces. _____

To find a fraction *of* a fraction, multiply.

| **Try This** |

Write and solve a number model to find the fractional part of the pie left after subtracting dessert and the piece saved for Linda's mom.

_____

LESSON 8·6 **Fraction Problems**

1. Ailene is baking corn bread. She will cover $\frac{3}{4}$ of the cornbread with cheese. Then she plans to give $\frac{2}{3}$ of the cornbread with cheese to her friend Alex.

   a. Use the rectangle to show an area model for the problem.

   b. Write an open number model for the problem. Choose a letter to stand for the portion that will be given to Alex. _____

   c. Ailene will give _____ of the cornbread to Alex.

2. A recipe for granola bars calls for $\frac{1}{2}$ cup almonds. Cy is making $\frac{3}{4}$ of the recipe.

   a. Write an open number model to show how many ounces of almonds Cy will use. _____

   b. Cy will use _____ cup of almonds.

3. An ant weighs $\frac{1}{10}$ the weight of a crumb that it is carrying. Suppose the crumb weighs $\frac{3}{100}$ gram.

   a. Write an open number model to show the weight of the ant in grams.

   _____

   b. The ant weighs _____ gram.

4. Walker plans to hike a trail that is $\frac{8}{10}$ of a mile long. So far, he has walked $\frac{1}{4}$ that distance.

   a. Write an open number model for the problem. _____

   b. So far, Walker has walked _____ mi.

5. In Mrs. Ortiz's class, $\frac{9}{22}$ of the students are boys. Of the boys, $\frac{1}{9}$ are left-handed.

   a. Write an open number model to show how to find what fraction of the class are left-handed boys. _____

   b. _____ of the class are left-handed boys.

STUDY LINK 8·7 Multiplying Fractions and Whole Numbers

Use the fraction multiplication algorithm to calculate the following products.

1. $\frac{5}{3} * 9 =$ _____

2. $\frac{3}{8} * 12 =$ _____

3. $\frac{1}{8} * 5 =$ _____

4. $20 * \frac{3}{4} =$ _____

5. $\frac{5}{6} * 14 =$ _____

6. $27 * \frac{2}{9} =$ _____

7. Use the given rule to complete the table.

Rule	in (□)	out (△)
$\triangle = \square * 4$	$\frac{2}{3}$	
	$\frac{4}{5}$	
	$\frac{8}{9}$	
	$\frac{5}{4}$	
	$\frac{7}{3}$	

8. What is the rule for the table below?

Rule	in (□)	out (△)
	2	$\frac{1}{2}$
	3	$\frac{3}{4}$
	$\frac{5}{6}$	$\frac{5}{24}$
	$\frac{2}{3}$	$\frac{1}{6}$

9. Make and complete your own "What's My Rule?" table on the back of this page.

LESSON 8·7   # Simplifying Fraction Factors

An Algorithm for Fraction Multiplication

$$\frac{a}{b} * \frac{c}{d} = \frac{a * c}{b * d}$$

The denominator of the product is the product of the factor denominators, and the numerator of the product is the product of the factor numerators.

The commutative property lets us write $\frac{a * c}{b * d}$ as $\frac{c * a}{d * b}$. Study the examples.

Example 1: $\frac{7}{8} * \frac{16}{21} = \frac{7 * 16}{8 * 21} = \frac{112}{168}$. $\frac{112}{168} \div \frac{8}{8} = \frac{14}{21}$, or $\frac{2}{3}$

Example 2: $\frac{7}{8} * \frac{16}{21} = \frac{7 * 16}{8 * 21} = \frac{16}{8} * \frac{7}{21} = \frac{2}{1} * \frac{1}{3} = \frac{2 * 1}{1 * 3} = \frac{2}{3}$

1. Describe the similarities and differences between Examples 1 and 2.

_____

_____

_____

_____

Example 3: $\overset{1}{\cancel{\frac{7}{8}}}_{1} * \overset{2}{\cancel{\frac{16}{21}}}_{3} = \frac{1 * 2}{1 * 3} = \frac{2}{3}$

2. Describe the similarities and differences between Examples 2 and 3.

_____

_____

_____

_____

Use what you have discovered to solve the following problems. Show your work.

3. $\frac{14}{60} * \frac{12}{21} =$ _____

4. $\frac{36}{88} * \frac{33}{72} =$ _____

5. $\frac{25}{54} * \frac{36}{45} =$ _____

STUDY LINK 8·8 **Multiplying Fractions and Mixed Numbers**

1. Multiply.

a. $5\frac{3}{4} * \frac{2}{6} =$ _____

b. $\frac{5}{8} * \frac{2}{5} =$ _____

c. $4\frac{1}{4} * \frac{5}{6} =$ _____

d. $2\frac{1}{3} * 3\frac{1}{8} =$ _____

e. $3\frac{1}{12} * 1\frac{3}{5} =$ _____

f. $2\frac{4}{5} * 3\frac{2}{8} =$ _____

2. Find the area of each figure below.

Area of a Rectangle	Area of a Triangle	Area of a Parallelogram
$A = b * h$	$A = \frac{1}{2} * b * h$	$A = b * h$

a.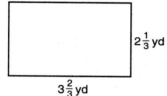

$2\frac{1}{3}$ yd

$3\frac{2}{3}$ yd

b.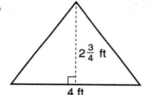

$2\frac{3}{4}$ ft

4 ft

c.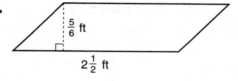

$\frac{5}{6}$ ft

$2\frac{1}{2}$ ft

Area = _____ yd²   Area = _____ ft²   Area = _____ ft²

3. The dimensions of a large doghouse are $2\frac{1}{2}$ times the dimensions of a small doghouse.

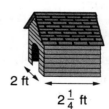

a. If the width of the small doghouse is 2 feet, what is the width of the large doghouse?

_____ feet

b. If the length of the small doghouse is $2\frac{1}{4}$ feet, what is the length of the large doghouse?

_____ feet

2 ft

$2\frac{1}{4}$ ft

STUDY LINK 8·9 Fractions, Decimals, and Percents

1. Complete the table so each number is shown as a fraction, decimal, and percent.

Fraction	Decimal	Percent
		45%
	0.3	
$\frac{2}{10}$		
	0.15	

2. Use your percent sense to estimate the discount for each item. Then calculate the discount for each item. (If necessary, round to the nearest cent.)

Item	List Price	Percent of Discount	Estimated Discount	Calculated Discount
Saguaro cactus with arms	$400.00	25%		
Life-size wax figure of yourself	$10,000.00	16%		
Manhole cover	$78.35	10%		
Live scorpion	$14.98	5%		
10,000 honeybees	$29.00	30%		
Dinner for one on the Eiffel Tower	$88.00	6%		
Magician's box for sawing a person in half	$4,500.00	18%		
Fire hydrant	$1,100.00	35%		

Source: *Everything Has Its Price*

238

LESSON 8·9

Finding the Percent of a Number

The unit percent is 1% or 0.01. For example, the unit percent of 100 is 1; the unit percent of 200 is 2; the unit percent of 10 is 0.1.

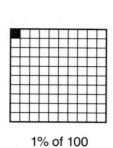

1% of 100

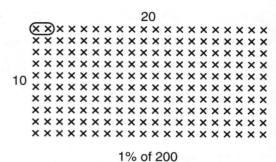

1% of 200

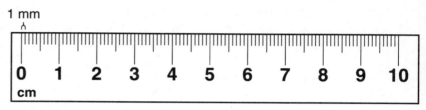

1% of 10 cm

Another way to think of the unit percent of a number is to think: *What number times 100 equals the whole?* For example, 1 * 100 = 100; 2 * 100 = 200; 0.1 * 100 = 10

To find the unit percent of a whole, multiply by 0.01 or $\frac{1}{100}$.

Solve.

1. 1% of 84 = _____ *

2. 1% of 35 = _____

3. 1% of 628 = _____

The unit percent can be used to find other percents of a whole. For example, if you want to find 8% of 200:

◆ Calculate the unit percent: 1% of 200 = 200 * 0.01 = 2

◆ Check your answer: 2 * 100 = 200.

◆ Multiply your answer by the percent you are finding: 2 * 8 = 16; 8% of 200 = 16

Solve.

4. 19% of 84 = _____

5. 72% of 35 = _____

6. 37% of 628 = _____

7. Think about the steps you followed in Problems 4–6. First you multiplied the unit percent by 0.01, and then you multiplied the product by the number of percents. How can you find the percent of a number by multiplying only once? Provide an example.

_____

_____

_____

LESSON 8·9 Calculating Discounts

There are 2 steps to finding a discounted total:

◆ Calculate the amount that represents the percent of discount.

◆ Subtract the calculated discount from the original total. This is the discounted total.

Calculate the discounted total for the following problems. Show your work on the back of this sheet.

1. A computer store has an Internet special for their customers. If Carla spends $50.00 or more, she gets 10% off her order. The shipping and handling charge is 4% of the original total. Carla buys $68.00 in software. What is her total charge?

_____

2. The Hartfield School District wants to get the government discount for telephone service. The discount is based on the percent of students qualifying for the National School Lunch Program. 32% of students in this urban district qualify. The district pays about $3,500 per month for telephone service. Use the table below to find how much the district would save.

Percent of Students	Urban Discount	Rural Discount
Less than 1%	20%	25%
1% to 19%	40%	50%
20% to 34%	50%	60%
35% to 49%	60%	70%
50% to 74%	80%	80%
75% to 100%	90%	90%

The Hartfield School District is eligible for a _____ discount. The district will save about _____ per month for its telephone service. With the government discount, the district will pay about _____ per month.

3. At the Goose Island Family Restaurant, if the original bill is $75.00 or more, the kids' meals are discounted 3%. If the original bill is $95.70, with $23.00 for kids' meals, what is the discounted amount? _____ What is the discounted total? _____

240

STUDY LINK 8·10 | Unit Fractions

Finding the worth of the unit fraction will help you solve each problem below.

1. If $\frac{4}{5}$ of a number is 16, what is $\frac{1}{5}$ of the number? _____

What is the number? _____

2. Our football team won $\frac{3}{4}$ of the games that it played. It won 12 games. How many games did it play?

_____
(unit)

3. When a balloon had traveled 800 miles, it had completed $\frac{2}{3}$ of its journey. What was the total length of its trip?

_____ *
(unit)

4. Grandpa baked cookies. Twenty cookies were oatmeal raisin. The oatmeal raisin cookies represent $\frac{5}{8}$ of all the cookies. How many cookies did Grandpa bake?

_____
(unit)

5. Tiana jogged $\frac{6}{8}$ of the way to school in 12 minutes. If she continues at the same speed, how long will her entire jog to school take?

_____
(unit)

6. After 35 minutes, Hayden had completed $\frac{7}{10}$ of his math test. If he has a total of 55 minutes to complete the test, do you think he will finish in time?

_____

Explain: _____

_____

7. Complete the table using the given rule.

Rule	in	out
out = 60% of in	100	
	60	
		42
	110	
		72
	35	

8. Find the rule. Then complete the table.

Rule	in	out
out = _____ of in	24	9
	72	27
	56	21
	80	30
		15
	32	

241

LESSON 8·10   Fraction of and Percent of a Number

George practiced finding the fraction of and the percent of a number. He completed the tables below. George thinks there is something wrong with his answers, but he doesn't know how to fix it.

$\frac{1}{4}$ of 12 =	3
$\frac{2}{4}$ of 12 =	6
$\frac{3}{4}$ of 12 =	12
$\frac{4}{4}$ of 12 =	24

20% of 40 =	6
40% of 40 =	12
60% of 40 =	18
80% of 40 =	24
100% of 40 =	30

1. Study George's tables and then explain how he should correct his work.

_____

_____

_____

_____

_____

_____

_____

2. Write the correct answers.

$\frac{1}{4}$ of 12 =	
$\frac{2}{4}$ of 12 =	
$\frac{3}{4}$ of 12 =	
$\frac{4}{4}$ of 12 =	

20% of 40 =	
40% of 40 =	
60% of 40 =	
80% of 40 =	
100% of 40 =	

LESSON 8·10 Fraction and Percent of a Number Methods

1. Alton collected 252 marbles but lost $\frac{4}{7}$ of them on his way to school.
When he arrived at school, how many marbles did Alton have left? _____

Explain how you found your answer.

_____

_____

2. Circle the letter of each method below that you could use to solve Problem 1.

a. You can find $\frac{4}{7}$ of 252 by multiplying $252 * \frac{4}{7}$ and simplifying.

b. You can find $\frac{4}{7}$ of 252 by dividing 252 by 4 and multiplying the result by 7.

c. You can find the unit fraction by dividing 252 by 7, and then find $\frac{4}{7}$ of 252 by multiplying the unit fraction value by 4.

3. For any method you did *not* circle, explain why it will not work.

_____

_____

4. The regular price for in-line skates is $125 at a local store. The store was having a promotion: Buy one pair of in-line skates and get a second pair for 75% of the regular price. How much would a second pair of in-line skates cost? _____

Explain how you found your answer.

_____

_____

5. Circle the letter of each method below that you could use to solve Problem 4.

a. You can rename 75% as a fraction and then multiply $125 by the fraction to find 75% of $125.

b. You can find the cost of the second pair by multiplying $125 by $\frac{1}{4}$ and subtracting the product from $125.

c. You can find the cost of the second pair by dividing $125 by 4.

6. For any method you did *not* circle, explain why it will not work.

_____

_____

243

Classroom Survey

Number in Household	Number of Students
1–2	
3–5	
6 or more	

Language at Home	Number of Students
English	
Spanish	
Other	

Handedness	Number of Students
right	
left	

Years at Current Address	Number of Students
0 or 1	
2	
3	
4	
5	
6 or more	

Name _____   Date _____   Time _____

Write three equivalent fractions for each fraction.

1. $\frac{7}{8}$ _____

2. $\frac{3}{4}$ _____

3. $\frac{6}{12}$ _____

4. $\frac{2}{3}$ _____

Circle the fraction that is closer to $\frac{1}{2}$.

5. $\frac{3}{8}$ or $\frac{4}{5}$ **6.** $\frac{4}{7}$ or $\frac{5}{9}$ **7.** $\frac{7}{8}$ or $\frac{7}{9}$ **8.** $\frac{4}{10}$ or $\frac{7}{12}$

9. Explain how you found your answer for Problem 8.

_____

_____

_____

_____

Solve. Write your answers in simplest form.

10. _____ $= \frac{5}{6} + \frac{3}{4}$

11. $\frac{7}{9} - \frac{1}{6} =$ _____

12. $8 - \frac{2}{3} =$ _____

13. $\frac{7}{8} - \frac{1}{6} =$ _____

14. $\frac{3}{4}$ of $\frac{2}{5}$ is _____.

15. $4 * \frac{5}{6} =$ _____

Practice

16. $64{,}072 - 15{,}978 =$ _____

17. $2{,}297 \div 45 \rightarrow$ _____

18. $1{,}674 - 1{,}204 =$ _____

19. $326 + 684 + 934 =$ _____

245

LESSON 8·11   # Using a Calculator with Percents

Finding the percent of a number is the same as multiplying the number by the percent. Usually, it's easiest to change the percent to a decimal and use a calculator.

Example: What is 65% of 55?

$65\% = \frac{65}{100} = 0.65$

Write the fraction and decimal for each percent.

1. 18% = _____ = _____   **2.** 60% = _____ = _____

3. 89% = _____ = _____   **4.** 7.5% = _____ = _____

Use your calculator and the percents in Problem 1 to find the percent of 55 by multiplying 55 by each decimal.

Example: 55 * 0.65

5. 18% of 55 = _____   **6.** 60% of 55 = _____

7. 89% of 55 = _____   **8.** 7.5% of 55 = _____

9. Write the calculator key sequence that you used.

_____

Sometimes you know a percent and how much it's worth, but you don't know what the ONE is. Use a unit percent strategy first to find 1%, and then multiply by 100 to get 100%.

Example: 60 million is 37%
            of what number? $60 \div 37 = 1.6216216$

                                    $1.6216216 * 100 = 162.16216$

        Using the fix function $1.6216216 * 100 = 162$ (rounded to the nearest
                                                            whole number)

37% of 162 million is 59.94 million, or 60 million (rounded to the nearest ten million).

Use your calculator and unit percents to solve the following problems.

10. 42% of _____ = 18   **11.** 87% of _____ = 65

12. 63% of _____ = 28 million

LESSON 8·11 | Charting Changes in Consumption

Many times the information that interests you has to be located in data displays with much more data than you need. Use the information on *Student Reference Book,* page 363 to complete the table below.

1. _____

(title)

Foods	1970	1980	1990	2000
Carrots				
Grapes				

Line graphs can make it easier to compare changes in data over time. Use the data from your table in Problem 1 to make a line graph of the pounds of carrots and grapes eaten per person, per year in the United States. Use one color for the carrots data and a different color for the grapes data. Indicate your choices by coloring in the boxes of the graph key.

2.

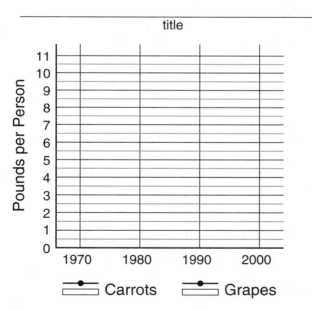

3. What is one conclusion you could draw from the data in your line graph?

_____

_____

STUDY LINK 8·12 | Mixed-Number Review

1. a. Four pizzas will each be cut into eighths. Show how they can be cut to find how many slices there will be in all.

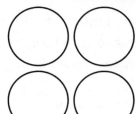

  b. The drawing shows that $4 \div \frac{1}{8} =$ _____, so there will be

     _____ slices in all.

2. a. Two families equally share $\frac{1}{3}$ of a garden. Show how they can divide their portion of the garden.

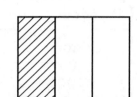

  b. The drawing shows that $\frac{1}{3} \div 2 =$ _____, so each family

     gets _____ of the total garden.

Common Denominator Division

Step 1 Rename the numbers using a common denominator.

Step 2 Divide the numerators, and divide the denominators.

Solve. Show your work.

3. $5 \div \frac{2}{3} =$ _____

4. $\frac{4}{7} \div \frac{3}{5} =$ _____

5. $4\frac{1}{8} \div \frac{3}{4} =$ _____

6. $6\frac{2}{3} \div \frac{7}{9} =$ _____

Practice

7. $4\frac{1}{4} = 3\frac{\square}{4}$ _____

8. $\frac{\square}{5} = 3\frac{7}{5}$ _____

9. $1\frac{3}{5} + 2\frac{1}{5} =$ _____

10. $3\frac{3}{8} - 1\frac{5}{8} =$ _____

11. $7\frac{4}{9} - 5\frac{8}{9} =$ _____

12. $3\frac{2}{7} + 1\frac{4}{5} =$ _____

13. $5\frac{2}{3} + 2\frac{3}{4} =$ _____

14. $4 - 1\frac{3}{4} =$ _____

15. $3 * 3\frac{3}{4} =$ _____

16. $4\frac{2}{3} * \frac{6}{7} =$ _____

248

LESSON 8·12 | **Exploring the Meaning of the Reciprocal**

Lamont and Maribel have to divide fractions. Lamont doesn't want to use common denominators. He thinks using the reciprocal is faster, but he's not sure what a reciprocal is. Maribel looks it up on the Internet and finds this: One number is the **reciprocal** of another number if their product is 1.

Example 1:	Example 2:
$3 * ? = 1$	$\frac{1}{2} * ? = 1$
$3 * \frac{1}{3} = \frac{3}{3} = 1$	$\frac{1}{2} * 2 = \frac{2}{2} = 1$
$\frac{1}{3}$ is the reciprocal of 3	2 is the reciprocal of $\frac{1}{2}$
3 is the reciprocal of $\frac{1}{3}$	$\frac{1}{2}$ is the reciprocal of 2

1. Find the reciprocals.

　a. 6 _____　　**b.** $\frac{1}{7}$ _____　　**c.** 20 _____　　**d.** $\frac{1}{9}$ _____

2. What do you think would be the reciprocal of $\frac{5}{6}$? _____

Reciprocals on a Calculator

On all scientific calculators, you can find a reciprocal of a number by raising the number to the −1 power.

3. Write each number in standard notation as a decimal and a fraction.

　a. 8^{-1} _____, _____　　**b.** 5^{-2} _____, _____　　**c.** 2^{-3} _____, _____

4. Write the key sequence you could use to find the reciprocal of 36.

_____

5. Write the key sequence you could use to find the reciprocal of $\frac{3}{7}$.

_____

6. What pattern do you see for the reciprocal of a fraction?

_____

_____

_____

STUDY LINK 8·13 | **Unit 9: Family Letter**

Coordinates, Area, Volume, and Capacity

In the beginning of this unit, your child will practice naming and locating ordered number pairs on a coordinate grid. Whole numbers, fractions, and negative numbers will be used as coordinates. Your child will play the game *Hidden Treasure,* which provides additional practice with coordinates. You might want to challenge your child to a round.

In previous grades, your child studied the perimeters (distances around) and the areas (amounts of surface) of geometric figures. *Fourth Grade Everyday Mathematics* developed and applied formulas for the areas of rectangles, parallelograms, and triangles. In this unit, your child will review these formulas and explore new area topics, including the rectangle method for finding areas of regular and irregular shapes.

Students will also examine how mathematical transformations change the area, perimeter, and angle measurements of a figure. These transformations resemble changes and motions in the physical world. In some transformations, figures are enlarged in one or two dimensions; in other transformations, figures are translated (slid) or reflected (flipped over).

In the Earth's Water Surface exploration, students locate places on Earth with latitude and longitude. Then they use latitude and longitude in a sampling experiment that enables them to estimate, without measuring, the percent of Earth's surface that is covered by water. In the School's Land Area exploration, students use actual measurements and scale drawings to estimate their school's land area.

The unit concludes with a look at volume (the amount of space an object takes up) and capacity (the amount of material a container can hold). Students develop a formula for the volume of a prism (volume = area of the base * the height). They observe the metric equivalents 1 liter = 1,000 milliliters = 1,000 cubic centimeters, and they practice making conversions between U.S. customary measures (1 gallon = 4 quarts, and so on).

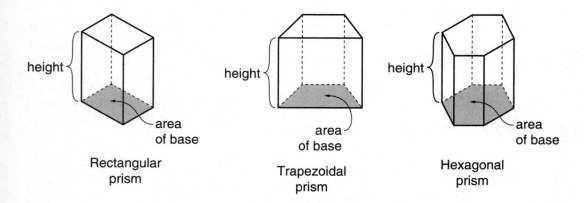

height — area of base
Rectangular prism

height — area of base
Trapezoidal prism

height — area of base
Hexagonal prism

Please keep this Family Letter for reference as your child works through Unit 9.

Vocabulary

Important terms in Unit 9:

area The amount of surface inside a 2-dimensional figure. Area is measured in square units, such as square inches (in^2) and square centimeters (cm^2).

axis of a coordinate grid Either of the two number lines that intersect to form a coordinate grid.

capacity The amount of space occupied by a *3-dimensional* shape. Same as *volume.* The amount a container can hold. Capacity is often measured in units such as *quarts, gallons, cups,* or *liters.*

coordinate A number used to locate a point on a number line, or one of two numbers used to locate a point on a coordinate grid.

coordinate grid A reference frame for locating points in a plane using ordered number pairs, or coordinates.

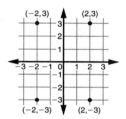

Rectangular coordinate grid

formula A general rule for finding the value of something. A formula is usually an equation with quantities represented by letter *variables.* For example, the formula for the area of a rectangle may be written as $A = \ell * w$, where A represents the area of the rectangle, ℓ represents the length, and w represents the width.

latitude A measure, in degrees, of the distance of a place north or south of the equator.

longitude A measure, in degrees, of how far east or west of the prime meridian a place is.

ordered number pair Two numbers that are used to locate a point on a *coordinate grid.* The first number gives the position along the horizontal axis; the second number gives the position along the vertical axis. Ordered number pairs are usually written inside parentheses: (2,3).

perpendicular Two lines or two planes that intersect at right angles. Line segments or rays that lie on perpendicular lines are perpendicular to each other. The symbol ⊥ means *is perpendicular to.*

rectangle method A method for finding area in which one or more rectangles are drawn around a figure or parts of a figure.

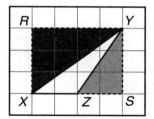

To find the area of triangle *XYZ,* first draw rectangle *XRYS* through its vertices. Then subtract the areas of the two shaded triangles from the area of rectangle *XRYS.*

transformation Something done to a geometric figure that produces a new figure. Common transformations are translations (slides), reflections (flips), and rotations (turns).

volume The amount of space occupied by a 3-dimensional shape. Same as *capacity.* The amount a container can hold. Volume is usually measured in cubic units, such as cubic centimeters (cm^3), cubic inches (in^3), or cubic feet (ft^3).

Do-Anytime Activities

To work with your child on concepts taught in this unit, try these interesting and rewarding activities:

1. Find an atlas or map that uses letter-number pairs to locate places. For example, an atlas might say that Chattanooga, Tennessee, is located at D-9. Use the letter-number pairs to locate places you have visited or would like to visit.

2. Estimate the area of a room in your home. Use a tape measure or ruler to measure the room's length and width, and multiply to find the area. Make a simple sketch of the room, including the length, the width, and the area. If you can, find the area of other rooms or of your entire home.

Building Skills through Games

In Unit 9, your child will develop his or her understanding of coordinates and coordinate grids by playing the following games. For detailed instructions, see the *Student Reference Book.*

Frac-Tac-Toe See *Student Reference Book,* pages 309–311. Two players use a set of number cards 0–10 (4 of each), a gameboard, counters, and a calculator to play one of many versions. Students practice converting between fractions, decimals, and percents.

Hidden Treasure See *Student Reference Book,* page 319. This game for 2 players provides practice using coordinates and coordinate grids. It also offers the opportunity for players to develop good search strategies. Each player will need a pencil and two 1-quadrant playing grids with axes labeled from 0 to 10.

Polygon Capture See *Student Reference Book,* page 328. This game involves two to four players. Materials include polygon pieces and property cards. Players strengthen skills with identifying attributes of polygons. Players may also use 4-quadrant grids with axes labeled from −7 to 7. Practice is extended to coordinates and grids that include negative numbers.

As You Help Your Child with Homework

As your child brings assignments home, you might want to go over the instructions together, clarifying them as necessary. The answers listed below will guide you through some of the Study Links in this unit.

Study Link 9∙1

2. Rectangular prism

3. a. (11,7)   **4.** 13,297

5. 872.355   **6.** $10\frac{2}{8}$, or $10\frac{1}{4}$

Study Link 9∙2

1. Sample answers: (8,16); (0,5); (16,5)

2. isosceles   **4.** quadrangle

Study Link 9∙3

2. The first number

3.

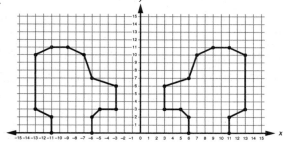

4. 26,320   **6.** $\frac{14}{24}$, or $\frac{7}{12}$

Study Link 9∙4

1. 150 sq ft; 12 hr 30 min   **2.** 114 square feet

3. 80 yd²   **4.** 33 ft²

5.

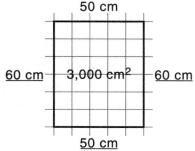

50 cm

60 cm — 3,000 cm² — 60 cm

50 cm

6.

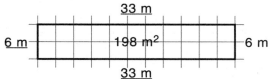

33 m

6 m — 198 m² — 6 m

33 m

Study Link 9∙5

1. 4 cm²   **2.** 6 cm²   **3.** 16 cm²

4. 10 cm²   **5.** 15 cm²   **6.** 4 cm²

Study Link 9∙6

1. 4.5 cm²; $\frac{1}{2} * 3 * 3 = 4.5$

2. 7.5 cm²; $\frac{1}{2} * 5 * 3 = 7.5$

3. 3 cm²; $\frac{1}{2} * 2 * 3 = 3$

4. 24 cm²; $6 * 4 = 24$

5. 12 cm²; $4 * 3 = 12$

6. 8 cm²; $4 * 2 = 8$

Study Link 9∙7

1. yd²   **2.** cm²   **3.** cm²

4. in²   **5.** ft²

6. $A = \frac{1}{2} * 20 * 13$; 130 ft²   **7.** $A = 8 * 2$; 16 cm²

8. $A = \frac{1}{2} * 22 * 7$; 77 yd²   **9.** $A = 8 * 9\frac{1}{2}$; 76 m²

Study Link 9∙8

1. 15 cm²; 15 cm³; 45 cm³   **2.** 8 cm²; 8 cm³; 16 cm³

3. 9 cm²; 9 cm³; 27 cm³   **4.** 14 cm²; 14 cm³; 56 cm³

5. $\frac{3}{40}$ **6.** 960   **7.** 3,840

Study Link 9∙9

1. 72 cm³   **2.** 144 cm³   **3.** 70 in³

4. 162 cm³   **5.** 45 in³   **6.** 140 m³

7. 4   **8.** −245   **9.** 160

Study Link 9∙10

2. $A = \frac{1}{2} * 7 * 6$; 21 cm²   **3.** $A = 8 * 6$; 48 in²

LESSON 8·2 | **Solving Mixed-Number Addition Problems**

Add. Write each sum as a mixed number in simplest form. Show your work.

1. $5\frac{1}{5} + 2\frac{4}{5} =$ _____

2. $3\frac{2}{5} + 5\frac{3}{10} =$ _____

3. $4\frac{3}{4} + 2\frac{1}{12} =$ _____

4. $4\frac{2}{3} + 2\frac{3}{4} =$ _____

5. Josiah was painting his garage. Before lunch, he painted $1\frac{2}{3}$ walls. After lunch, he painted another $1\frac{2}{3}$ walls. How many walls did he paint during the day?

_____

6. Julie's mom made muffins for Julie and her friends to share. Julie ate $1\frac{3}{4}$ muffins. Her friends ate $3\frac{1}{2}$ muffins. How many muffins did Julie and her friends eat altogether?

_____

Without adding the mixed numbers, insert <, >, or =.
Explain how you got your answer.

7. $1\frac{3}{8} + 6\frac{2}{3}$ _____ 8

_____

_____

_____

8. 5 _____ $2\frac{1}{5} + 2\frac{7}{8}$

_____

_____

_____

253A

LESSON 8·12 **Number Stories: Division with Fractions**

1. Five pies will each be sliced into fourths. Ira would like to find out how many slices there will be in all.

   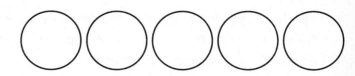

   a. Show how the pies will be cut.

   b. The drawings show that $5 \div \frac{1}{4} =$ _____, so there will be _____ slices in all.

2. Jake has a 3-inch strip of metal. He would like to find out how many $\frac{1}{2}$-inch strips he can cut.

   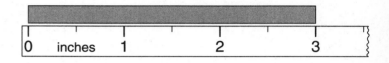

   Jake can cut _____ strips. So, $3 \div \frac{1}{2} =$ _____.

3. Two students equally share $\frac{1}{4}$ of a granola bar. They would like to know how much of the bar each will get.

   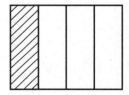

   a. Show how the piece of granola bar will be cut.

   b. The drawing shows that $\frac{1}{4} \div 2 =$ _____, so each

   student will get _____ of a granola bar.

4. a. Drawing A can be used to find $\frac{1}{3} \div 5$.
   Drawing B can be used to find $\frac{1}{3}$ of $\frac{1}{5}$,
   or $\frac{1}{3} * \frac{1}{5}$. Use the drawings to show
   that $\frac{1}{3} \div 5 = \frac{1}{3} * \frac{1}{5}$.

   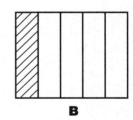
   A   B

   b. Complete.

   $\frac{1}{3} * \frac{1}{5} =$ _____

   $\frac{1}{3} \div 5 =$ _____

   $\frac{1}{3} \div 5 = \frac{1}{3} *$ _____ = _____

253B

STUDY LINK 9·1 | **Plotting Points**

1. Plot the following points on the grid below. After you plot each point, draw a line segment to connect it to the last point you plotted.
Reminder: Use your straightedge!

(3,6); (11,11); (15,11); (15,7); (7,2); (3,2); (3,6); (7,6)

Draw a line segment connecting (7,6) and (7,2).
Draw a line segment connecting (7,6) and (15,11).

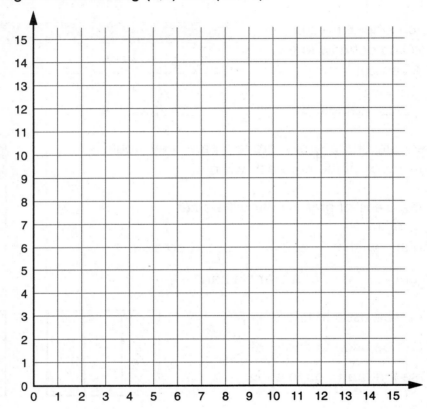

2. What 3-dimensional shape could this drawing represent? _____

3. **a.** What ordered pair would name the missing vertex to represent a prism? _____

b. Draw the missing vertex, and then add dashed lines for the missing edges.

Practice

4. $3{,}745 + 8{,}761 + 791 =$ _____

5. $3.745 + 87.61 + 781 =$ _____

6. $4\frac{3}{8} + 5\frac{7}{8} =$ _____

7. $\frac{1}{5} + \frac{3}{4} =$ _____

LESSON 9·1 — A Botanical Garden Map

A fifth-grade class is visiting a botanical garden. They plan to see every attraction and have lunch in the picnic area. Each student has a copy of the map below. They want to use ordered pairs of numbers to label each attraction and the picnic area.

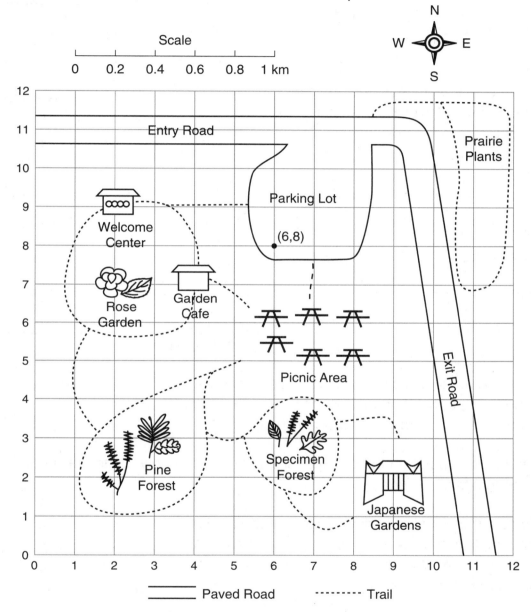

Find and plot the ordered pairs of numbers for each location.

School Bus (6,8)   Welcome Center _____

Prairie Plants _____   Rose Garden _____

Pine Forest _____   Picnic Area _____

Specimen Forest _____   Japanese Gardens _____

255

LESSON 9·1   Traveling the Grid by Bus

Mrs. Thrasher's fifth-grade class is taking a fieldtrip to two different locations: the aquarium, museum, or planetarium, depending on which two places are closest to each other.

1. Choose where the class should go and connect the points.

2. Think of the grid lines as streets. The class must take the bus, and the bus can travel along the grid lines only. Which location is closer to the museum now?

   _____

   Is it the same as your first choice?

   _____

   Why or why not?

   _____

   _____

Scale: 0.75 cm represents 1 block

At the museum, the class learned about plans for the new Skateboard Park. Everyone thought that it should be located an equal distance from the aquarium, museum, and planetarium by bus.

3. Draw and label a point on the grid that shows where the new Skateboard Park should be located.

   Maggie said the city should have built Skateboard Park first. You could just draw a circle using Skateboard Park as the center. Then there would be many locations that were the same distance away.

4. Use the grid to the right to check Maggie's idea. Remember that the bus can go along the gridlines only. Mark every point that is the same distance from Skateboard Park.

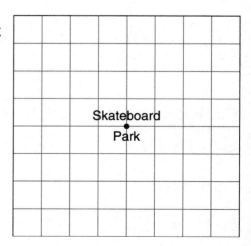

5. Do you agree or disagree with Maggie? _____

   Explain your answer on the back of this page.

STUDY LINK 9·2 | **Plotting Figures on a Coordinate Grid**

1. Plot three points, and make a triangle on the grid below. Label the points as *A, B,* and *C*. List the coordinates of the points you've drawn.

   A: (_____,_____)   *B:* (_____,_____)   *C:* (_____,_____)

2. Circle the name of the kind of triangle you drew.

   scalene   equilateral   isosceles

3. Plot four points, and make a parallelogram on the grid below. Label the points as *M, N, O,* and *P*. List the coordinates of the points you've drawn.

   M: (_____,_____)   *N:* (_____,_____)   *O:* (_____,_____)   *P:* (_____,_____)

4. Circle another name for the parallelogram you've drawn.

   quadrangle   rhombus   rectangle   square

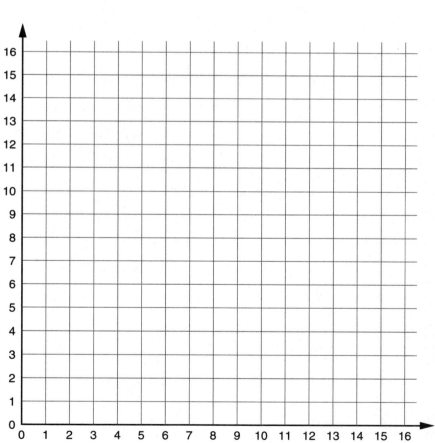

LESSON 9·2 **Plotting a Picture**

1. Draw a simple picture on the grid by connecting points with straight lines. (Use at least 8 points, but no more than 14 points.)

2. Record the ordered pairs you have plotted on a separate sheet of paper. Be sure you record your points in the order in which they need to be connected.

3. Give your list of coordinates and a blank grid to your partner, and have your partner reproduce your drawing by plotting and connecting the points.

4. Compare your original picture with your partner's copy.

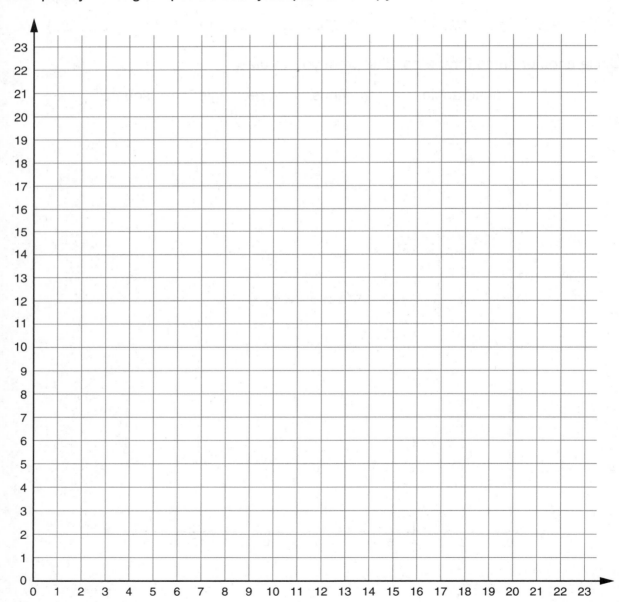

LESSON 9·2 | Scaling Graphs

Scaling a figure on a coordinate grid makes the figure larger or smaller along the coordinate directions. Using a notation to write the scale is another way to represent the rule used to transform a figure.

For example, using (M2,M2) doubles the width and the height of a figure.

This is "double scale" notation that shows how the ordered number pairs change. The M stands for multiplication. The *x*-axis coordinate is multiplied by 2, and the *y*-axis coordinate is multiplied by 2.

◆ (M1,M0.5) compresses the figure on the *y*-axis to half the original dimensions.

◆ (M2,M1) expands the figure on the *x*-axis to twice the original dimensions.

1. How would you describe a new figure that was scaled (M1,M1) from the original?

_____

_____

2. Plot and connect the following coordinates on the grid below:
(4,0.5); (2.5,0.5); (2.5,3.5); (0.5,1); (2.5,0.5); (0,0.5); (1,0); (3.5,0); (4,0.5)

3. Scale the Problem 2 figure to graph two new figures.

Each figure should be a different size. Locate the coordinates, and connect the points so the scaled figures are one behind the other on the grid. *For example:*

4. Write your rules and the corresponding double scales for each of the new figures on the back of this page.

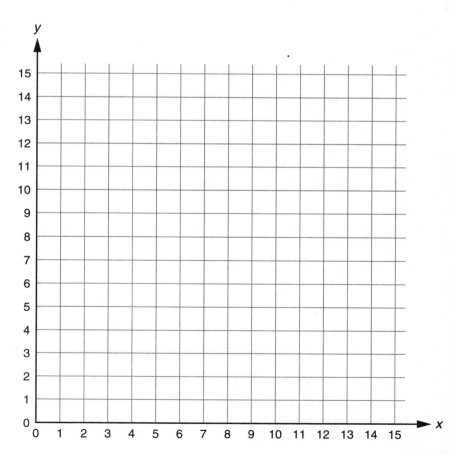

259

LESSON 9·2

Plotting a Map

1. **a.** Plot the following ordered number pairs on the grid:

(21,14); (17,11); (17,13); (15,14); (2,16); (1,11);
(2,8); (3,6); (7.5,5.5); (11,2.5); (12.5,4)

b. Connect all the points in the same order in which they were plotted. Then connect (12.5,4) to (17.5,5) and (21.5,15.5) to (21,14). When you have finished, you should see an outline map of the continental United States.

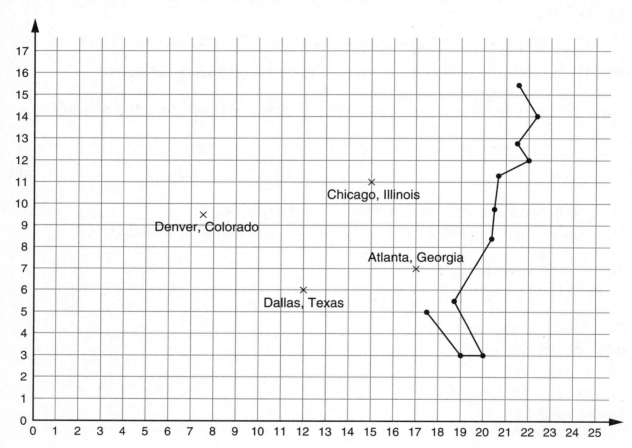

2. Write the coordinates of each city.

a. Chicago, Illinois (_____,_____)   **b.** Atlanta, Georgia (_____,_____)

c. Dallas, Texas (_____,_____)   **d.** Denver, Colorado (_____,_____)

3. Plot each city on the grid and write in the city name.

a. Billings, Montana (7.5,13)   **b.** Salt Lake City, Utah (5.5,10.5)

4. The U.S.–Mexican border is shown by line segments from (3,6) to (7.5,5.5) and from (7.5,5.5) to (11,2.5). Write the border name on the grid.

260

STUDY LINK 9·3 | Reflections on a Coordinate Grid

SRB
157 208

1. Plot the points listed below. Use a straightedge to connect the points in the same order that you plot them.

   (6,0); (6,2); (5,3); (3,3); (3,6); (6,7); (7,10); (9,11); (11,11); (13,10); (13,3); (11,2); (11,0)

2. Which number (the first number or the second number) in the pair do you need to change to the opposite in order to draw the reflection of this design on the other side of the *y*-axis?

   _____

3. Draw the reflection described above. Plot the points and connect them.

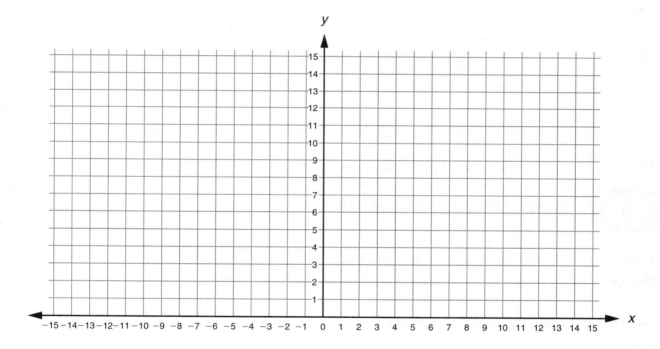

Practice

Multiply.

4. 752 * 35 = _____

5. 75.2 * 0.35 = _____

6. $\frac{7}{8} * \frac{2}{3}$ = _____

7. $2\frac{1}{2} * \frac{3}{4}$ = _____

LESSON 9·3   **Building a Coordinate Grid**

A **rectangular coordinate grid** is used to name points in the plane. A plane is a flat surface that extends forever. Every point on a coordinate grid can be named by an ordered number pair.

Write four true statements about rectangular coordinate grids.

_____

_____

_____

_____

_____

_____

_____

✂ -

Name   Date   Time

LESSON 9·3   **Building a Coordinate Grid**

A **rectangular coordinate grid** is used to name points in the plane. A plane is a flat surface that extends forever. Every point on a coordinate grid can be named by an ordered number pair.

Write four true statements about rectangular coordinate grids.

_____

_____

_____

_____

_____

_____

_____

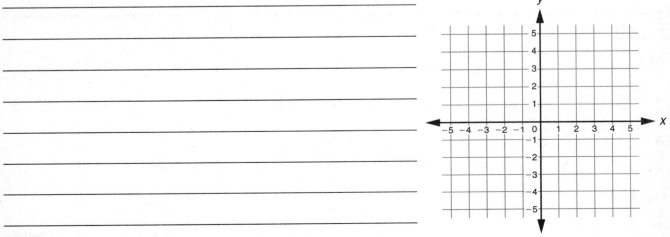

LESSON 9·3 Exploring the Line of Reflection

In geometry, when a line divides a figure into two parts that look exactly alike, but are facing opposite directions, the figure is said to be symmetric. The line is called a *line of symmetry* for the figure. Think of the line of symmetry as a line of reflection. The left side and its reflection together form the figure.

The line of reflection may also be used to produce a new figure that has the same size and shape. The original figure is called the preimage and the new figure is called the image. The preimage and the image are reversed, and each point and its matching point are the same distance from the line of reflection.

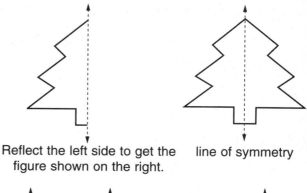

Reflect the left side to get the   line of symmetry
figure shown on the right.

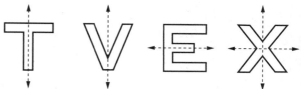

1. Graph the initial of your first name on the coordinate grid below. Record the coordinates.

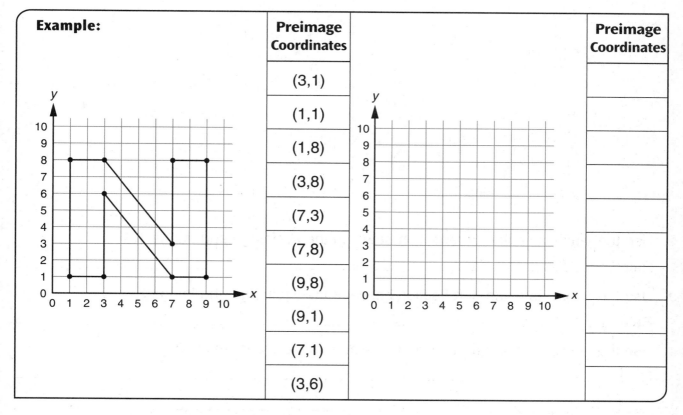

Example:	Preimage Coordinates		Preimage Coordinates
	(3,1)		
	(1,1)		
	(1,8)		
	(3,8)		
	(7,3)		
	(7,8)		
	(9,8)		
	(9,1)		
	(7,1)		
	(3,6)		

2. Follow the instructions on *Math Masters,* page 264 to graph reflections of your initial.

263

LESSON 9·3   Graphing Initials

1. Plot the points of your initial on the coordinate grid below.

   Find and record the rule for each of the following images and plot them on the coordinate grid.

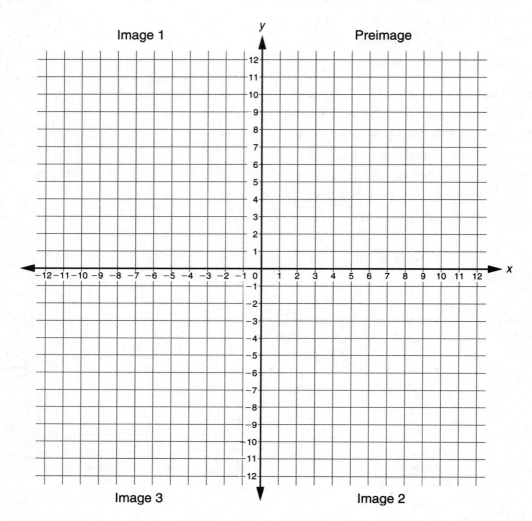

Image 1   Preimage

Image 3   Image 2

2. Use the y-axis as a line of reflection between the Preimage and Image 1.

   Rule: _____

3. Use the x-axis as a line of reflection between the Preimage and Image 2.

   Rule: _____

4. Use the y-axis as a line of reflection between Image 2 and Image 3.

   Rule: _____

   _____

5. Draw a letter that has more than one line of symmetry. _____

264

STUDY LINK
9·4

More Area Problems

1. Rashid can paint 2 square feet of fence in 10 minutes. Fill in the missing parts to tell how long it will take him to paint a fence that is 6 feet high by 25 feet long. Rashid will be able to paint

_____ of fence in ._____
(area)   (hours/minutes)

SRB
104 105
189

2. Regina wants to cover one wall of her room with wallpaper. The wall is 9 feet high and 15 feet wide. There is a doorway in the wall that is 3 feet wide and 7 feet tall. How many square feet of wallpaper will she need to buy?

_____

Calculate the areas for the figures below.

3.

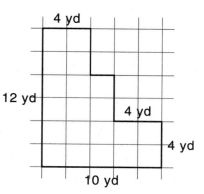

4.

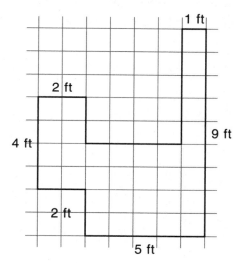

Area = _____ yd²

Area = _____ ft²

Fill in the missing lengths for the figures below.

5.

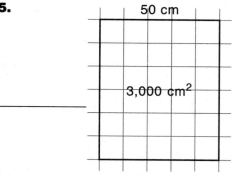

6.

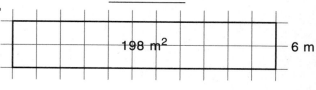

LESSON 9·4   Comparing Perimeter and Area

◆ Roll 2 six-sided dice. The numbers on top are the lengths of 2 sides of a rectangle.

◆ Draw the rectangle in the grid below.

◆ Record the perimeter and the area of the rectangle in the table.

◆ Use centimeter cubes to find other rectangles that have the same area, but different perimeters. Draw the rectangles and record their perimeters and areas in the table.

◆ Repeat until you have filled the table. You might need to roll the dice several times.

Rectangle	Perimeter	Area
A		
B		
C		
D		
E		
F		

LESSON 9·4 **Perimeter and Area of Irregular Figures**

◆ Cut 6 rectangles that are 6 columns by 7 rows from the centimeter grid paper.

◆ Record the area and the perimeter of one of these rectangles in Problem 1.

◆ Divide each rectangle by using 3 different colored pencils to shade three connected parts with the same number of boxes. The parts must follow the grid, and the squares must be connected by sides.

◆ Divide each rectangle in a different way.

1. For a rectangle that is 6 cm by 7 cm:

Area = _____   Perimeter = _____

2. Record the perimeters for the divisions of the 6 rectangles in the table.

Rectangle	Perimeters		
	Part 1	**Part 2**	**Part 3**
1			
2			
3			
4			
5			
6			

3. What is the area for each of the parts? _____

4. What is the range of the perimeters for each of the parts? _____

5. a. Describe one relationship between perimeter and area.

_____

_____

b. Is the relationship the same for rectangles and irregular figures? Explain.

_____

_____

STUDY LINK 9·5

The Rectangle Method

Use the rectangle method to find the area of each figure below.

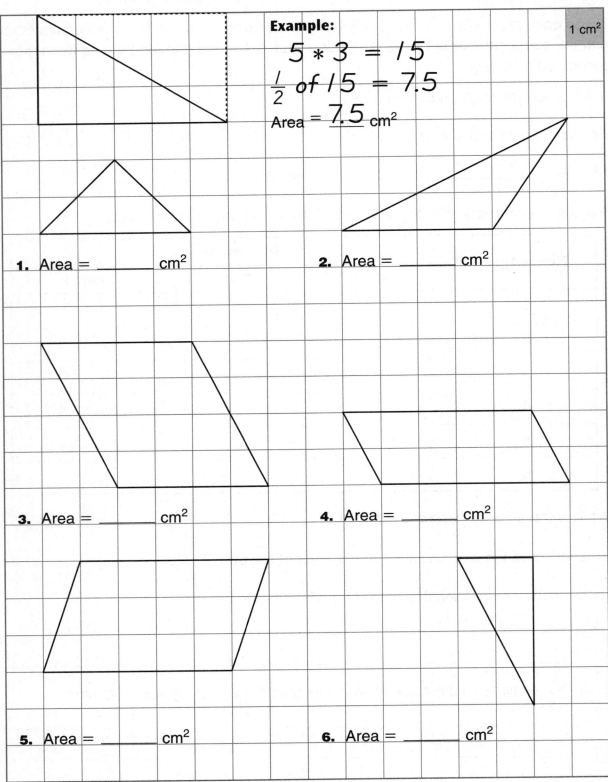

Example:

$5 * 3 = 15$

$\frac{1}{2}$ of $15 = 7.5$

Area = __7.5__ cm²

1 cm²

1. Area = _____ cm²

2. Area = _____ cm²

3. Area = _____ cm²

4. Area = _____ cm²

5. Area = _____ cm²

6. Area = _____ cm²

**STUDY LINK
9·6** | **Area Formulas**

For each figure below, label the base and the height, find the area, and record
the number model you use to find the area.

> Area of a parallelogram: $A = b * h$
>
> Area of a triangle: $A = \frac{1}{2} * b * h$

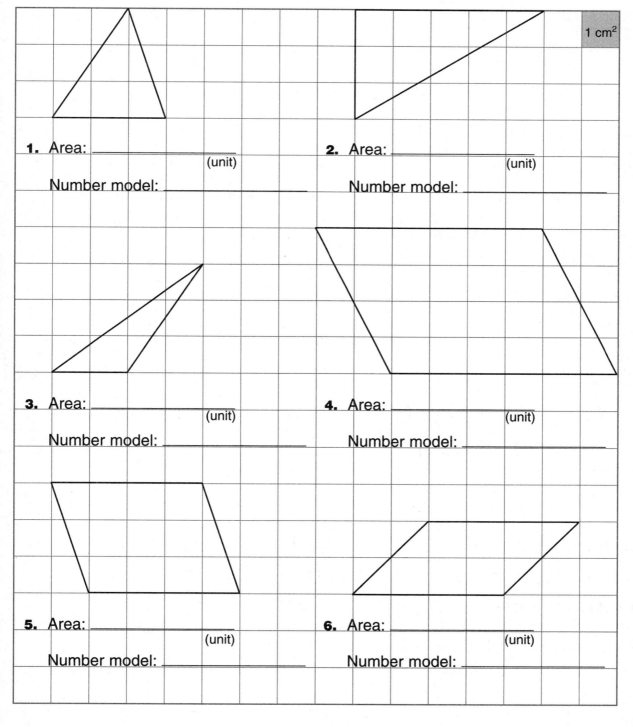

1. Area: _____
(unit)

    Number model: _____

2. Area: _____
(unit)

    Number model: _____

3. Area: _____
(unit)

    Number model: _____

4. Area: _____
(unit)

    Number model: _____

5. Area: _____
(unit)

    Number model: _____

6. Area: _____
(unit)

    Number model: _____

1 cm²

LESSON 9·6 | **Areas of Parallelograms**

1. Cut out Parallelogram A on *Math Masters,* page 272 and form a rectangle. Do *not* cut out the shapes on this page. Tape the parallelogram to form a rectangle.

Parallelogram A

Tape your rectangle in the space below.

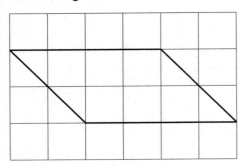

Base = _____ cm

Height = _____ cm

Area of parallelogram = _____ cm²

Length = _____ cm

Width = _____ cm

Area of rectangle = _____ cm²

2. Do the same with Parallelogram B on *Math Masters,* page 272.

Parallelogram B

Tape your rectangle in the space below.

Base = _____ cm

Height = _____ cm

Area of parallelogram = _____ cm²

Length = _____ cm

Width = _____ cm

Area of rectangle = _____ cm²

3. Write a formula for finding the area of a parallelogram.

_____

LESSON 9·6 | **Areas of Triangles and Parallelograms**

1. Cut out Triangles C and D from *Math Masters,* page 272 and form a parallelogram. Do *not* cut out the shapes below. Tape the two triangles together to form a parallelogram.

Triangle C

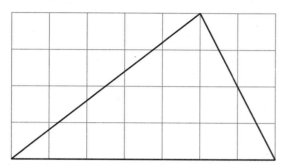

Tape your parallelogram in this space.

Base = _____ cm

Height = _____ cm

Area of triangle = _____ cm²

Length = _____ cm

Height = _____ cm

Area of parallelogram = _____ cm²

2. Do the same with Triangles E and F on *Math Masters,* page 272.

Triangle E

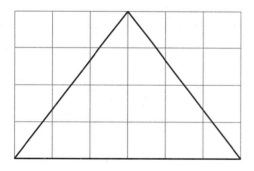

Tape your parallelogram in this space.

Base = _____ cm

Height = _____ cm

Area of triangle = _____ cm²

Base = _____ cm

Height = _____ cm

Area of parallelogram = _____ cm²

3. Write a formula for finding the area of a triangle.

_____

LESSON 9·6 | **Areas of Parallelograms and Triangles**

Cut out Parallelogram A. (Use the second Parallelogram A if you make a mistake.)
Cut it into 2 pieces so that it can be made into a rectangle. Tape the rectangle on
Math Masters, page 270.

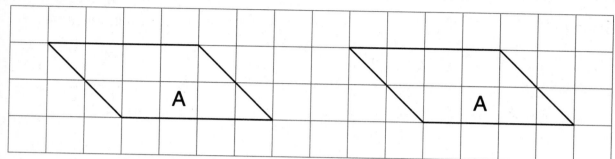

Do the same with Parallelogram B.

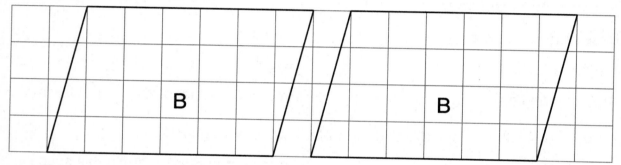

Cut out Triangles C and D. Tape them together at the shaded corners to form
a parallelogram. Tape the parallelogram in the space next to Triangle C on
Math Masters, page 271.

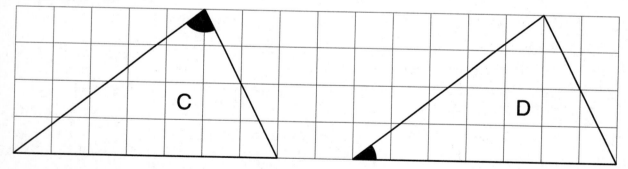

Do the same with Triangles E and F.

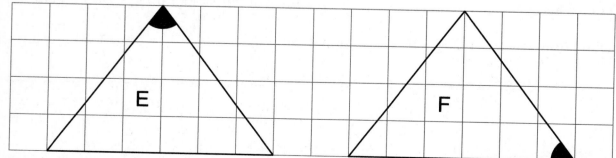

LESSON 9·6 Calculating Area

1. Determine the area of the shaded path on the grid below.

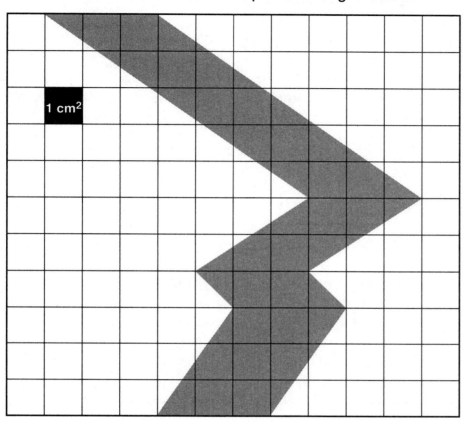

1 cm²

The area of the path is about _____ cm².

2. Describe the strategy that you used to calculate the area of the path.

_____

_____

_____

_____

_____

_____

_____

_____

_____

LESSON 9·7 **Latitudes**

North

0° Latitude (Equator)	10°N	20°N	30°N	40°N
50°N	60°N	70°N		

South

0° Latitude (Equator)	10°S	20°S	30°S	40°S
50°S	60°S	70°S		

In squares for latitude, note that poles (90°N and 90°S) and latitudes 80°N and 80°S are not used.

LESSON 9·7 Longitudes

0° Longitude (prime meridian)	10°W	20°W	30°W	40°W	50°W
60°W	70°W	80°W	90°W	100°W	110°W
120°W	130°W	140°W	150°W	160°W	170°W
180° Longitude	10°E	20°E	30°E	40°E	50°E
60°E	70°E	80°E	90°E	100°E	110°E
120°E	130°E	140°E	150°E	160°E	170°E

STUDY LINK 9·7

An Area Review

Circle the most appropriate unit to use for measuring the area of each object.

1. The area of a football field

cm²	ft²	yd²	in²

2. The area of your hand

cm²	ft²	yd²	in²

3. The area of a postage stamp

cm²	ft²	yd²	in²

4. Area of a triangular kite

cm²	ft²	yd²	in²

5. Area of a parallelogram-shaped
sign on the highway

cm²	ft²	yd²	in²

Use a formula to find the area of each figure. Write the appropriate number sentence
and the area.

6.

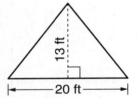

13 ft

20 ft

Number sentence: _____

Area: _____
(unit)

7.

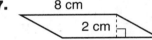

8 cm

2 cm

Number sentence: _____

Area: _____
(unit)

8.

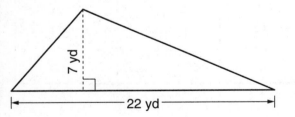

7 yd

22 yd

Number sentence: _____

Area: _____
(unit)

9.

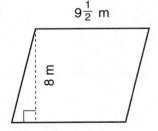

$9\frac{1}{2}$ m

8 m

Number sentence: _____

Area: _____
(unit)

276

LESSON 9·7 Estimation Challenge: Area

What is the ground area of your school? In other words, what area of land is taken up by the ground floor?

Work alone or with a partner to come up with an estimation plan. How can you estimate the ground area of your school without measuring it with a tape measure? Discuss your ideas with your classmates.

My estimation plan:

_____

_____

_____

_____

_____

_____

My best estimate:

_____

_____

_____

_____

_____

How accurate is your estimate? In what range of areas might the actual area fall?

_____

_____

_____

_____

_____

_____

LESSON 9·7 **Practice with Area Formulas**

Write the following formulas.

Area of a triangle: _____

Area of a parallelogram: _____

Use a formula to find the area of each figure.

1.

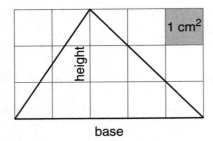

base

Area: _____

2.

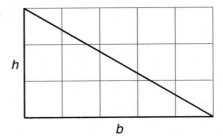

Area: _____

3.

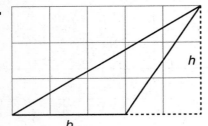

Area: _____

4.

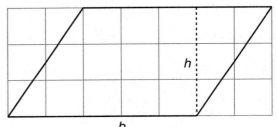

Area: _____

5.

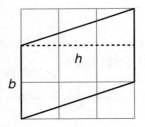

Area: _____

6.

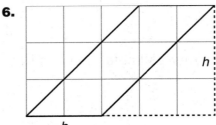

Area: _____

STUDY LINK 9·8 | Volumes of Cube Structures

The structures below are made up of centimeter cubes.

1.

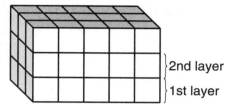

2nd layer
1st layer

Area of base = _____ cm²

Volume of first layer = _____ cm³

Volume of entire
cube structure = _____ cm³

2.

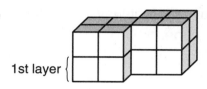

1st layer

Area of base = _____ cm²

Volume of first layer = _____ cm³

Volume of entire
cube structure = _____ cm³

3.

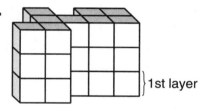

1st layer

Area of base = _____ cm²

Volume of first layer = _____ cm³

Volume of entire
cube structure = _____ cm³

4.

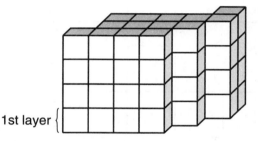

1st layer

Area of base = _____ cm²

Volume of first layer = _____ cm³

Volume of entire
cube structure = _____ cm³

Practice

5. $\frac{3}{5} * \frac{1}{8} =$ _____

6. $3,840 / 4 =$ _____

7. $960 * 4 =$ _____

8. $\frac{4}{5} * \frac{5}{6} =$ _____

LESSON 9·8 | Unfolding Prisms

If you could unfold a prism so that its faces are laid out as a set attached at their edges, you would have a flat diagram for the shape. Imagine unfolding a cube. There are many different ways that you could make diagrams, depending on how you unfold the cube.

Which of the following are diagrams that could be folded to make a cube? Write *yes* or *no* in the blank next to each diagram.

1. _____

2. _____

3. _____

4. _____

LESSON 9·8 | Comparing Volume

What is the volume of one stick-on note? In other words, how much space is taken up by a single stick-on note? How does the volume of a stick-on note compare to the volume of a centimeter cube?

1. An unused pad of stick-on notes is an example of what shape?

_____

2. Estimate the volume of one stick-on note.

_____

3. Calculate the volume of one stick-on note. Volume = _____

Record your strategy.

_____

_____

_____

_____

_____

4. Use a formula to calculate the volume of one centimeter cube. Volume = _____

Write the number sentence for this calculation.

_____

5. Explain how the volume of one stick-on note compares with the volume of one centimeter cube.

_____

_____

_____

_____

_____

LESSON 9·9 | Triangular Prism Base Template

This template is a pattern for the base of a triangular prism. Place the template on a sheet of foam board. Using a pencil or ballpoint pen, mark the position of the six dots by piercing the template. Remove the template and connect the points with solid or dashed lines, the same as on the template. Cut out the prism along the outer solid line, using a serrated knife or saw, making sure that your cuts are made perpendicular to the base.

LESSON 9·9 Parallelogram Prism Base Template

This template is a pattern for the base of a parallelogram prism.
Place the template on a sheet of foam board. Using a pencil or
ballpoint pen, mark the position of the five dots by piercing the
template. Remove the template and connect the points with
solid or dashed lines, the same as on the template.
Cut out the prism along the solid line, using a
serrated knife or saw, making sure that
your cuts are made perpendicular
to the base.

STUDY LINK
9·9

Volumes of Prisms

The volume *V* of any prism can be found with the formula $V = B * h$, where *B* is the area of the base of the prism, and *h* is the height of the prism from that base.

SRB
197

1.

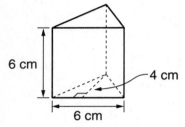

6 cm
4 cm
6 cm

Volume = _____ cm³

2.

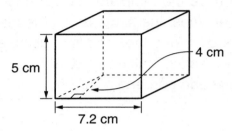

5 cm
4 cm
7.2 cm

Volume = _____ cm³

3.

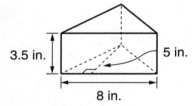

3.5 in.
5 in.
8 in.

Volume = _____ in³

4.

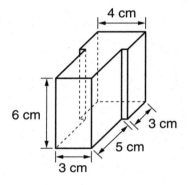

4 cm
6 cm
3 cm
5 cm
3 cm

Volume = _____ cm³

5.

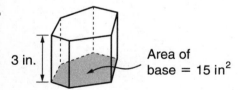

3 in.
Area of base = 15 in²

Volume = _____ in³

6.

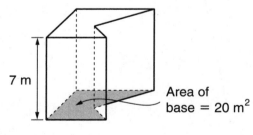

7 m
Area of base = 20 m²

Volume = _____ m³

Practice

Solve each equation.

7. $36 * r = 144$ _____

8. $3{,}577 - t = 3{,}822$ _____

9. $3{,}577 - m = 3{,}417$ _____

10. $d * 68 = 340$ _____

LESSON 9·9 **Triangular Prism Template**

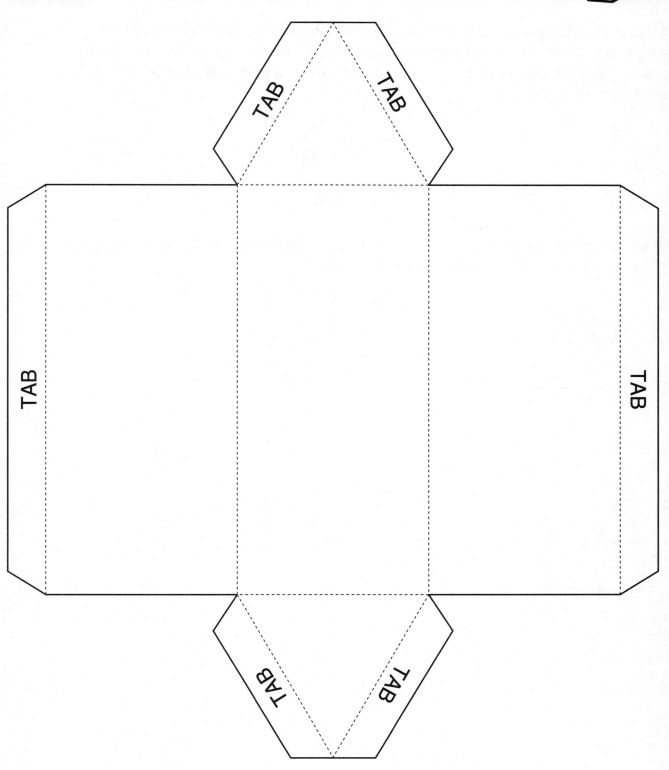

**LESSON
9·9**

Unfolding Geometric Solids

If you could unfold a prism so that its faces are laid out as a set attached at their edges, you would have a flat diagram for the shape. Imagine unfolding a triangular prism. There are different ways that you could make diagrams, depending on how you unfold the triangular prism.

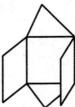

Which of the following are diagrams that could be folded to make a triangular prism? Write *yes* or *no* in the blank under each diagram.

1.

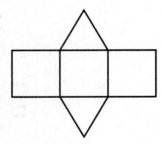

_____

2.

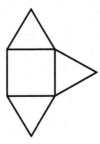

_____

3.

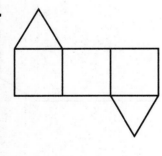

_____

4.

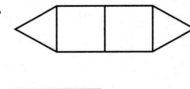

_____

LESSON 9·9 | Faces and Bases

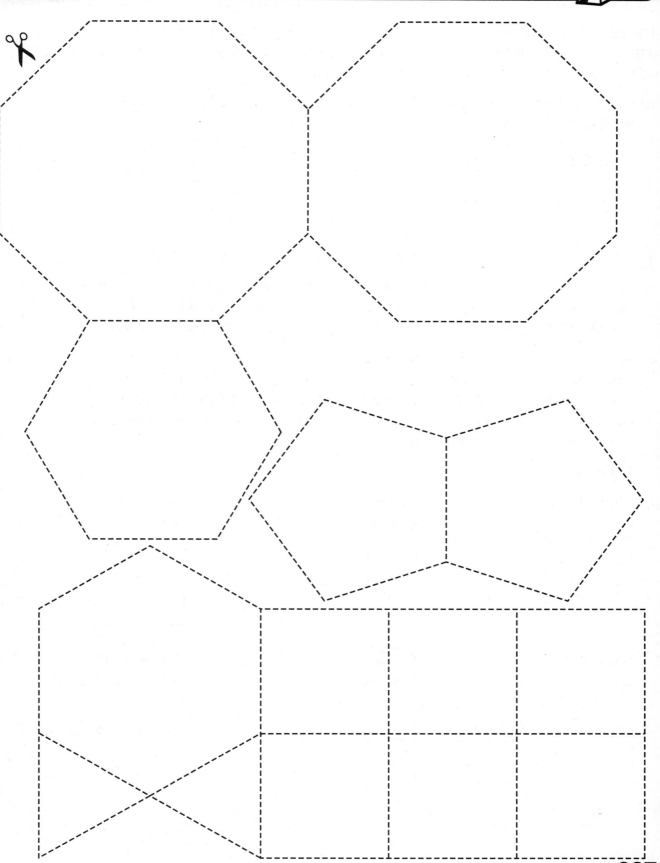

287

LESSON 9·9 | **Using Faces and Bases**

The flat diagram formed from unfolding a prism so that its faces are laid out flat and attached at their edges is called a **geometric net.** For a given prism, there are different nets, depending on how you think about unfolding the prism.

1. Cut out the figures on *Math Masters,* page 287. You and your partner will use the figures to build nets for the prisms below.

   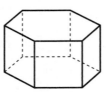 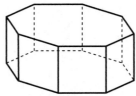

2. Take turns to select, draw, and place figures to form a net for a prism.

3. The partner who places the figure that completes the net states the number of faces and the number of bases. For example, if the net for a cube were completed, the partner would say, "4 faces, 2 bases." This ends the round.

4. A partner can also block the completion of a net. In this case, the partner would put down a figure that would prevent completing the net in the following placement and say "block." The blocked partner then has the opportunity to complete the net by placing two figures and stating the number of faces and bases. Again, this would end the round.

Example:

Student 1
Draw 1:

Student 2
Draw 2:

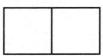

Student 1
Draw 3:

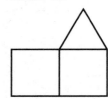

Student 2
Draw 4:

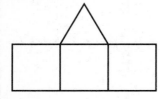

Student 1
Draw 5:

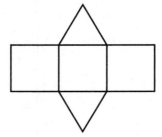

Student 1 states,
"3 faces, 2 bases."

This ends the round.

STUDY LINK
9·10 | # Unit 9 Review

1. Plot 6 points on the grid below and connect them to form a hexagon.
List the coordinates of the points you plotted.

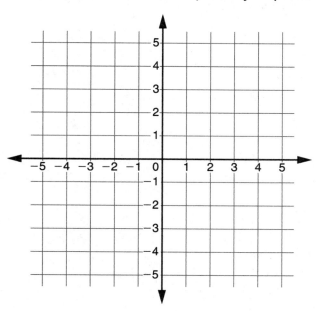

(_____ , _____)

(_____ , _____)

(_____ , _____)

(_____ , _____)

(_____ , _____)

(_____ , _____)

Find the area of the figures shown below.
Write the number model you used to
find the area.

> Area of a rectangle: $A = b * h$
>
> Area of a parallelogram: $A = b * h$
>
> Area of a triangle: $A = \frac{1}{2} * b * h$

2.

Number model: _____

Area: _____
(unit)

3.

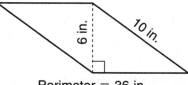

Perimeter = 36 in.

Number model: _____

Area: _____
(unit)

4. On the back of this page, explain how you solved Problem 3.

Unit 10: Family Letter

Algebra Concepts and Skills

In this unit, your child will be introduced to solving simple equations with a pan balance, thus developing basic skills of algebra. For example, a problem might ask how many marbles in the illustration below weigh as much as a cube. You can solve this problem by removing 3 marbles from the left pan and 3 marbles from the right pan. Then the pans will still balance. Therefore, you know that one cube weighs the same as 11 marbles.

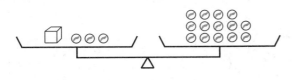

You can think of this pan-balance problem as a model for the equation $c + 3 = 14$, in which the value of c is 11.

A "What's My Rule?" table has been a routine since the early grades of *Everyday Mathematics.* In this unit, your child will follow rules to complete tables, such as the one below and will then graph the data. Your child will also determine rules from information provided in tables and graphs. Students will begin to express such rules using algebraic expressions containing variables.

Rule
+ 6

in	out
−1	5
2	8
5	
	12
12	
	15

As the American Tour continues, your child will work with variables and formulas to predict eruption times of the famous geyser, Old Faithful, in Yellowstone National Park.

In previous grades, your child studied the perimeter (distance around) and the area (amount of surface) of geometric figures. In Unit 9, students developed and applied formulas for the area of rectangles, parallelograms, and triangles. In this unit, your child will explore and apply formulas for the circumference (distance around) and area of circles.

Please keep this Family Letter for reference as your child works through Unit 10.

290

Vocabulary

Important terms in Unit 10:

algebraic expression An expression that contains a variable. For example, if Maria is 2 inches taller than Joe, and if the variable M represents Maria's height, then the algebraic expression $M - 2$ represents Joe's height.

line graph A graph in which data points are connected by line segments.

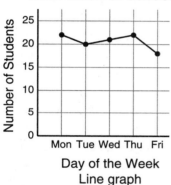

Attendance for the First Week of School

Number of Students

Day of the Week
Line graph

pan balance A tool used to weigh objects or compare weights.

Pan balance

predict In mathematics, to say what will happen in the future based on experimental data or theoretical calculation.

rate A comparison by division of two quantities with unlike units. For example, a speed such as 55 miles per hour is a rate that compares distance with time.

Do-Anytime Activities

To work with your child on concepts taught in this unit and in previous units, try these interesting and rewarding activities:

1. Have your child list different timed distances for a mile. For example, the fastest mile run by a human and by a race car; your child's own fastest mile completed by running, biking, or walking; the fastest mile run for a handicapped athlete; the fastest mile completed by a swimmer, and so on.

2. Have your child keep a running tally of when the school bus arrives. Or have your child time himself or herself to see how long it takes to walk to school in the morning compared to walking home in the afternoon. After a week, have your child describe landmarks for their data and interpret these landmarks.

Building Skills through Games

In this unit, your child will practice using algebraic expressions containing variables by playing the following game. For more detailed instructions, see the *Student Reference Book.*

First to 100 See *Student Reference Book,* page 308.
This is a game for two to four players and requires 32 Problem Cards and a pair of six-sided dice. Players answer questions after substituting numbers for the variable on the Problem Cards. The questions offer practice on a variety of mathematical topics.

As You Help Your Child with Homework

As your child brings assignments home, you might want to go over the instructions together, clarifying them as necessary. The answers listed below will guide you through some of the Study Links in this unit.

Study Link 10◆1

1. 3   **2.** 3   **3.** 36   **4.** 4   **5.** 3

Study Link 10◆2

3. 5, 10   **4.** 2, 2   **5.** 4, 6   **6.** 26
7. 2   **8.** 50   **9.** 0

Study Link 10◆3

1. $2 * (L + M)$, or $2 (L + M)$

2. $\frac{1}{4} * (m - (l + s))$, or $\frac{1}{4} (m - (l + s))$

3. a. Multiply N by 3 and add 5.
   b. $Q = 3N + 5$

4. a. Multiply E by 6 and add 15.
   b. $R = (E * 6) + 15$

Study Link 10◆4

1. a.

Weight (lb) (w)	Cost ($) ($2.50 * w$)
1	2.50
3	7.50
6	15.00
10	25.00

2. a.

Gasoline (gal) (g)	Distance (mi) ($24 * g$)
1	24
4	96
7	168
13	312

Study Link 10◆5

2. 60°F   **4.** 72°F   **5. a.** 70°F   **b.** 67°F

Study Link 10◆6

Time	Distance (yd)	
	Natasha	Derek
Start	0	10
1	6	15
2	12	20
3	18	25
4	24	30
9	54	55
10	60	60
11	66	65
12	72	70
13	78	75

Study Link 10◆7

Answers vary.

Study Link 10◆8

1. a. 22.0   **b.** 40.2

2. a. 85   **b.** 85

3. 21

Study Link 10◆9

1. circumference   **2.** area   **3.** area

4. circumference   **5.** 50 cm^2

6. 6 in.   **7.** 5 m

8. Sample answer: The circumference is 31.4 meters, and this equals $\pi * d$, or about $3.14 * d$. Since $3.14 * 10 = 31.4$, the diameter is about 10 meters. The radius is half the diameter, or about 5 meters.

293

LESSON 9·4 | ## Area: Tiling and Using a Formula

For each rectangle below, cut out a rectangle from the centimeter grid paper (*Math Masters,* page 436) that has the same dimensions. Follow the directions for each problem.

1. The length of the base of the rectangle is 6 cm and the height is $2\frac{1}{2}$ cm.

    a. Tape the centimeter grid over the rectangle, and then use the counting method to find the area of the rectangle. _____ cm²

    b. Use the formula to write an open number model that can be used to find the area. _____

    c. Area = _____ cm²

2. The length of the base of the rectangle below is $12\frac{1}{2}$ cm and the height is $2\frac{1}{2}$ cm.

    a. Tape the centimeter grid over the rectangle, and then use the counting method to find the area of the rectangle. _____ cm²

    b. Use the formula to find the area. _____ cm²

3. a. Use the formula to find the area of the rectangle below. _____ cm²

    b. Tape the centimeter grid over the rectangle, and then use the counting method to find the area of the rectangle. _____ cm²

$1\frac{1}{2}$ cm

$10\frac{1}{2}$ cm

    c. Explain why the formula and the counting method produce the same area.

_____

_____

_____

293A

STUDY LINK
10·1 Pan-Balance Problems

In each figure below, the two pans are in perfect balance. Solve these
pan-balance problems.

1. One triangle weighs

as much as _____ squares.

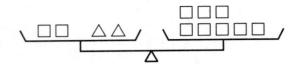

2. One cube weighs

as much as _____ marbles.

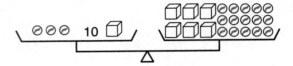

3. Two cantaloupes weigh

as much as _____ apples.

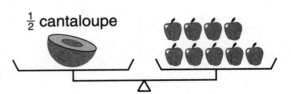

4. One *X* weighs

as much as _____ *Y*s.

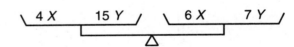

5. One *B* weighs

as much as _____ *M*s.

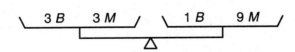

Practice

6.   4,217
      − 2,849

7.   16,000
      − 8,245

8. $11.47 - 8.896 =$ _____

9. $36 - 42 =$ _____

Exploring Pan Balances

Find combinations of objects where the weights balance the pans.
Record the combinations below using pictures and words.

Example:

One nickel weighs about as much as 5 blocks.

1.

One _____ weighs about as much as _____.

2.

One _____ weighs about as much as _____.

3.

One _____ weighs about as much as _____.

4.

One _____ weighs about as much as _____.

LESSON
10·1 **Penny Weights**

The materials used to make a penny were changed at the beginning
of one of these years: 1981, 1982, or 1983. As a result, the weight of
a penny has changed. Your task is to find the year the weight
of pennies changed.

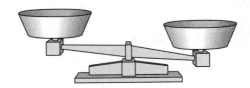

1. Compare 1981 pennies to 1982 pennies.
    Put ten 1981 pennies in one pan and ten 1982 pennies in the other pan.

    Do the pans balance? _____

2. Return the pennies to their correct containers.
    Put ten 1982 pennies in one pan and ten 1983 pennies in the other pan.

    Do the pans balance? _____

3. I think penny weights changed beginning in the year _____ because

    _____

    _____

4. Why do you think it is better to compare the weights using 10 pennies for each year

    rather than only 1 penny for each year? _____

    _____

    _____

    _____

    _____

5. Why do you think they changed the materials used to make a penny?

    _____

    _____

296

STUDY LINK 10·2 Pan-Balance Problems

In each figure below, the two pans are in perfect balance. Solve these
pan-balance problems.

SRB
222 228
229

1.

One triangle weighs

as much as _____ balls.

2.

One pen weighs

as much as _____ paper clips.

3.

M weighs

as much as _____ marbles.

N weighs

as much as _____ marbles.

4.

```
5 △ □        11 □
```

One △ weighs

as much as _____ □s.

```
△ □ □        8 marbles
```

One □ weighs

as much as _____ marbles.

5.

One cup of juice weighs

as much as _____ blocks.

One apple weighs

as much as _____ blocks.

Practice

Fill in the missing numbers to make true sentences.

6. _____ = (7 + 45) / 2

7. ((28 / 7) + 12) / 8 = _____

8. ((14 * 3) + 14) − 6 = _____

9. _____ = (3 − 3) * ((34 / 2) * 115)

LESSON 10·2   Measuring Time

Franz buys two sandglasses from an antique dealer.
However, when he gets home he realizes the sand in the
sandglasses does not measure 1 hour. The first sandglass
measures a nine-minute interval, and the other sandglass
measures a thirteen-minute interval.

Franz wants to make a special cleaning solution to clean his new
sandglasses. The solution needs to boil for 30 minutes. Can Franz
use his sandglasses to measure 30 minutes from the time the
solution starts to boil?

Explain your solution by describing what Franz should do.

_____

_____

_____

_____

_____

_____

_____

_____

_____

_____

_____

_____

_____

_____

Writing Algebraic Expressions

Complete each statement below with an algebraic expression, using the suggested variable.

SRB
218 231 232

1. Lamont, Augusto, and Mario grow carrots in three garden plots. Augusto harvests two times as many carrots as the total number of carrots that Lamont and Mario harvest. So Augusto harvests

Augusto

Lamont and Mario harvested
$L + M$ carrots.

_____ carrots.

2. Rhasheema and Alexis have a lemonade stand at their school fair. They promise to donate one-fourth of the remaining money (m) after they repay the school for lemons (l) and sugar (s). So the girls donate

_____ dollars.

3. **a.** State in words the rule for the "What's My Rule?" table at the right.

_____

_____

b. Circle the number sentence that describes the rule.

$Q = (3 + N) * 5$ $Q = 3 * (N + 5)$ $Q = 3N + 5$

N	Q
2	11
4	17
6	23
8	29
10	35

4. **a.** State in words the rule for the "What's My Rule?" table at the right.

_____

_____

b. Circle the number sentence that describes the rule.

$R = E * 6 * 15$ $R = (E * 6) + 15$ $R = E * 15 + 6$

E	R
7	57
10	75
31	201
3	33
108	663

Practice

5. $384 * 1.5 =$ _____

6. $50.3 * 89 =$ _____

7. $\frac{843}{7} =$ _____

8. $70.4 / 8 =$ _____

LESSON 10·3   **"What's My Rule?"**

1. Write a rule in words for the "What's My Rule?" table.

in	out

2. Work with a partner to complete the table. Take turns: one partner enters an *in* value, and the other partner follows the rule to enter an *out* value.

3. Write the rule as an algebraic expression.

_____

4. Think of a rule for the "What's My Rule?" table. Then use your rule to complete 3 rows in the table. Have your partner find the rule and complete the table.

in	out

5. Write your rule in words and as an algebraic expression.

   a. Rule in words:

   _____

   _____

   b. Rule as an algebraic expression:

   _____

6. What are important things to remember when writing rules or making a "What's My Rule?" table for a partner to find the rule?

_____

_____

_____

_____

300

LESSON 10·3 | Patterns and Relationships

A car is traveling at a given speed over a stretch of highway. You can find the distance the car travels by multiplying its speed by the amount of time it travels.

1. Car A travels at a speed of 30 miles per hour (mph). Car B travels at 60 miles per hour. Complete the tables to find the distance each car travels for the given times.

Car A	
Speed: 30 mph	
Time (hr)	**Distance (mi)**
0	0
1	30
2	
3	
4	

Car B	
Speed: 60 mph	
Time (hr)	**Distance (mi)**
0	
1	
2	
3	
4	

2. For each car, write the rule that is used to find the distance.
Car A: Car B:

_____   _____

3. Use the tables to write a set of ordered pairs in the form (Time, Distance) for each car. Then graph the data and connect the points for each car. Label each graph.

Car A	Car B
(0,0)	_____
(1,30)	_____
_____	_____
_____	_____
_____	_____

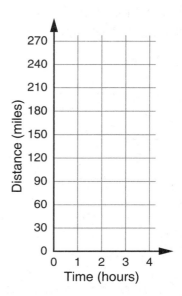

4. As the amount of time increases, explain how the distance Car B travels compares with the distance Car A travels?

_____

LESSON 10·4 | Analyzing Two Rates

Each day, Taylor practices the piano $1\frac{1}{2}$ hours and Kim practices $\frac{3}{4}$ hour.

1. In the tables below, write a rule for each student that gives the total number of hours (h) practiced for a given number of days (d).

2. Complete the tables to show the total amount of time each student practiced during a 5-day period.

Taylor's Practice	
Rule:	
Days	**Hours**
1	$1\frac{1}{2}$
2	3
3	
4	
5	

Kim's Practice	
Rule:	
Days	**Hours**
1	$\frac{3}{4}$
2	
3	
4	
5	

3. Use the data to write a set of ordered pairs in the form (Days, Hours) for Taylor and Kim. Graph the data, connect the points for each student, and label each graph.

Taylor   Kim

$(1,1\frac{1}{2})$ _____

_____   _____

_____   _____

_____   _____

_____   _____

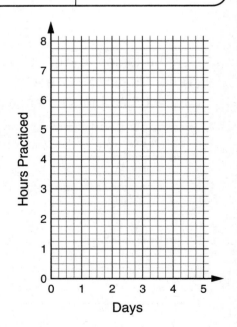

4. After each day, how does the total amount of time practiced by Taylor compare to Kim's time? Explain.

_____

_____

300B

STUDY LINK
10·4

Representing Rates

Complete each table below. Then graph the data and connect the points.

1. **a.** Cherry tomatoes cost $2.50 per pound.
Rule: Cost = $2.50 * number of pounds

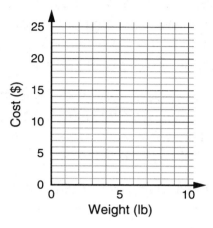

Weight (lb) (*w*)	Cost ($) (2.50 * *w*)
1	
3	
	15.00
10	

b. Plot a point to show the cost of 8 pounds.
How much would 8 pounds of cherry tomatoes cost? _____

c. Would you use the graph, the rule, or the table to find out how much
50 pounds of cherry tomatoes would cost? Explain.

_____

_____

2. **a.** Chantel is planning a trip to drive across country.
Her car uses 1 gallon of gasoline every 24 miles.
Rule: distance = 24 * number of gallons

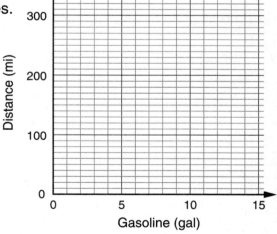

Gasoline (gal) (*g*)	Distance (mi) (24 * *g*)
1	
4	
	168
13	

b. Plot a point to show the distance the car would travel
on 6 gallons of gasoline. How many miles would it go? _____

c. Would you use the graph, the rule, or the table to find out
how far the car would travel on 9 gallons of gasoline? Explain. _____

_____

301

LESSON 10·4 Solving Rate Problems

Rate describes a relationship between two quantities with different units. Rate tells how many of one type of thing there are for a certain number of another type of thing. Rates are often expressed with phrases that include the word *per.* For example, miles per hour, cost per ounce, or books per student.

One example of rate is speed. A basic formula is distance = rate * time. Multiplication can be used for many different problems involving rates. For example, distance = rate * gallons, total cost = rate * ounces, or total books = rate * students.

To solve a problem using a formula, first replace variables with the known values.

Example:

Maribel can travel 5 miles per hour on her skateboard. How far will she travel in 2 hours?

distance = rate * time	d	$=$	r	$*$	t
distance = 5 miles per hour * 2 hours	10	$=$	5	$*$	2
distance = 10 miles					

Maribel can travel 10 miles.

Use the formula to solve the following problem.

1. Samuel's go-kart can travel 357 miles on 14 gallons of gas. His go-kart travels how many miles per gallon?

distance = rate * gallons of gas	d	$=$	r	$*$	g
distance = miles per gallon * 14 gallons of gas	___	$=$	___	$*$	___
rate = _____					

2. Samuel's go-kart can travel _____ miles per gallon of gas.

Explain your solution.

_____

_____

_____

302

LESSON 10·4 — "What's My Rule?"

Complete each table below according to the rule.

1. Rule: Subtract the *in* number from 15.

in (n)	out (15 − n)
1	
2	
8	
	5
18	
	0

2. Rule: Triple the *in* number.

in (d)	out (3 * d)
7	
12	
	24
0.3	
	1
$\frac{1}{2}$	

3. Rule: Double the *in* number and add 3.

in (x)	out ((2 * x) + 3)
2	
4	
6	
	19
12	
	3

Complete each table below. Write the rule in words or as a formula. On the back of the page, graph the data in Problems 4 and 5.

4. Rule: _____

_____

_____

in	out
4	2
12	6
16	8
2	
	$3\frac{1}{2}$
310	

5. Rule: _____

_____

_____

in	out
1	1
2	3
3	5
4	
5	
	19

6. Make up your own.

Rule: _____

_____

in	out

STUDY LINK 10·5 Cricket Formulas

In 1897, the physicist, A. E. Dolbear, published an article titled "The Cricket as a Thermometer." In it he claimed that outside temperatures can be estimated by counting the number of chirps made by crickets and then by using that number in the following formula:

Outside temperature (°F) = $\dfrac{\text{(number of cricket chirps per minute } - 40)}{4} + 50$

1. Write a number model for the formula. _____

2. According to this formula, what is the estimated outside temperature if you count 80 chirps in a minute? _____

    Other cricket formulas exist. The following formula is supposed to work particularly well with field crickets:

    Outside temperature (°F) = (number of chirps in 15 seconds) + 37

3. Write a number model for the formula. _____

4. According to this formula, what is the estimated outside temperature if you counted 35 chirps in 15 seconds? _____

5. Compare the two formulas. If you count 30 chirps in 15 seconds, what is the estimated outside temperature for each formula?

    a. First formula: _____

    b. Second formula: _____

Practice

6. $7 - 2\frac{2}{5} =$ _____

7. $1\frac{1}{2} + 2\frac{2}{3} + 3\frac{3}{4} + \frac{1}{12} =$ _____

8. $\left(\frac{2}{3} * \frac{2}{3}\right) - \frac{2}{9} =$ _____

9. $\frac{12}{9} \div \frac{1}{3} =$ _____

LESSON 10·5

Graphing "What's My Rule?" Tables

Complete the "What's My Rule?" tables. Record the rule on the lines provided, and graph the data from the tables.

1. Rule: _____

_____

_____

in (x)	out ((2 * x) + 3)
1	
2	
3	
	15
8	
	3

2. Rule: _____

_____

_____

in n	out n ÷ 2
6	3
9	$4\frac{1}{2}$
1	0.5
12	
	8

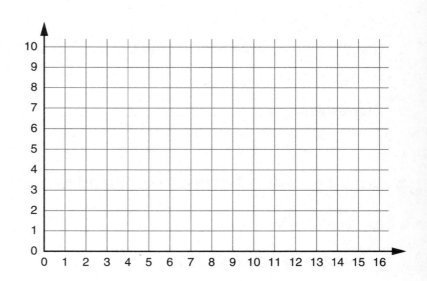

305

Interpreting Tables and Graphs

Natasha is 12 years old and runs an average of 6 yards per second. Derek is 8 years old and runs about 5 yards per second. Natasha challenged Derek to an 80-yard race and told him she would win even if he had a 10-yard head start.

1. Complete the table showing the distances Natasha and Derek are from the starting line after 1 second, 2 seconds, 3 seconds, and so on.

Time (sec)	Distance (yd)	
	Natasha	Derek
Start	0	10
1		
2		20
3	18	
4		
9		55
10		
11		
12		
13		

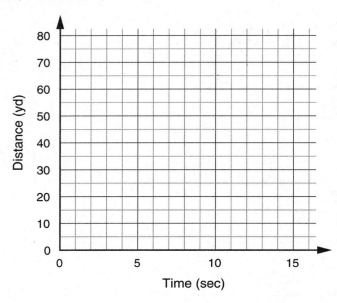

2. Use the table to write rules for the distance covered by Natasha and Derek.

Natasha's Rule: _____

Derek's Rule: _____

_____

3. Graph the results of the race between Natasha and Derek on the grid above. Label each line.

4. a. Who wins the race? _____

  b. What is the winning time? _____

  c. At what time in the race did Natasha take the lead? _____

306

LESSON 10·6   Interpreting Table Data

There are a number of choices when making a graph from table data.

◆ The type of graph is determined by the type of data represented.

◆ The title and labels for the graph are often the easiest to recognize from the table.

◆ Deciding on the scale to use for the y-axis of a line graph is more of a challenge. The intervals in the data can guide the choice of a scale.

1. Make a graph for each of the tables below.

Table 1	
Pinto bean plants grow an average of 1.5 inches each day.	
Day	**Plant Height (in.)**
0	0
1	1.5
2	3.0
3	4.5
4	6.0
5	7.5

Table 2	
Exterior colors of cars in the movie theater parking lot	
Exterior Color	**Percent**
Silver	25%
Yellow	5%
Black	25%
Red	10%
Blue	25%
White	10%

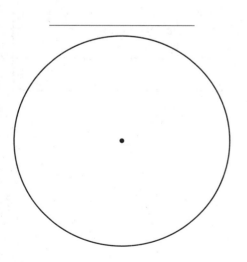

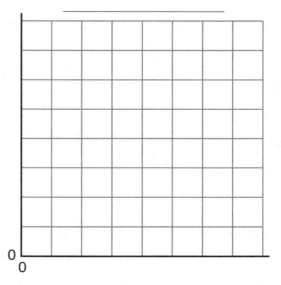

2. On the back of this page, explain why you chose which graph to use for each table.

LESSON 10·6 Analyzing Two Rules

Ivan earns $50 every 2 days. Elise earns $70 every 3 days.

1. Write a rule to describe how much money Ivan earns in a given number of days.

   Amount earned = _____ * number of days

2. Write a rule to describe how much money Elise earns in a given number of days.

   _____

3. Complete the table for the outputs in the cells that are not shaded.

4. a. After 6 days, who has earned more money?

   _____

   b. After 12 days, who has earned more money?

   _____

   c. Who earns more money per day? Explain your answer.

   _____

   _____

   _____

   _____

Days	Money Earned	
	Ivan	Elise
0		
1	(shaded)	(shaded)
2		(shaded)
3	(shaded)	
4		(shaded)
5	(shaded)	(shaded)
6		
7	(shaded)	(shaded)
8		(shaded)
9	(shaded)	
10		(shaded)
11	(shaded)	(shaded)
12		
13	(shaded)	(shaded)
14		(shaded)
15	(shaded)	
16		(shaded)

5. How long does it take each person to make $350?

   Ivan: _____ days   Elise: _____ days

LESSON 10·6 | **Analyzing Two Rules** *continued*

6. Write three ordered pairs to show the relationship between number of days and the amount earned for each person.

Ivan: _____

Elise: _____

7. Use the grid to graph your ordered pairs. Use a straightedge to connect the points for each person, and label the lines Ivan and Elise.

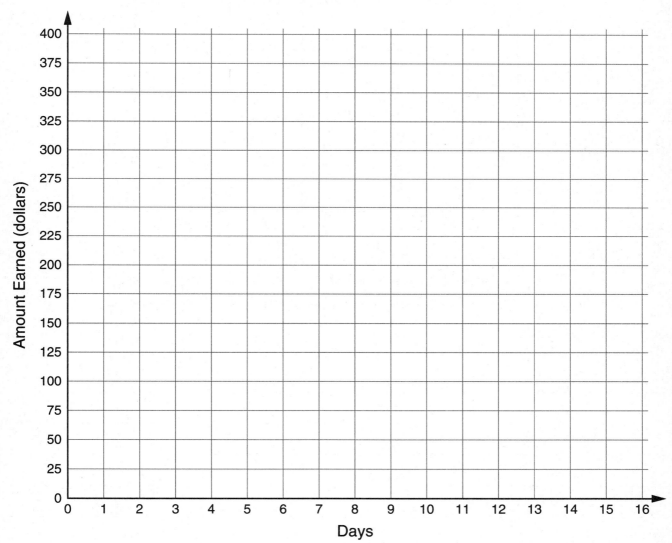

8. About how much more did Ivan earn after 13 days? _____

9. Extend the graph to find out about how much Elise earned in 16 days. _____

307B

STUDY LINK 10·7 | **Mystery Graphs**

Create a mystery graph on the grid below. Be sure to label the horizontal and vertical axes. Describe the situation that goes with your graph on the lines provided.

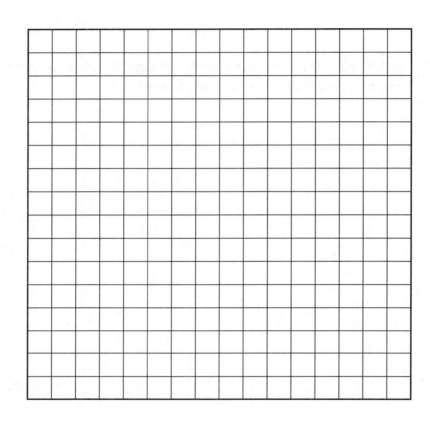

_____

_____

_____

_____

_____

_____

_____

Reminder: Look for examples of ratios and bring them to school.

LESSON 10·7 | **Exploring Silhouettes**

Objects and actions can often be recognized from their shapes, called **silhouettes.**
For each of the silhouettes below, write a description of the object or activity.

1.	**2.**
3.	**4.**
5.	**6.**

LESSON 10·7 | Making Tables from Graphs

When you plot the values of a table as coordinates on a grid and connect the points, the resulting figure can be called a **line graph.**

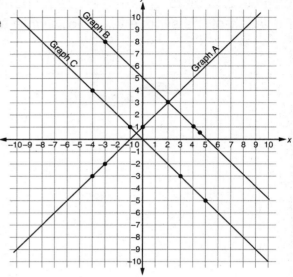

For each graph on the grid to the right:

◆ Find the coordinates of four points that lie on the graph.

◆ Write the four points in the "What's My Rule?" table.

◆ Write the rule for the table.

◆ Check that your rule works for all the points on the graph.

1. Rule for Graph A: _____

x	y

2. Rule for Graph B: _____

x	y

3. Rule for Graph C: _____

x	y

LESSON 10·7 | Analyzing Graph Errors

For each graph below, describe a possible error in the graph.

Favorite Colors

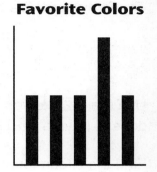

1. The students in Ms. Wyn's fifth-grade class took a favorite color survey. About the same number of people voted for red, blue, and green. Orange and yellow got about the same number of votes, but the votes were a lot less than the other three colors. They made a bar graph of their results.

Describe at least one error in the Favorite Colors graph. Explain how you know this is an error.

_____

_____

_____

2. There are 26 students in Ms. Wyn's class. They wanted to find the mean number of books that students had read in their class. They found out that half the class had read five or fewer books and the other half had read more than 15 books. The mode for the class was 19 books. They made a line plot of their results.

Books We Have Read

```
    X
    X                           X
    X                           X       X
    X                           X      X X
  X X                       X   X      X X
  X X   X                 X X  X X   X  X X
  ─────────────────────────────────────────
  0   2   4   6   8  10  12  14  16  18  20  22  24  26  28  30
```

Describe at least one error in the Books We Have Read graph. Explain how you know this is an error.

_____

_____

_____

STUDY LINK 10·8

Finding Circumferences

The formula for the circumference of a circle is:

> Circumference = π * diameter, or $C = \pi * d$

Use the π key on your calculator to solve these problems. If your calculator doesn't have a π key, enter 3.14 each time you need π.

Find the circumference of each circle below. Show answers to the nearest tenth.

1. a.

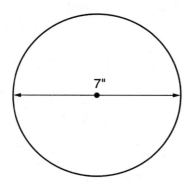

7"

b.

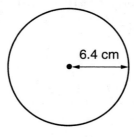

6.4 cm

Circumference ≈ _____ inches

Circumference ≈ _____ centimeters

2. The wheels on Will's bicycle have a diameter of about 27 inches, including the tire.

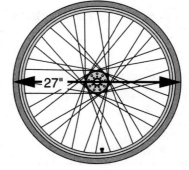

←27"→

   a. What is the circumference of the tire?

      About _____ inches

   b. About how far will Will's bicycle travel if the wheels go around exactly once?

      About _____ inches

3. Sofia measured the circumference of her bicycle tire. She found it was 66 inches. What is the diameter of the tire?

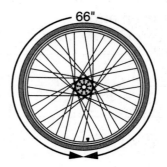

66"

   About _____ inches

LESSON 10·8   Can Your Body Pass through an Index Card?

1. Fold a 5-inch-by-8-inch index card in the middle, along the 5-inch width of the card.

2. Hold the halves of the folded card together. Cut the card as shown by the lines in Diagram A. Some cuts start at the fold and go almost to the edge of the card. Other cuts start at the edge and go almost to the fold. Be sure the first and last cuts start at the fold. Cuts should alternate between starting at the fold and starting at the edge.

3. Open the card. Cut along the fold from X to Y as shown in Diagram B. Be careful not to cut to the edges of the card.

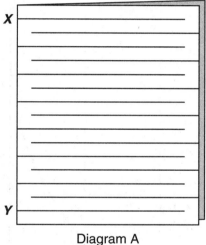

Diagram A

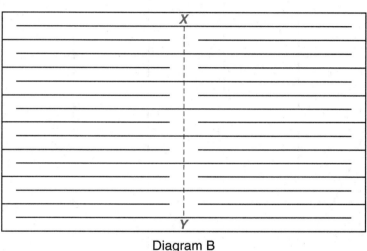

Diagram B

4. Pull the card apart carefully. You'll have a paper ring. Is it large enough for your body to pass through?

Try This

Use another 5-inch-by-8-inch index card. Can you cut out a ring that has a perimeter twice the perimeter of the ring you just made? Explain how you would do it.

_____

_____

_____

LESSON 10·9

Counting Squares to Find the Area of a Circle

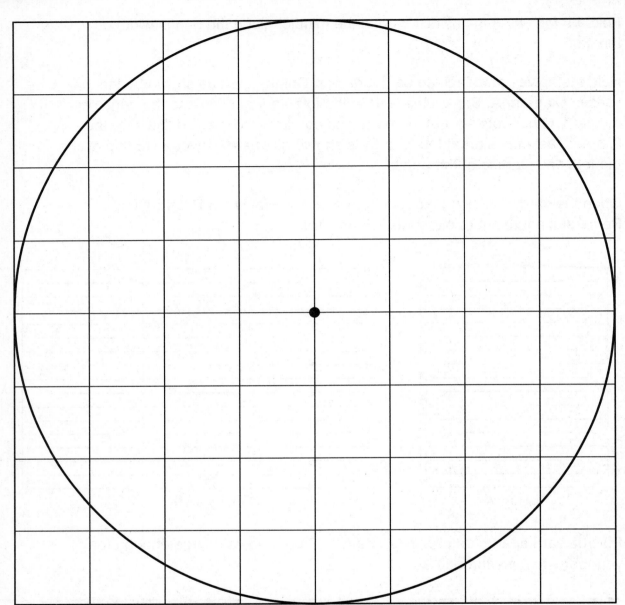

STUDY LINK 10·9 | **Area and Circumference**

Circle the best measurement for each situation described below.

SRB
187 194

1. What size hat to buy (*Hint:* The hat has to fit around a head.)

area   circumference   perimeter

2. How much frosting covers the top of a round birthday cake

area   circumference   perimeter

3. The amount of yard that will be covered by a circular inflatable swimming pool

area   circumference   perimeter

4. The length of a can label when you pull it off the can

area   circumference   perimeter

Fill in the oval next to the measurement that best completes each statement.

> Area of a circle: $A = \pi * r^2$
> Circumference of a circle: $C = \pi * d$

5. The radius of a circle is about 4 cm. The area of the circle is about

○ 12 cm²   ○ 39 cm²   ○ 50 cm²   ○ 25 cm²

6. The area of a circle is about 28 square inches. The diameter of the circle is about

○ 3 in.   ○ 6 in.   ○ 9 in.   ○ 18 in.

7. The circumference of a circle is about 31.4 meters. The radius of the circle is about

○ 3 m   ○ 5 m   ○ 10 m   ○ 15 m

8. Explain how you found your answer for Problem 7.

_____

_____

_____

_____

_____

315

LESSON 10·9   **Modeling πr^2**

The figure of a circle drawn inside a square is a model that shows how the circumference of the circle is greater than 2 lengths around, but less than 4 lengths. This makes the circumference about 3 times the circle's diameter.

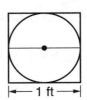

← 1 ft →

Follow the directions below to make a model that shows how the area of a circle can be found using the formula $A = \pi r^2$.

1. Cut along the lines of the circle to cut it into 8 pieces.

2. Arrange and glue the pieces on a sheet of construction paper so they approximate a parallelogram.

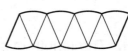

3. Use a colored pencil or marker to draw the outline of a parallelogram along the edges of your arranged circle pieces, and mark the measure of the height and the base.

The height of this figure is the same as the radius of the circle.

The base is $\frac{1}{2}$ the circumference of the circle. The circumference is approximately π times the diameter. Since the radius is $\frac{1}{2}$ of the diameter, the measure of $\frac{1}{2}$ the diameter can be written as π times the radius, or πr.

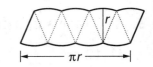

πr

The formula for the area of a parallelogram is $A = b * h$. In our model, the formula can be written as $A = \pi r * r$, $A = \pi * (r * r)$, or $A = \pi r^2$.

4. Label your figure: $A = \pi * (r * r) = \pi r^2$.

5. Describe what you think is the most interesting thing about this model.

_____

_____

_____

_____

LESSON 10·9 | **A Model for πr^2**

Cut along the dotted lines. Use the pieces for your model of the formula for the area of a circle.

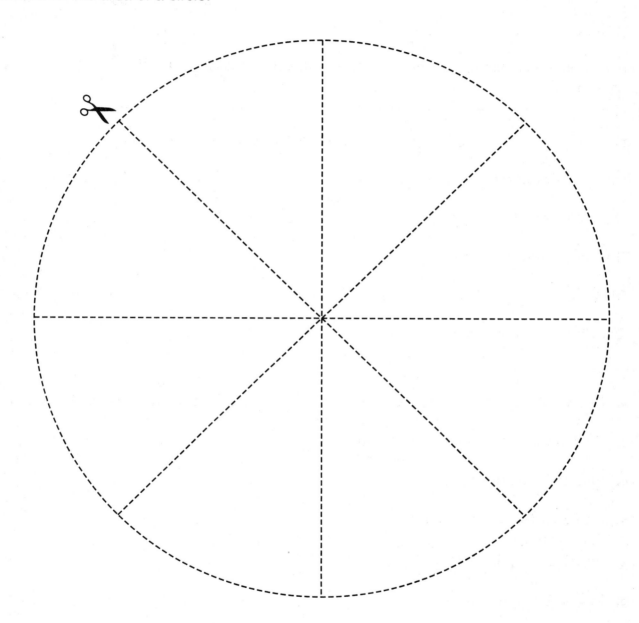

LESSON 10·9   ## More Area and Circumference Problems

Circle Formulas

Circumference: $C = \pi * d$

Area: $A = \pi * r^2$

where C is the circumference of a circle, A is its area, d is its diameter, and r is its radius.

Measure the diameter of the circle at the right to the nearest centimeter.

1. The diameter of the circle is _____.

2. The radius of the circle is _____.

3. The circumference of the circle is _____.

4. The area of the circle is _____.

5. Explain the meaning of the word *circumference.* _____

_____

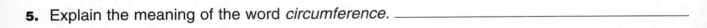

6. **a.** Use your Geometry Template to draw a circle that has a diameter of 2 centimeters.

   b. Find the circumference of your circle. _____

   c. Find the area of your circle.   _____

7. **a.** Use your Geometry Template
      to draw a circle that has
      a radius of $1\frac{1}{2}$ inches.

   b. Find the circumference of

      your circle. _____

   c. Find the area of your circle.

      _____

STUDY LINK 10·10

Unit 11: Family Letter

Volume

Unit 11 focuses on developing your child's ability to think spatially. Many times, students might feel that concepts of area and volume are of little use in their everyday lives compared with computation skills. Encourage your child to become more aware of the relevance of 2- and 3-dimensional shapes. Point out geometric solids (pyramids, cones, and cylinders) as well as 2-dimensional shapes (squares, circles, and triangles) in your surroundings.

Volume (or capacity) is the measure of the amount of space inside a 3-dimensional geometric figure. Your child will develop formulas to calculate the volume of rectangular and curved solids in cubic units. The class will also review units of capacity, such as cups, pints, quarts, and gallons. Students will use units of capacity to estimate the volume of irregular objects by measuring the amount of water each object displaces when submerged. Your child will also explore the relationship between weight and volume by calculating the weight of rice an average Thai family of four consumes in one year and by estimating how many cartons would be needed to store a year→s supply.

Area is the number of units (usually squares) that can fit onto a bounded surface, without gaps or overlaps. Your child will review formulas for finding the area of rectangles, parallelograms, triangles, and circles and use these formulas in calculating the surface area of 3-dimensional shapes.

The goal of this unit is not to have students memorize formulas, but to help them develop an appreciation for using and applying formulas in various settings. By the end of this unit, your child will have had many experiences using 2- and 3-dimensional geometry.

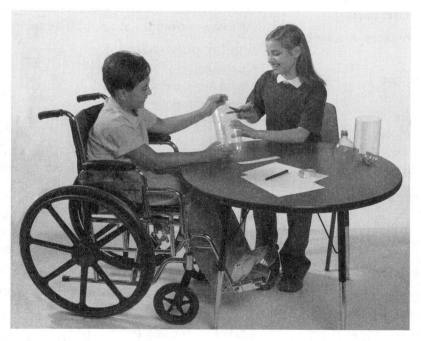

Please keep this Family Letter for reference as your child works through Unit 11.

Vocabulary

Important terms in Unit 11:

apex In a pyramid or cone, the vertex opposite the base.

base of a parallelogram The side of a parallelogram to which an altitude is drawn. The length of this side.

base of a prism or cylinder Either of the two parallel and congruent faces that define the shape of a prism or a cylinder.

base of a pyramid or cone The face of a pyramid or cone that is opposite its apex.

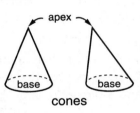

calibrate To divide or mark a measuring tool, such as a thermometer, with gradations.

cone A geometric solid with a circular base, a vertex (apex) not in the plane of the base, and all of the line segments with one endpoint at the apex and the other endpoint on the circumference of the base.

cones

cube A polyhedron with 6 square faces. A cube has 8 vertices and 12 edges.

cylinder A geometric solid with two congruent, parallel circular regions for bases, and a curved face formed by all the segments with an endpoint on each circle that are parallel to the segment with endpoints at the center of the circles.

cylinder

edge A line segment where two faces of a polyhedron meet.

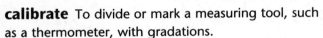

face A flat surface on a polyhedron.

geometric solid The surface or surfaces that make up a 3-dimensional shape, such as a prism, pyramid, cylinder, cone, or sphere. Despite its name, a geometric solid is hollow; it does not contain the points in its interior.

polyhedron A 3-dimensional shape formed by polygons with their interiors (faces) and having no holes.

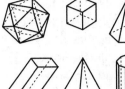
polyhedrons

prism A polyhedron with two parallel and congruent polygonal regions for bases and lateral faces formed by all the line segments with endpoints on corresponding edges of the bases. The lateral faces are all parallelograms. Prisms get their names from the shape of their bases.

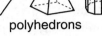
triangular prism · rectangular prism

pyramid A polyhedron made up of any polygonal region for a base, a point (apex) not in the plane of the base, and all of the line segments with one endpoint at the apex and the other on an edge of the base. All the faces except perhaps the base are triangular. Pyramids get their names from the shape of their base.

square pyramid

regular polyhedron A polyhedron whose faces are all congruent regular polygons and in which the same number of faces meet at each vertex.

tetrahedron · cube · octahedron

dodecahedron · icosahedron
The five regular polyhedrons

sphere The set of all points in space that are a given distance from a given point. The given point is the center of the sphere, and the given distance is the radius.

surface area A measure of the surface of a 3-dimensional figure.

vertex (vertices or vertexes) The point where the rays of an angle, the sides of a polygon, or the edges of a polyhedron meet.

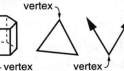
vertex · vertex · vertex

Do-Anytime Activities

To work with your child on the concepts taught in this unit and in previous units, try these interesting and rewarding activities.

1. Have your child compile a 2- and 3-dimensional shapes portfolio or create a collage of labeled shapes. Images can be taken from newspapers, magazines, photographs, and so on.

2. Explore Kitchen Measures

The most common use of measuring volume is cooking. Work with your child to make a favorite recipe. (Doubling the recipe can be good practice in computing with fractions.) Ask your child to use measuring spoons and cups to find the capacity of various containers. The data can be organized in a table.

Container	Capacity
Coffee mug	$1\frac{1}{4}$ cups
Egg cup	3 tablespoons

Building Skills through Games

In Unit 11, your child will practice operations with whole numbers and geometry skills by playing the following games. Detailed instructions for each game are in the *Student Reference Book* or the journal:

Name That Number See *Student Reference Book,* page 325.
This is a game for two or three players using the Everything Math Deck or a complete deck of number cards. Playing *Name That Number* helps students review operations with whole numbers, including the order of operations.

3-D Shape Sort See *Student Reference Book,* page 332.
This game is similar to *Polygon Capture.* Partners or 2 teams each with 2 players need 16 Property cards and 12 Shape cards to play. *3-D Shape Sort* gives students practice identifying properties of 3-dimensional shapes.

Rugs and Fences See journal page 380.
This game uses 32 Polygon cards and 16 Area and Perimeter cards and is played by partners. *Rugs and Fences* gives students practice finding the area and perimeter of polygons.

As You Help Your Child with Homework

As your child brings assignments home, you might want to go over the instructions together, clarifying them as necessary. The answers listed below will guide you through some of this unit's Study Links.

Study Link 11•1

1. Answers vary.

2. D

Study Link 11•2

1.

triangular
pyramid

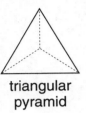 vertex

vertices

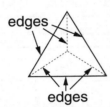 edges

edges

Study Link 11•3

Sample answers:

1. 2.8 cm; 4.3 cm; 24.6 cm²; 105.9 cm³

3a. 30 * 30 * 18 = 16,200

5. more; 283,500,000 cm³

7. $5\frac{3}{8}$

Study Link 11•4

1. <　　**2.** <　　**3.** >

4. Because both pyramids have the same height, compare the areas of the bases. The base of the square pyramid has an area of 5 * 5 = 25 m². The base area of the triangular pyramid is $\frac{1}{2}$ * 5 * 5 or $12\frac{1}{2}$ m².

5. $10\frac{16}{27}$　　**6.** $1\frac{11}{21}$　　**7.** 600,000　　**8.** 25.39

Study Link 11•5

Most of the space taken up by a handful of cotton is air between the fibers.

Study Link 11•6

1. >　　　　**2.** =　　　　**3.** <

4. <　　　　**5.** <　　　　**6.** =

7. cubic inches

8. gallons

9. gallons

10. milliliters

11. cubic centimeters

12. capacity

13. volume

14. –250　　**15.** 137,685

16. $10\frac{2}{5}$　　**17.** 0.48

Study Link 11•7

1. 88 in²; Sample answer: I found the area of each of the 6 sides and then added them together.

2. Yes. A 4 in. by 4 in. by $3\frac{1}{2}$ in. box has a volume of 56 in³ and a surface area of 88 in².

3. Volume: 502.4 cm³; Surface area: 351.7 cm²

4. Volume: 216 in³; Surface area: 216 in²

LESSON 11·1 Cube Pattern

1. Cut on the solid lines.

2. Fold on the dashed lines.

3. Tape or glue the tabs inside or outside the shape.

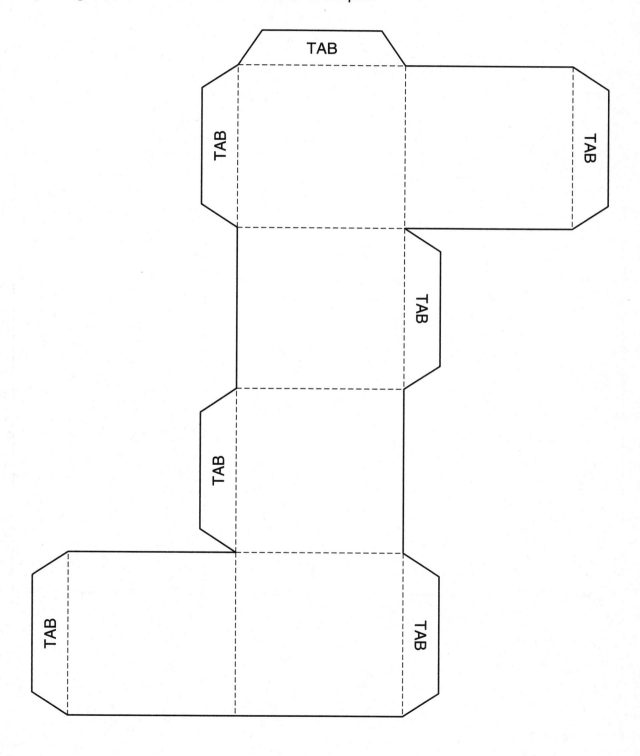

LESSON 11·1 Triangular Prism Pattern

1. Cut on the solid lines.

2. Fold on the dashed lines.

3. Tape or glue the tabs inside or outside the shape.

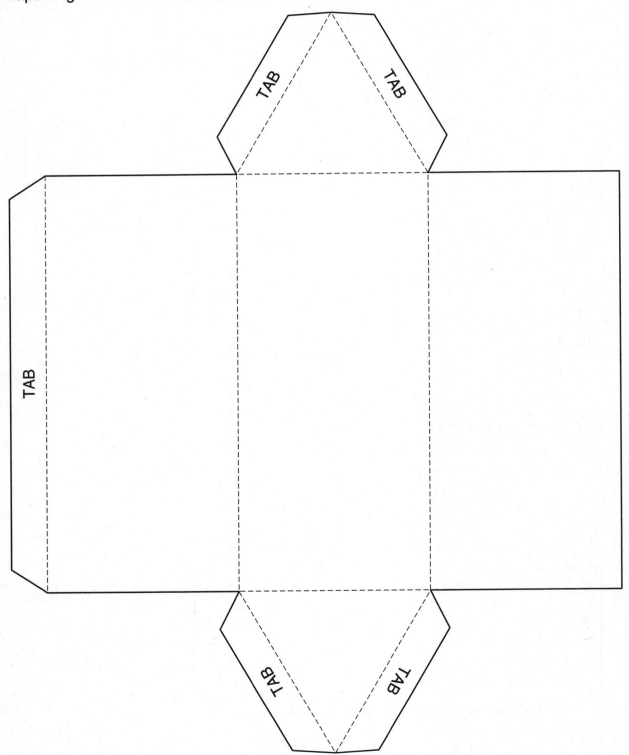

LESSON 11·1 | Triangular Pyramid Pattern

1. Cut on the solid lines.

2. Fold on the dashed lines.

3. Tape or glue the tabs inside or outside the shape.

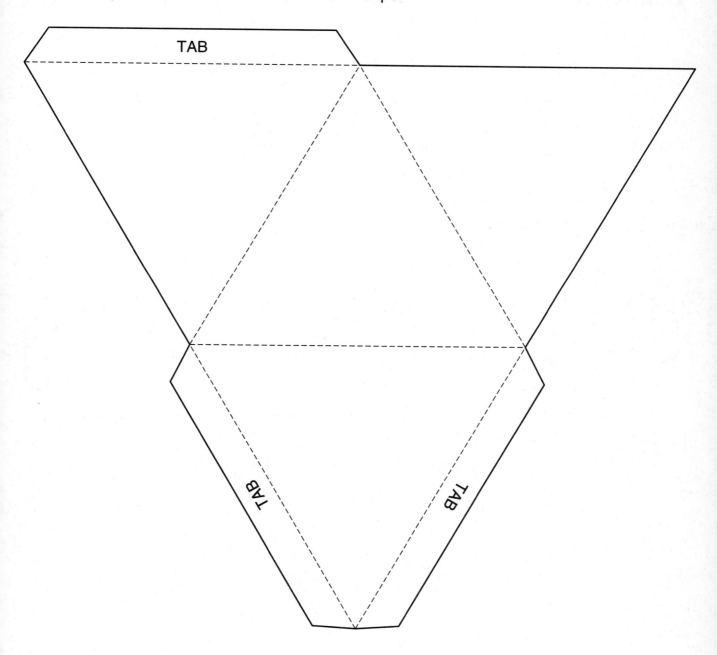

TAB

TAB

TAB

LESSON 11·1 | **Square Pyramid Pattern**

1. Cut on the solid lines.

2. Fold on the dashed lines.

3. Tape or glue the tabs inside or outside the shape.

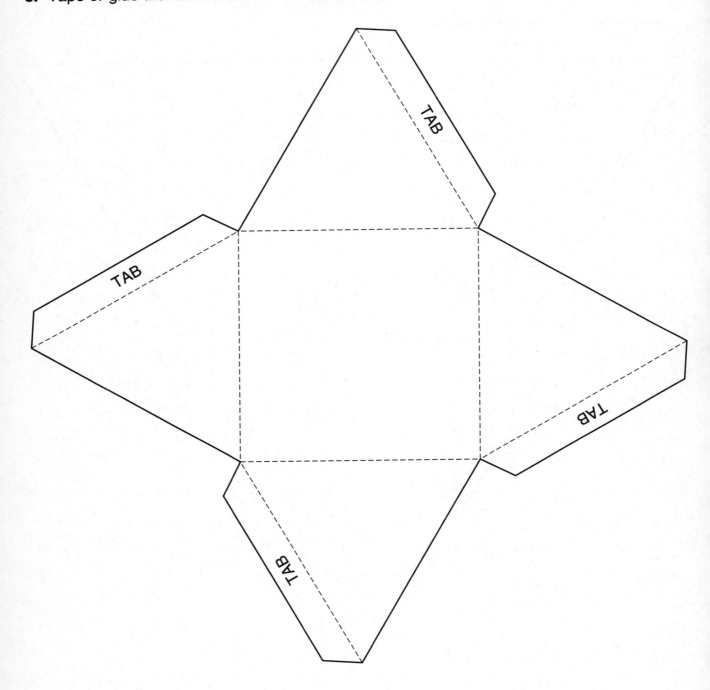

STUDY LINK
11·1 Cube Patterns

There are four patterns below. Three of the patterns can be folded to form a cube.

SRB
147–149

1. Guess which one of the patterns below cannot be folded into a cube.

   My guess: Pattern _____ (A, B, C, or D) cannot be folded into a cube.

2. Cut on the solid lines, and fold the pattern on the dashed lines to check your guess. Did you make the correct guess? If not, try other patterns until you find the one that does not form a cube.

   My answer: Pattern _____ (A, B, C, or D) cannot be folded into a cube.

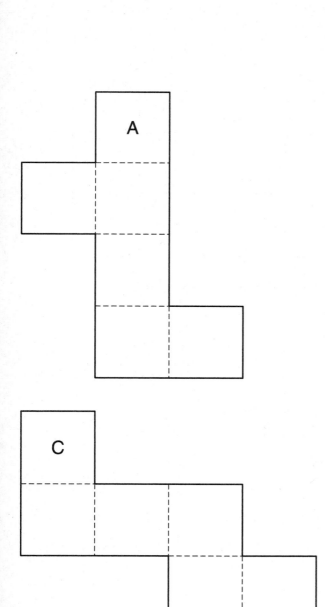

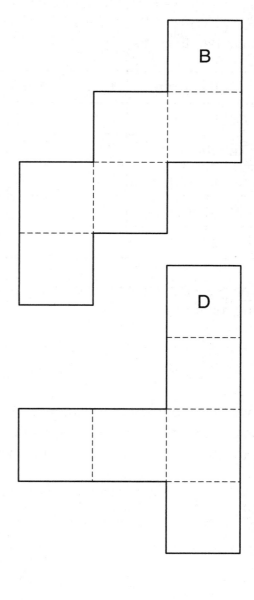

LESSON 11·1   Exploring Faces, Vertices, and Edges

◆ A flat surface of a geometric solid is called a face.

◆ A corner of a geometric solid is called a vertex. The plural of vertex is vertices.

◆ An edge of a geometric solid is a line segment or curve where two surfaces meet.

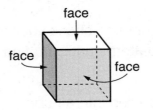

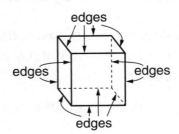

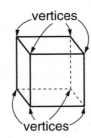

1. Complete the table.

Polyhedron	Faces	Vertices	Faces + Vertices	Edges
Cube	6	8	6 + 8 = 14	12
Tetrahedron				
Octahedron				
Dodecahedron				
Icosahedron				

2. Compare the values in the Faces + Vertices column with the Edges column. What do you notice?

_____

_____

3. Two of the patterns below can be folded to make a tetrahedron. Cross out the patterns that will not make a tetrahedron. Circle the patterns that will make a tetrahedron. Explain your solution strategy.

_____

_____

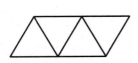

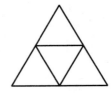
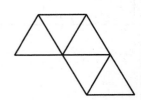

LESSON 11·1   Rectangular Prism Pattern

1. Cut on the solid lines.

2. Fold on the dashed lines.

3. Tape or glue the tabs inside or outside the shape.

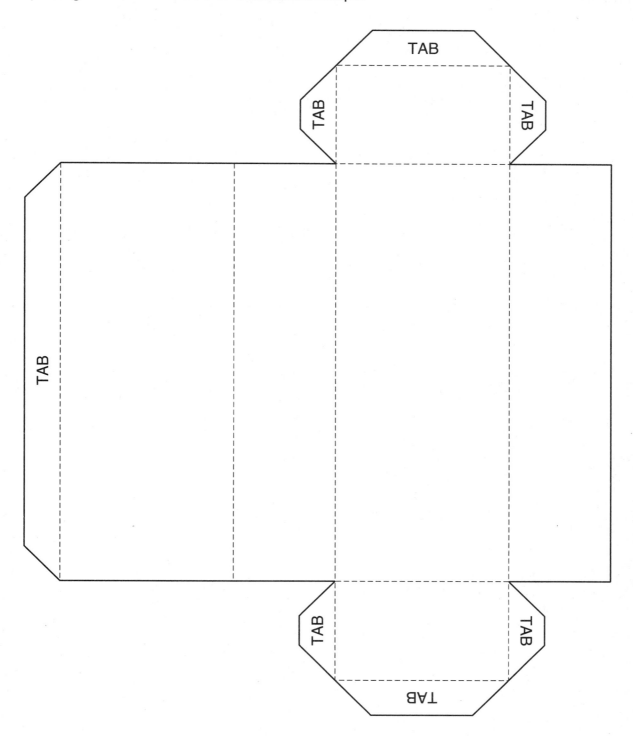

LESSON 11·1 | Octahedron Pattern

1. Cut on the solid lines.

2. Fold on the dashed lines.

3. Tape or glue the tabs inside or outside the shape.

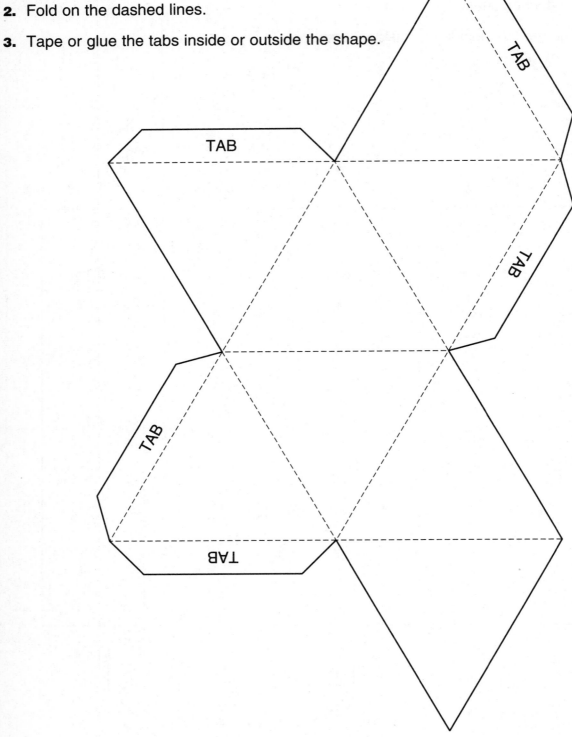

STUDY LINK 11·2

Comparing Geometric Solids

Name the figures, and label their bases, vertices, and edges.

Geometric Solids			
Name	**Bases**	**Vertices**	**Edges**
Example cube	base base	vertices vertices	edges edges edges edges
1. _____			
2. _____			
3. _____			

LESSON 11·2 Exploring Truncated Polyhedrons

Truncated polyhedrons are formed by shortening the edges of the solid and cutting off the vertices. Follow the steps below to make models of an octahedron and a truncated octahedron.

Part 1: Octahedrons

1. Use a centimeter ruler to mark dots on the lines of the pattern on *Math Masters,* page 330 so that the lines are divided into thirds.

2. Use a colored pencil or marker to connect the dots to form triangles around the vertices of the octahedron.

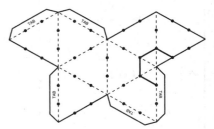

3. Cut out and assemble the octahedron model.

4. Hold the model so that a vertex is facing you. What shape is formed by the colored lines? _____

Part 2: Truncated Octahedrons

5. Repeat steps 1 and 2 with your second copy of the octahedron pattern.

6. Cut out the pattern. Then cut along the colored lines. You will cut off the vertices and parts of the tabs. Assemble the model.

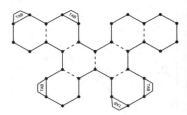

7. What two shapes are contained in the model?

_____

8. What shapes are contained in a truncated hexahedron?

_____

9. What shapes are contained in a truncated icosahedron?

_____

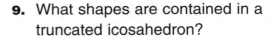

Hexahedron   Truncated Hexahedron

Icosahedron   Truncated Icosahedron

Name _____ Date _____ Time _____

  Volume of Cylinders

Use these two formulas to solve the problems below.

Formula for the Volume of a Cylinder	**Formula for the Area of a Circle**
$V = B * h$	$A = \pi * r^2$
where V is the volume of the cylinder, B is the area of the cylinder's base, and h is the height of the cylinder.	where A is the area of the circle and r is the length of the radius of the circle.

1. Find the smallest cylinder in your home. Record its dimensions, and calculate its volume.

radius = _____ height = _____

Area of base = _____ Volume = _____

2. Find the largest cylinder in your home. Record its dimensions, and calculate its volume.

radius = _____ height = _____

Area of base = _____ Volume = _____

3. Write a number model to estimate the volume of:

a. Your toaster _____

b. Your television _____

4. Is the volume of the largest cylinder more or less than the volume of your toaster? _____

About how much more or less? _____

5. Is the volume of the largest cylinder more or less than the volume of your television set? _____

About how much more or less? _____

Practice

6. $6\frac{1}{3} * \frac{2}{5} =$ _____ **7.** $10\frac{6}{8} * \frac{1}{2} =$ _____ **8.** $4 - 2.685 =$ _____

Prism and Pyramid Patterns

LESSON 11·4

1. Cut each pattern along the solid lines, and score along the dashed lines.

2. Then assemble with the *dashed lines* on the inside.

STUDY LINK
11·4

Comparing Volumes

Use >, <, or = to compare the volumes of the two figures in each problem below.

SRB 196–199

1.

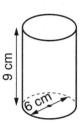

_____

9 cm, 6 cm, 6 cm

2.

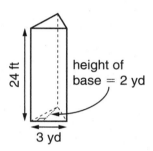

height of base = 2 yd

24 ft

3 yd

_____

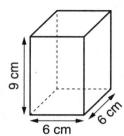

6 ft

8 yd

3.

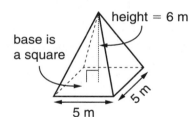

height = 6 m

base is a square

5 m

5 m

_____

height = 6 m

height of base = 5 m

5 m

4. Explain how you got your answer for Problem 3.

_____

_____

_____

_____

_____

Practice

5. $4\frac{1}{3} + 2\frac{4}{9} =$ _____

6. $2\frac{6}{7} - 1\frac{1}{3} =$ _____

7. $6 * 10^5 =$ _____

8. $584 \div 23 =$ _____

335

Finding the Area of Concentric Circles

Concentric circles are circles that have the same center, but the radius of each circle has a different length.

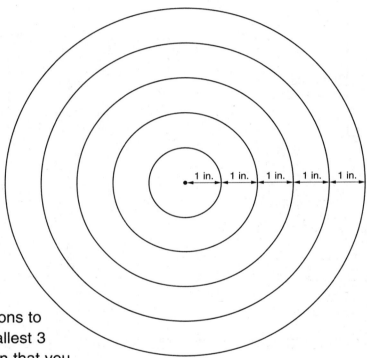

The smallest of the 5 concentric circles below has a radius of 1 in. The next largest circle has a radius of 2 in. The next has a radius of 3 in. The next has a radius of 4 in., and the largest circle has a radius of 5 in. The distance from the edge of one circle to the next larger circle is 1 in.

1 in.   1 in.   1 in.   1 in.   1 in.

1. Use colored pencils or crayons to shade the region of the smallest 3 circles red. Shade the region that you can see of the next circle yellow, and the region that you can see of the largest circle orange.

   Which region has the greater area, the red region or the orange region?

   _____

2. **a.** How can you change the distance between the circles to make the area of the yellow region equal to the area of the red region? Explain your answer on the back of this page.

   b. How can you change the distance between the circles to make the area of the yellow region equal to the area of the orange region? Explain your answer on the back of this page.

STUDY LINK 11·5   A Displacement Experiment

Try this experiment at home.

Materials
- ☐   drinking glass
- ☐   water
- ☐   2 large handfuls of cotton
  (Be sure to use real cotton. Synthetic materials will not work.)

Directions

◆ Fill the drinking glass almost to the top with water.

◆ Put the cotton, bit by bit, into the glass. Fluff it as you go.

If you are careful, you should be able to fit all of the cotton into the glass without spilling a drop of water.

Think about what you know about displacement and volume. Why do you think you were able to fit the cotton into the glass without the water overflowing?

_____

_____

_____

_____

_____

_____

_____

_____

_____

_____

_____

_____

LESSON 11·5 | # A Boat and a Stone

A thought experiment uses the imagination to solve a problem. Mathematicians, physicists, philosophers, and others use thought experiments to investigate ideas about nature and the universe.

One early example of a thought experiment attempts to show that space is infinite. Use your imagination to picture what is being described in the experiment below.

> If there is a boundary to the universe, we can toss a spear at it. If the spear flies through, it isn't a boundary after all. If the spear bounces back, then there must be something beyond the supposed edge of space—a cosmic wall which is itself in space that stopped the spear. Either way, there is no edge of the universe; space is infinite.

Often it is impossible to investigate the situation in a thought experiment directly. This might be because of physical or technological limitations. But the thought experiment in Problem 1 can be modeled directly. Solve Problem 1, and then follow the directions in Problem 2 to model the experiment.

1. Imagine that you are in a small boat. There is a large stone in the bottom of the boat. The boat is floating in a swimming pool. If you throw the stone overboard, does the level of the boat on the water go up, down, or stay the same? Does the level of the water in the pool go up, down, or stay the same?

_____

_____

_____

_____

_____

LESSON 11·5 | **A Boat and a Stone** *continued*

2. Model the thought experiment, "A Boat and a Stone."

Materials

☐   bucket or clear container

☐   small container that floats and fits in the bucket or clear container with plenty of space all around

☐   several rocks   ☐   water

☐   waterproof marker

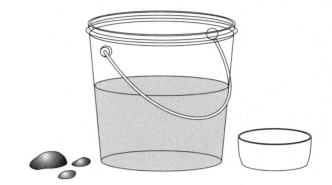

Directions:

a. Fill the bucket part way up with water. Make sure the water is deep enough to cover the rock.

b. Place a rock in the small container, and float it in the bucket. If the small container sinks, try a smaller rock. If the small container tilts over into the water, try a larger rock.

c. After the water settles, mark the height of the water on the bucket with the marker. If your bucket is clear, mark the outside. If not, mark the inside wall. Also, mark the height of the water on the outside of the small container.

d. Take the rock out of the small container, and gently drop it into the water.

e. Describe the changes in the height of the water on the outside of the small container.

_____

_____

f. Describe the changes in the height of the water in the bucket.

_____

_____

_____

g. Do the changes agree with your thought experiment solutions? Why or why not?

_____

_____

339

STUDY LINK 11·6 Units of Volume and Capacity

Write >, <, or = to compare the measurements below.

1. 5 cups _____ 1 quart   **2.** 30 mL _____ 30 cm³   **3.** 1 quart _____ 1 liter

4. 15 pints _____ 8 quarts   **5.** 100 cm³ _____ 1 gallon   **6.** 10 cups _____ 5 pints

Circle the unit you would use to measure each of the following.

7. The volume of a square pyramid

    gallons   cubic inches   ounces   meters

8. The amount of milk a fifth grader drinks in a week

    gallons   milliliters   ounces   meters

9. The amount of water used to fill a swimming pool

    gallons   milliliters   ounces   meters

10. The amount of penicillin given in a shot

    gallons   milliliters   liters   meters

11. The volume of a rectangular prism

    gallons   cubic centimeters   liters   meters

12. Would you think of volume or capacity if
you wanted to know how much juice a jug holds? _____

13. Would you think of volume or capacity if you wanted to
know how much closet space a stack of boxes would take up? _____

Practice

14. $-200 + (-50) =$ _____   **15.** $685 * 201 =$ _____

16. $13\frac{1}{5} - 2\frac{4}{5} =$ _____   **17.** $3.84 \div 8 =$ _____

STUDY LINK
11·7

Volume and Surface Area

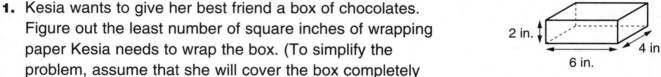

Area of rectangle:	**Circumference of circle:**
$A = l * w$	$c = \pi * d$
Volume of rectangular prism:	**Area of circle:**
$V = l * w * h$	$A = \pi * r^2$
	Volume of cylinder:
	$V = \pi * r^2 * h$

SRB
197 198
200 201

---

1. Kesia wants to give her best friend a box of chocolates. Figure out the least number of square inches of wrapping paper Kesia needs to wrap the box. (To simplify the problem, assume that she will cover the box completely with no overlaps.)

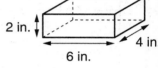

2 in. 6 in. 4 in.

Amount of paper needed: _____

Explain how you found the answer.

_____

_____

_____

2. Could Kesia use the same amount of wrapping paper to cover a box with a larger volume than the box in Problem 1? _____ Explain.

_____

_____

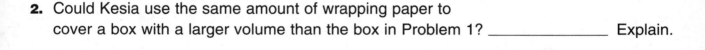
Find the volume and the surface area of the two figures in Problems 3 and 4.

3. Volume:

_____

Surface area:

_____

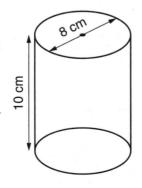

8 cm

10 cm

4. Volume:

_____

Surface area:

_____

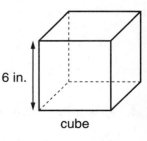

6 in.

cube

341

LESSON 11·7   A Surface-Area Investigation

In each problem below, the volume of a rectangular prism is given. Your task is to find the dimensions of the rectangular prism (with the given volume) that has the smallest surface area. To help you, use centimeter cubes to build as many different prisms as possible having the given volume.

Record the dimensions and surface area of each prism you build in the table. Do not record different prisms with the same surface area. Put a star next to the prism with the smallest surface area.

1.

Dimensions (cm)	Surface Area (cm²)	Volume (cm³)
2 × 6 × 1	40	12
		12
		12
		12

2.

Dimensions (cm)	Surface Area (cm²)	Volume (cm³)
		24
		24
		24
		24
		24
		24

3. If the volume of a prism is 36 cm³, predict the dimensions that will result in the smallest surface area. Explain.

_____

_____

_____

4. Describe a general rule for finding the surface area of a rectangular prism in words or

with a number sentence. _____

_____

342

LESSON 11·7 | # Area, Surface Area, and Volume

Area of rectangle: $A = l * w$

Volume of rectangular prism: $V = B * h$
or $V = l * w * h$

Circumference of circle: $c = \pi * d$

Area of circle: $A = \pi * r^2$

Volume of cylinder: $V = \pi * r^2 * h$

---

1. Record the dimensions and find the area.

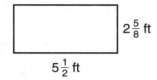

$2\frac{5}{8}$ ft

$5\frac{1}{2}$ ft

Length = _____

Width = _____

Area = _____

How many square tiles, each 1 ft long on a side, would be needed to fill the rectangle?

_____

2. Record the dimensions and find the volume.

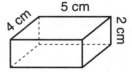

5 cm

4 cm

2 cm

Length of base = _____

Width of base = _____

Area of base = _____

Height of prism = _____

Number of
1-centimeter unit cubes
needed to fill the box: _____

Volume = _____

Record the dimensions, and find the volume and surface area for each figure below. Round results to the nearest hundredth.

3. Rectangular prism

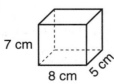

7 cm

8 cm 5 cm

Length of base = _____

Width of base = _____

Height of prism = _____

Volume = _____

Surface area = _____

4. Cylinder

7 ft

9 ft

Diameter = _____

Height = _____

Volume = _____

Surface area = _____

343

Unit 12: Family Letter

Probability, Ratios, and Rates

A **ratio** is a comparison of two quantities with the same unit. For example, if one house has a floor area of 2,000 ft^2, and a second house has a floor area of 3,000 ft^2, the ratio of the areas is 2,000 to 3,000, or 2 to 3, simplified.

To prepare students for working with ratios in algebra, the class will review the meanings and forms of ratios and will solve number stories involving ratios of part of a set to the whole set. Your child will find, write, and solve many number models (equations) for ratio problems.

Your child will continue to use the American Tour section of the *Student Reference Book* as part of the discussion of ratios. We will also be doing projects based on information in the American Tour.

A **rate** is a comparison of two quantities with different units. For example, speed is expressed in miles per hour. In our study of rates, students will determine their own heart rates (heartbeats per minute). Then they will observe the effect of exercise on heart rate and represent the class results graphically.

We will continue our study of probability by looking at situations in which a sequence of choices is made. For example, if a menu offers you 2 choices of appetizer, 4 choices of entrée, and 3 choices of dessert, and you choose one of each kind, there are 2 ∗ 4 ∗ 3 or 24 different possible combinations for your meal. If all the choices were equally appealing (which is unlikely), and you chose at random, the probability of any one combination would be $\frac{1}{24}$.

Your child will play *Frac-Tac-Toe,* which was introduced in Unit 5, as well as a new game, *Spoon Scramble,* to practice operations and equivalencies with fractions, decimals, and percents.

You can help your child by asking questions about homework problems; by pointing out fractions, percents, and ratios that you encounter in everyday life; and by playing *Frac-Tac-Toe* and *Spoon Scramble* to sharpen his or her skills.

Please keep this Family Letter for reference as your child works through Unit 12.

344

Vocabulary

Important terms in Unit 12:

common factor Any number that is a factor of two or more counting numbers. The common factors of 18 and 24 are 1, 2, 3, and 6.

equally likely outcomes Outcomes of a chance experiment or situation that have the same probability of happening. If all the possible outcomes are equally likely, then the probability of an event is equal to: $\dfrac{\text{number of favorable outcomes}}{\text{number of possible outcomes}}$

factor tree A method used to obtain the prime factorization of a number. The original number is written as a product of factors. Then each of these factors is written as a product of factors, and so on, until the factors are all prime numbers. A factor tree looks like an upside down tree with the root (the original number) at the top, and the leaves (the factors) beneath it.

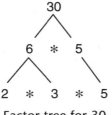

Factor tree for 30

greatest common factor The largest factor that two or more counting numbers have in common. For example, the common factors of 24 and 36 are 1, 2, 3, 4, 6, and 12. Thus, the greatest common factor of 24 and 36 is 12.

least common multiple The smallest number that is a multiple of two or more numbers. For example, while some common multiples of 6 and 8 are 24, 48, and 72, the least common multiple of 6 and 8 is 24.

multiplication counting principle A way of determining the total number of possible outcomes for two or more separate choices. Suppose, for example, you roll a die and then flip a coin. There are 6 choices for which number on the die lands up and 2 choices for which side of the coin shows. Then there are 6 * 2, or 12 possible outcomes all together: (1,H), (1,T), (2,H), (2,T), (3,H), (3,T), (4,H), (4,T), (5,H), (5,T), (6,H), (6,T).

prime factorization A counting number expressed as a product of prime number factors. For example, the prime factorization of 24 is 2 * 2 * 2 * 3, or $2^3 * 3$.

probability A number from 0 to 1 that tells the chance that an event will happen. For example, the probability that a fair coin will show heads is $\frac{1}{2}$. The closer a probability is to 1, the more likely it is that the event will happen. The closer a probability is to 0, the less likely it is that the event will happen.

rate A comparison by division of two quantities with unlike units. For example, traveling 100 miles in 2 hours is an average rate of 100 mi/2 hr, or 50 miles per hour. In this case, the rate compares distance (miles) to time (hours).

ratio A comparison by division of two quantities with the same units. Ratios can be fractions, decimals, percents, or stated in words. Ratios can also be written with a colon between the two numbers being compared. For example, if a team wins 3 out of 5 games played, the ratio of wins to total games can be written as $\frac{3}{5}$, 3/5, 0.6, 60%, 3 to 5, or 3:5 (read "three to five").

tree diagram A network of points connected by line segments and containing no closed loops. Factor trees are tree diagrams used to factor numbers. Probability trees are tree diagrams used to represent probability situations in which there is a series of events.

The first tree diagram below represents flipping one coin two times. The second tree diagram below shows the prime factorization of 30.

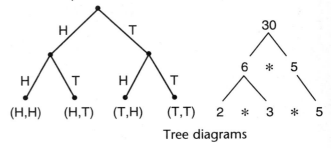

Tree diagrams

345

Do-Anytime Activities

To work with your child on the concepts taught in this unit and in previous units, try these interesting and rewarding activities:

1. Identify different ratios, and ask your child to write each ratio using words, a fraction, a decimal, a percent, and a colon. For example, the ratio of 1 adult for every 5 students could be written as 1 to 5, $\frac{1}{5}$, 0.2, 20%, or 1:5.

2. Play one of the games in this unit with your child: *Frac-Tac-Toe, Name That Number,* or *Spoon Scramble.*

3. Read the book *Jumanji* with your child, and review the possible outcomes when rolling two dice. Ask your child to verify the probabilities of rolling certain number combinations by recording the outcomes for 100 rolls of a pair of dice.

4. Identify rate situations in everyday life, and ask your child to solve problems involving rates. For example, find the number of miles your car travels for each gallon of gas, or find the number of calories that are burned each hour or minute for different types of sports activities.

Building Skills through Games

In Unit 12, your child will practice skills with probability, ratios, and rates by playing the following games. For detailed instructions, see the *Student Reference Book.*

Frac-Tac-Toe See *Student Reference Book,* pages 309–311. This is a game for two players. Game materials include 4 each of the number cards 0–10, pennies or counters of two colors, a calculator, and a gameboard. The gameboard is a 5-by-5 number grid that resembles a bingo card. Several versions of the gameboard are shown in the *Student Reference Book. Frac-Tac-Toe* provides students with practice in converting fractions to decimals and percents.

Name That Number See *Student Reference Book,* page 325. This is a game for two or three players. Game materials include the Everything Math Deck or a complete deck of number cards. Playing *Name That Number* provides students with practice in working with operations and in using the order of operations.

Spoon Scramble See *Student Reference Book,* page 330. This is a game for four players using 3 spoons and a deck of 16 *Spoon Scramble* Cards. *Spoon Scramble* provides students with practice identifying equivalent expressions for finding a fraction, a decimal, or a percent of a number.

As You Help Your Child with Homework

As your child brings assignments home, you might want to go over the instructions together, clarifying them as necessary. The answers listed below will guide you through this unit's Study Links.

Study Link 12·1

1. a. 66   **b.** 72

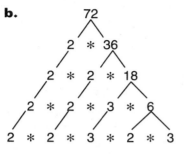

2. a. $\frac{10}{33}$ **b.** $\frac{11}{12}$ **c.** $\frac{5}{18}$

3. $250 = 5 * 5 * 5 * 2$

4. a. 32   **b.** 49   **5.** $\frac{2}{3}$

Study Link 12·2

1. $5 * 5 = 25$

2.

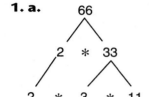

Entry Gate   A   B   C   X   Y

Exit Gate   A B C X Y A B C X Y A B C X Y A B C X Y A B C X Y

3. No; Sample answer: Some gates will probably be used more than other gates.

4. 20

5. a.

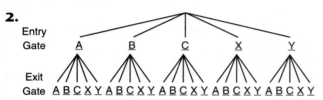

Question 1:   R   W

Question 2:   R   W   R   W

Question 3: R   W   R   W   R   W   R   W

R = right answer   W = wrong answer

b. $\frac{1}{8}$

Study Link 12·3

1. Sixteen out of twenty-five

2. $\frac{16}{25}$ **3.** 64%   **4.** 16:25

5. 23:50; 0.46 of the cars were blue

6. $\frac{2}{3}$; 6:9; $66\frac{2}{3}$% of the people were swimmers

7. 7 out of 8; 35:40 of the caps sold were baseball caps

Study Link 12·4

1. a. 4   **b.** 16   **2.** 15

3. 16   **4.** 8   **5.** 32

6. 98 R38   **7.** 9,016   **8.** 90.54

Study Link 12·5

1. 8   **2.** 24   **3.** 45

4. 60   **5.** 20   **6.** 26

7. $\frac{2}{5} = \frac{\square}{115}$; 46 students

9. $\frac{1.50}{3} = \frac{\square}{90}$; $45.00

11. 216   **12.** 729

Study Link 12·6

1. a.

Number of Spiders	27,000	54,000	81,000	108,000	135,000
Pounds of Spider Web	1	2	3	4	5

b. 270,000

3. 1,000   **4.** 930   **5.** $7\frac{1}{2}$, or 7.5

Study Link 12·7

1. $3\frac{3}{4}$ in.   **3.** $1\frac{3}{4}$ lb   **5.** $20\frac{7}{8}$ in.

7. $50\frac{2}{5}$ kg   **9.** 34   **11.** 180

Study Link 12·8

2. 8 lunches

4. a. 1 to 1   **b.** 26 to 104, or $\frac{1}{4}$ **c.** 8 to 16, or $\frac{1}{2}$

5. $3\frac{4}{7}$ **6.** 5   **7.** 12.5   **8.** 8

LESSON 11·6 Adding and Subtracting Measurements

Example 1: Add.

```
   6 lb    7 oz
+  3 lb   11 oz
─────────────────
   9 lb   18 oz = 10 lb  2 oz
```

Because 18 oz > 1 lb, rename 18 oz as 1 lb 2 oz. So the sum in simplest form is 9 lb + 1 lb + 2 oz, or 10 lb 2 oz.

Example 2: Subtract.

```
   9 ft   5 in.
─  6 ft   8 in.
```

Because 8 in. > 5 in., rename 9 ft 5 in. as 8 ft 17 in. so that you can subtract the inches.

```
        8      17
        9̸ ft   5̸ in.
     ─  6 ft   8 in.
     ──────────────────
        2 ft   9 in.
```

Add or subtract. When you add, be sure your answer is in simplest form. When you subtract, you may have to rename in order to have enough of a given unit to subtract.

1.
```
    10 ft   9 in.
+   10 ft   7 in.
──────────────────
```

2.
```
    6 gal   3 qt
+   5 gal   3 qt
──────────────────
```

3.
```
    8 yd   1 ft
─   3 yd   2 ft
──────────────────
```

4.
```
    7 ft   0 in.
─   1 ft   9 in.
──────────────────
```

5.
```
    89 lb   10 oz
+   76 lb   15 oz
──────────────────
```

6.
```
    20 qt   1 pt
─   19 qt   2 pt
──────────────────
```

Convert the measurements so that their units match the unit given in the answer. Then add or subtract.

7. 10 m + 15 cm = _____ cm

8. 8 m + 8 cm + 8 mm = _____ mm

9. 50 kg − 50 g = _____ g

10. 10,000 L − 2 kL = _____ kL

347A

STUDY LINK 12·1 | **Factor Trees**

1. Make factor trees and find the prime factorization for the following numbers.

   Example: 20

   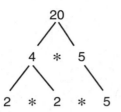

   $20 = 2 * 2 * 5$

   a. 66

   b. 72

   66 = _____   72 = _____

2. Write each fraction in simplest form. Use factor trees to help you. Show your work.

   a. $\frac{20}{66}$ = _____   **b.** $\frac{66}{72}$ = _____   **c.** $\frac{20}{72}$ = _____

3. Find the prime factorization for 250. _____

4. **a.** Circle the number that has the most prime factors.

   63   32   49   100

   b. Which has the fewest prime factors? _____

5. Simplify the fraction to the right. $\frac{150}{225}$ = _____

Practice

6. $\frac{1}{4} * 36 =$ _____   7. $0.25 * 360 =$ _____

8. $\frac{1}{3} * 90 =$ _____   9. $33\frac{1}{3}\%$ of 90 = _____

348

**LESSON
12·1**   # The Division Method for Prime Factorization

Use the method below to find the prime factorization of the following numbers.

Example: Find the prime factorization for 732.

Step 1 Divide, using the smallest prime factor of the number as the divisor.

Step 2 The quotient becomes the dividend. Use the smallest prime factor as the divisor, and continue dividing until the quotient is a prime number.

$$2 \,\underline{|\,732}$$ Divide: $732 \div 2 = 366$

$$2 \,\underline{|\,366}$$ Divide: $366 \div 2 = 183$
2 is not a factor of 183.
The next smallest prime factor is 3.

$$3 \,\underline{|\,183}$$ Divide: $183 \div 3 = 61$

$$\underline{|\,61}$$ 61 is a prime number.

The prime factorization of 732 is
2 * 2 * 3 * 61

Step 3 Write the divisors as a multiplication expression.

$$732 = 2 * 2 * 3 * 61$$

This is the prime factorization of 732.

Use the division method to find the prime factorizations. Show your work.

1. 1,056   **2.** 3,190   **3.** 24,598

**LESSON
12·1** # Factor Trees and Adding Fractions

1. Make factor trees and write the prime factorization for each number below.

a. 12 **b.** 42 **c.** 32

12 = _____ 42 = _____ 32 = _____

2. Add the following fractions. Use the factor trees above to help you find the least common multiple of the denominators. Use this least common multiple as a common denominator.

a. $\dfrac{5}{12} = \dfrac{\Box}{\Box}$

$+ \dfrac{7}{32} = \dfrac{\Box}{\Box}$
_____

b. $\dfrac{41}{42} = \dfrac{\Box}{\Box}$

$+ \dfrac{1}{12} = \dfrac{\Box}{\Box}$
_____

3. Use factor trees or some other method to find a common denominator for the fraction pairs below. If you do not use factor trees, explain how you found the least common denominators.

a. $\dfrac{5}{14}$ and $\dfrac{2}{21}$ _____

b. $\dfrac{7}{18}$ and $\dfrac{16}{36}$ _____

c. $\dfrac{9}{24}$ and $\dfrac{21}{64}$ _____

350

Probability Investigations

SRB
134

Multiplication Counting Principle

Suppose you can make a first choice in *m* ways and a second choice in *n* ways. Then there are *m* * *n* ways to make the first choice followed by the second choice. Three or more choices can be counted in the same way, by multiplying.

1. A person can enter the stadium shown at the right through any gate and can exit through any gate. In how many different ways can a person enter and exit the stadium?

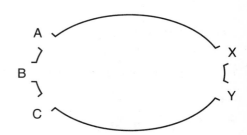

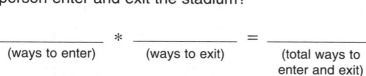

(ways to enter)   (ways to exit)   (total ways to enter and exit)

2. Draw a **tree diagram** to show all possible ways to enter and exit the stadium.

Entry gate: ____   ____   ____   ____   ____

Exit gate: __ __ __ __ __   __ __ __ __ __   __ __ __ __ __   __ __ __ __ __   __ __ __ __ __

3. Do you think that all the ways to enter and exit are equally likely? _____

Explain your answer. _____

_____

4. How many ways are there to enter and exit the same stadium if a person may not leave by the same gate through which he or she entered? _____

5. Sally takes a quiz with three true or false questions. She does not know the answer to any of the questions, so she guesses on all three.

   a. On the back of this page, draw a tree diagram to show Sally's possible results.

   b. What is the probability that she will get all three questions correct? _____

351

LESSON 12·2 Chance and Probability

Things that happen are called **events.** For some events, you can be sure that they will or will not happen. For example, you can be sure that water will freeze at the North Pole, and you can be just as sure that tropical plants will not grow there.

When a number between 0 and 1 is used to tell the likelihood of something happening, the number is called a **probability.** The closer a probability is to 1, the more likely it is that the event will happen.

For many events, you cannot be sure that they will or will not happen, but you feel there is a chance. If Susan is a good soccer player, you might say, "Susan has a good chance of scoring in the soccer game." If she is not one of the better players, you might say, "Susan does not have a good chance of scoring in the game."

For the events below:

◆ Write C if you feel there is a chance that the event may or may not happen, but you cannot be sure.

◆ Write P if you feel you could assign a probability to the chance that the event may or may not happen.

1. You study for a test and feel you are prepared. What is the likelihood that you will pass the test?   _____

2. You ask an adult for permission to go to a movie with friends and the answer is "maybe." What is the likelihood that you will be able to go to the movie?   _____

3. What is the likelihood that a die will land on 1 or 2?   _____

4. What is the likelihood that next year, every student in your class will have a new baby brother?   _____

5. You have 4 pairs of white socks and 2 pairs of blue socks in a drawer. What is the likelihood that the first sock you pull from the drawer will be blue?   _____

Describe an event for each type.

6. C: _____

   _____

7. P: _____

   _____

352

STUDY LINK
12·3 **Ratios**

Ratios can be stated or written in a variety of ways. Sometimes a ratio is easier to understand or will make more sense if it is rewritten in another form.

Example: In a group of 25 students, 16 students walk to school and 9 take a bus. The ratio of students who take a bus compared to all students in the group can be expressed in the following ways:

◆ With words: Nine out of twenty-five students take a bus.

◆ With a fraction: $\frac{9}{25}$ of the students take a bus.

◆ With a percent: 36% of the students take a bus.

◆ With a colon between the two numbers being compared: The ratio of students who take a bus to all students in the group is 9:25 (nine out of twenty-five).

Revise the above statements to express the ratio of students who walk to school to all students.

1. With words: _____ students walk to school.

2. With a fraction: _____ of the students walk to school.

3. With a percent: _____ of the students walk to school.

4. With a colon: The ratio of students who walk to school to all students is _____.

In each problem, fill in the ovals next to each correct ratio.

5. Fifty cars drove past in 10 minutes. Twenty-three cars were blue.

   ○ 23:50 of the cars were blue.   ○ 23% of the cars were blue.   ○ 0.46 of the cars were blue.

6. In a group of 9 people, 6 were swimmers.

   ○ $\frac{2}{3}$ of the people were swimmers.   ○ 6:9 of the people were swimmers.   ○ $66\frac{2}{3}$% of the people were swimmers.

7. In a sports shop, 35 of the 40 caps sold the day before the World Series were baseball caps.

   ○ 7 out of 8 caps sold were baseball caps.   ○ 35% of the caps sold were baseball caps.   ○ 35:40 of the caps sold were baseball caps.

353

LESSON 12·3 Picturing Ratios

The following pictograph shows how the 785 students at Windward Academy responded to a survey about the activities they thought were the most summer fun.

Pictograph of Summer Fun Data

Swimming	☀ ☀ ☀ ☀ ☀ ☀ ☀ ☀
Traveling	☀ ☀ ☀ ☀ ☀ ☀ ☀ ☀ ☀ ☀ ☀ ☀ ☀ ☀ ☀ ☀
Organized Sports	☀ ☀ ☀ ☀ ☀ ☀ ☀ ☀
Bike Riding	☀ ☀ ☀ ☀
Reading	☀ ☀
Other	☀ ☀ ☀

Each ☀ represents 20 students.

Use the pictograph to answer the questions.

1. How many ☀ would represent 100 students? _____

2. Which activity is the most popular for students at Windward Academy? _____

3. Which activity is about $\frac{1}{2}$ as popular as traveling? _____

4. Which activity is five times more popular than reading? _____

5. Explain how using a pictograph to solve simple ratio problems is different from using only numbers. Use an example to support your explanation.

_____

_____

_____

_____

_____

_____

Name   Date   Time

 LESSON 12·3 | **Imagining 10 Times More or 10 Times Less**

On a separate sheet of paper, write a story about what your life might be like if suddenly . . .

◆ everything became 10 times larger or 10 times more;

  or

◆ everything became 10 times smaller or 10 times less.

Use your imagination, but be specific. Give counts and measurements. Compare the way things are now with the way they would change. Give at least five examples of how things would be different.

Example: If everything were 10 times less, I could get to school in 2 minutes instead of the 20 minutes it takes me now. There would be only 3 people on the bus instead of the usual 30. My lunch would cost 30 cents instead of $3.00.

Name   Date   Time

 LESSON 12·3 | **Imagining 10 Times More or 10 Times Less**

On a separate sheet of paper, write a story about what your life might be like if suddenly . . .

◆ everything became 10 times larger or 10 times more;

  or

◆ everything became 10 times smaller or 10 times less.

Use your imagination, but be specific. Give counts and measurements. Compare the way things are now with the way they would change. Give at least five examples of how things would be different.

Example: If everything were 10 times less, I could get to school in 2 minutes instead of the 20 minutes it takes me now. There would be only 3 people on the bus instead of the usual 30. My lunch would cost 30 cents instead of $3.00.

LESSON 12·3 | More Ratios

1. There are 12 children on a bus. In all, 50 people are on the bus. Express the ratio of children to all people on the bus.

   a. With words: _____ people on the bus are children.

   b. With a fraction: _____ of the people on the bus are children.

   c. With a percent: _____ of the people on the bus are children.

   d. With a colon: The ratio of
   children to all people on the bus is _____.

2. In Mrs. Horton's fifth-grade class, 6 students own a cat. In all, 20 students own pets. Express the ratio of cat owners to all pet owners in the class.

   a. With words: _____ pet owners are cat owners.

   b. With a fraction: _____ of all pet owners are cat owners.

   c. With a percent: _____ of all pet owners are cat owners.

   d With a colon: The ratio of
   cat owners to all pet owners is _____.

3. In a survey about favorite flavors of ice cream, 8 people said they liked chocolate ice cream best. A total of 24 people were surveyed. Express the ratio of people who chose chocolate ice cream as their favorite to all the people surveyed.

   a. With words: _____ people surveyed prefer chocolate.

   b. With a fraction: _____ of the people surveyed prefer chocolate.

   c. With a percent: _____ of the people surveyed prefer chocolate.

   d. With a colon: The ratio of people who
   prefer chocolate to all the people surveyed is _____.

STUDY LINK 12·4 | **Ratio Problems**

1. Draw 20 tiles so that 2 out of 10 tiles are white and the rest are shaded.

   a. How many tiles are white? _____ tiles

   b. How many tiles are shaded? _____ tiles

2. Draw 9 shaded tiles.

   Add white tiles until 2 out of 5 tiles are white.

   How many tiles are there in all? _____ tiles

3. Imagine 48 tiles. If 4 out of 12 tiles
   are white, how many tiles are white? _____ tiles

4. There are 24 players on the soccer team. Two out of
   every 3 players have not scored a goal yet this year.
   How many players have scored a goal this year? _____ players

5. For every 8 spelling tests Justine took, she earned
   3 perfect scores. If Justine earned 12 perfect
   scores this year, how many spelling tests did she take? _____ tests

---

Practice

6. $92\overline{)9{,}054}$ → _____

7. $98 * 92 =$ _____

8. $90.16 + 0.38 =$ _____

9. $90.54 * 10^2 =$ _____

357

LESSON 12·4 | Writing Ratios

Some **ratios** compare part of a collection of things to the total number of things in the collection. The statement *6 out of 24 fifth graders have a pet* compares the number of fifth graders who have pets to the total number of fifth graders. This ratio can be expressed in several ways.

In *words:* For every 24 fifth graders, 6 have a pet. Six in 24 fifth graders have a pet. The ratio of fifth graders who have pets to the total number of fifth graders is 6 to 24.

With a *fraction:* $\frac{6}{24}$ of fifth graders have a pet.

A ratio is in simplest form if, when expressed as a fraction, the fraction is in simplest form. For example, the ratio *9 out of 36 fifth graders wear braces on his or her teeth* can be expressed in simplest form as $\frac{1}{4}$ of fifth graders wear braces.

Express each ratio below with a fraction, using the simplest form.

1. Eighteen out of 24 fifth graders do not have a pet.

_____

2. There are 18 water birds in the pond and 3 are swans.

_____

3. Of the 54 tropical fish in the school aquarium, 27 are tiger fish.

_____

4. For every 6 hot dogs sold at the ballpark, 4 are chili dogs.

_____

LESSON 12·4 Ratios

Solve the following ratio problems. Use the Square Tiles from *Math Journal 2,*
Activity Sheet 7 to help you.

1. Place 20 tiles on your desk so that 3 out of 4 tiles are white and the rest are shaded.

How many tiles are white? _____

How many tiles are shaded? _____

2. Place 25 tiles on your desk so that 3 out of 5 tiles are white and the rest are shaded.

How many tiles are white? _____

How many tiles are shaded? _____

3. Place 4 white tiles on your desk. Add some tiles until 1 out of 5 tiles is white and the

rest are shaded. How many tiles are there in all? _____

4. Place 9 white tiles on your desk. Add some tiles until 3 out of 8 tiles are white and

the rest are shaded. How many tiles are there in all? _____

5. Imagine 28 tiles. If 4 out of 7 are white, how many are white? _____

6. Imagine 24 tiles. If 5 out of 6 are white, how many are white? _____

7. Place 18 tiles on your desk so that 6 are white and the rest are shaded.
One out of _____ tiles is white.

8. Place 30 tiles on your desk so that 20 are white and the rest are shaded.
Out of 3 tiles, _____ are white.

9. Make up a ratio number story for a partner to solve.

_____

_____

Answer: _____

LESSON 12·4 | Permission Slip

We plan to examine the effect of exercise on heart rate in an upcoming math class. Students will find their heart rates after stepping up onto and down from a chair 5, 10, 15, 20, and 25 times.

Although the activity is not especially strenuous, we ask that you complete and return this form giving permission for your child's participation.

The data we collect will be used to teach graphing and other statistical skills.

I give permission for _____ to participate in the heart-rate activity described above.

Signature _____ Date _____

- ✂

Name _____ Date _____ Time _____

LESSON 12·4 | Permission Slip

We plan to examine the effect of exercise on heart rate in an upcoming math class. Students will find their heart rates after stepping up onto and down from a chair 5, 10, 15, 20, and 25 times.

Although the activity is not especially strenuous, we ask that you complete and return this form giving permission for your child's participation.

The data we collect will be used to teach graphing and other statistical skills.

I give permission for _____ to participate in the heart-rate activity described above.

Signature _____ Date _____

Ratio Problems

SRB
106–109
243–245

Find the missing number.

1. $\frac{1}{5} = \frac{x}{40}$ $x = $ _____

2. $\frac{2}{3} = \frac{16}{y}$ $y = $ _____

3. $\frac{5}{6} = \frac{m}{54}$ $m = $ _____

4. $\frac{1}{4} = \frac{15}{n}$ $n = $ _____

5. $\frac{5}{8} = \frac{f}{32}$ $f = $ _____

6. $\frac{13}{50} = \frac{g}{100}$ $g = $ _____

Write a number model for each problem. Then solve the problem.

7. Of the 115 students in the sixth grade, 2 out of 5 belong to the Drama Club. How many students are members of the Drama Club?

Number model: _____   Answer: _____
(unit)

8. Three out of 4 students at Highland School ordered a hot lunch today. There are 156 students at the school. How many students ordered a hot lunch?

Number model: _____   Answer: _____
(unit)

9. Gina and the other members of her troop sell cookies for $3 a box. For each box they sell, the troop earns $1.50. One week, Gina's troop sold $90 worth of cookies. How much did the troop earn?

Number model: _____   Answer: _____

10. 30% of the tickets sold by a movie theater for the Friday night show were children's tickets at $4 each. The rest of the tickets were sold at the full price of $8.50. The movie theater collected $360 just for the children's tickets. How many tickets did they sell in all?

Number model: _____   Answer: _____
(unit)

Practice

11. $6^3 = $ _____   **12.** $3^6 = $ _____   **13.** $6^3 * 10^2 = $ _____

361

LESSON 12·5   Solving Ratio Problems with Cross Multiplication

Cross multiplication is a strategy for solving ratio problems that is based on the quick common denominator.

Example:

Josie tosses a penny 32 times. It lands heads up 5 out of 8 times. How many times does the penny land heads up?

Number Model: $\dfrac{5}{8} = \dfrac{x}{32}$

Cross multiply:

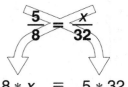

$$8 * x = 5 * 32$$

Solution: $8 * x = 160$
               $x = 20$

Answer: <u>   20 times   </u>
                       (unit)

Use cross multiplication to solve the following problems. Let the variable x represent the missing number in each problem.

1. Jeremy received 3 votes for every 5 votes cast. If he received 18 votes, how many votes were cast?

Number model: _____   Solution: _____

Cross multiply: _____   Answer: _____
                                                            (unit)

2. The restaurant at the mall sold 324 lunches. For every 9 lunches served, 3 were fish plates. How many fish plates were served?

Number model: _____   Solution: _____

Cross multiply: _____   Answer: _____
                                                            (unit)

3. The Nature Center has a total of 87 amphibians on display. For every 6 amphibians, 2 are types of salamanders. How many salamanders are there?

Number model: _____   Solution: _____

Cross multiply: _____   Answer: _____
                                                            (unit)

4. Write a ratio number story for your partner to solve using cross multiplication.

LESSON 12·5 — Solving Ratio Number Stories

Write a number model for each problem. Include key words for the numerators and denominators. Then solve the problem.

1. Of the 90 fifth-grade girls at Lincoln School, 1 out of 6 reported that they jumped rope 3 times last week. How many girls jumped rope 3 times last week?

Number model: _____

Answer: _____
           (unit)

2. The 175 seniors at Kennedy High School voted for the color of caps and gowns they would wear at the graduation ceremony. Six out of 7 voted for silver. How many students voted for silver?

Number model: _____

Answer: _____
           (unit)

3. Melissa's brother, Sidney, was explaining his college food budget to her. He told Melissa that he budgeted $160 a month for restaurants, but he spent 3 out of every 4 dollars at the campus pizza parlor. How much did he spend at the pizza parlor?

Number model: _____

Answer: _____
           (unit)

4. A survey was conducted at Sidney's college to find out how the 640 students budgeted their food money. Five out of 8 students reported that they spent less than $160 a month on food. How many students spent less than $160 on food?

Number model: _____

Answer: _____
           (unit)

363

Rates

Complete each table using the given information. Then answer the question below each table.

1. It would take 27,000 spiders, each spinning a single web, to produce a pound of spider webs.

a.

Number of Spiders	27,000	54,000			
Pounds of Spider Webs	1	2	3	4	5

b. At this rate, how many spiders, each spinning a single web, would be needed to produce 10 pounds of spider webs? _____ spiders

2. It used to be thought that the deer botfly flies so fast that it is almost invisible to the human eye. It has since been tested, and scientists found that it actually flies about 25 miles per hour.

a.

Miles	25				
Hours	1	2	3	4	5

b. At this rate, about how far could a deer botfly travel in 1 minute? _____ mile(s)

Solve the following rate problems. Make a table if it will help you.

3. About 50 gallons of maple sap are needed to make 1 gallon of maple syrup. How many gallons of maple sap are needed to make 20 gallons of maple syrup?

About _____ gallons

4. For 186 days a year, the sun is not visible at the North Pole. During a 5-year period, about how many days is the sun not visible?

About _____ days

5. In a beehive, about $1\frac{1}{2}$ ounces of beeswax are used to build a honeycomb that holds 4 pounds of honey. How much beeswax is needed to build a honeycomb that could hold 20 pounds of honey?

About _____ ounces

Source: *2201 Fascinating Facts*

STUDY LINK
12·7 | **Operations with Fractions**

SRB
70–73
243

1. In the Malagasay Indian tribes, it is against the law for a son to be taller than his father. If a son is taller, he must give his father money or an ox. Suppose a father is 5 feet $10\frac{1}{2}$ inches tall and his son is 5 feet $6\frac{3}{4}$ inches tall. How many more inches can the son grow before he is as tall as his father?

_____
(unit)

2. In the state of Indiana, it is illegal to travel on a bus within 4 hours of eating garlic. If you lived in Indiana and had eaten a bowl of pasta with garlic bread $2\frac{1}{3}$ hours ago, how many more hours would you need to wait before you could legally travel on a bus?

_____
(unit)

3. In Idaho, it is against the law to give a person a box of candy that weighs more than 50 pounds. It is Valentine's Day, and you give your mother a box of candy that weighs $48\frac{1}{4}$ pounds. How much more could the box weigh without breaking the law?

_____
(unit)

4. The body of an average jellyfish is about $\frac{9}{10}$ water. What fraction of the jellyfish is not water?

_____

5. The world record for a jump by a frog is 19 feet $3\frac{1}{8}$ inches. How much farther would a frog need to jump to set a new world record of 7 yards?

_____
(unit)

6. The maximum length for a typical king cobra is about $5\frac{4}{5}$ meters. If 6 of these snakes were lined up end to end, how far would they stretch?

_____
(unit)

7. An average trumpeter swan weighs about $16\frac{4}{5}$ kilograms. What is the approximate weight of 3 average trumpeter swans?

_____
(unit)

Sources: *The Top 10 of Everything; Beyond Belief!*

Practice

8. $(4 * 4) + \frac{4}{4} =$ _____

9. $4! + 4 + 4 + \sqrt{4} =$ _____

10. 75% of 12 = _____

11. 50% of 360 = _____

365

STUDY LINK 12·8 | **Rate and Ratio Problems**

1. The average American eats about 250 eggs per year. At this rate, about how many eggs will the average American eat in . . .

   a. five years? _____
   (unit)

   b. $\frac{1}{12}$ of a year? _____
   (unit)

2. The average fifth grader can eat $\frac{3}{8}$ of a pizza for lunch. At this rate, how many lunches will it take for an average fifth grader to eat the equivalent of 3 whole pizzas? _____
   (unit)

3. In 1975, a man in Washington state ate 424 clams in 8 minutes. At this rate, how many would he eat . . .

   a. in $\frac{1}{4}$ of this time? _____
   (unit)

   b. in $2\frac{1}{2}$ times as much time? _____
   (unit)

4. A deck has 52 playing cards. In two decks,

   a. what is the ratio of 2s to 10s? _____

   b. what is the ratio of Hearts to the total number of playing cards? _____

   c. what is the ratio of Jacks to Kings and Queens? _____

Practice

5. $3\frac{4}{7} * \frac{8}{8} =$ _____

6. $3n + 2n = 25$

   $n =$ _____

7. $25 = 2n$

   $n =$ _____

8. $12.5 * n = 100$

   $n =$ _____

366

Solving Ratio Problems

Instrument Players in the United States	
Piano/Keyboard	21 million
Guitar	19 million
Organ	6 million
Flute	4 million
Clarinet	4 million
Drums	3 million
Trumpet	3 million
Violin	2 million
Harmonica	1.7 million
Saxophone	1 million

Source: *America by the Numbers*

1. a. What is the ratio of flute players to harmonica players? _____

b. What is the ratio of drum players to piano players? _____

c. Record the ratio of violin and saxophone players to trumpet players. _____

2. Which two pairs of instrument players have a 1-to-1 ratio? _____

_____

3. In a fifth-grade band, the ratio of saxophonists to clarinetists is 2:3. If there are 10 saxophonists, how many clarinetists are there? _____

4. The school orchestra is performing tonight. There are 24 orchestra members. There are 6 violas. The ratio of violins to violas is 2:1. The ratio of cellos to basses is 2:1. There are no other instruments. How many chairs are needed in each section?

a. violins _____ **b.** violas _____

c. cellos _____ **d.** basses _____

End-of-Year Family Letter

Congratulations!

By completing *Fifth Grade Everyday Mathematics,* your child has accomplished a great deal. Thank you for your support!

This Family Letter provides a resource throughout your child's vacation. It includes an extended list of Do-Anytime Activities, directions for games that can be played at home, a list of mathematics-related books to check out over vacation, and a preview of what your child will be learning in *Sixth Grade Everyday Mathematics.* Enjoy your vacation!

Do-Anytime Activities

Mathematics means more when it is rooted in real-life situations. To help your child review many of the concepts he or she has learned in fifth grade, we suggest the following activities for you to do together over vacation. These activities will help your child build on the skills he or she has learned this year and will help prepare him or her for *Sixth Grade Everyday Mathematics.*

1. Review multiplication facts. For example, include basic facts such as $7 * 8 = 56$, and extended facts, such as $70 * 8 = 560$ and $70 * 80 = 5,600$.

2. Create opportunities to work with rulers, yardsticks, metersticks, tape measures, and scales. Have your child measure items using metric and U.S. customary units.

3. Ask your child to solve multiplication and division problems that are based on real-life situations. Vary the problems so that some are suitable for mental computation, some require paper-and-pencil calculation, and some require the use of a calculator.

4. Practice using percents by asking your child to calculate sales tax, percent discounts, sports statistics, and so on.

5. Continue the American Tour by reading about important people, events, inventions, explorations, and other topics in American history. Focus on data displays such as bar, line, and circle graphs, and on color-coded maps.

Building Skills through Games

The following section lists rules for games that can be played at home. The number cards used in some games can be made from 3" by 5" index cards.

Factor Captor

1. To start the first round, Player 1 (James) chooses a 2-digit number on the number grid. James covers it with a counter and records the number on scratch paper. This is James's score for the round.

2. Player 2 (Emma) covers all the factors of James's number. Emma finds the sum of the factors, and records it on scratch paper. This is Emma's score for the round.

   A factor may only be covered once during a round.

3. If Emma missed any factors, James can cover them with counters and add them to his score.

4. In the next round, players switch roles. Player 2 (Emma) chooses a number that is not covered by a counter. Player 1 (James) covers all factors of that number.

5. Any number that is covered by a counter is no longer available and may not be used again.

6. The first player in a round may not cover a number less than 10, unless no other numbers are available.

7. Play continues with players trading roles in each round, until all numbers on the grid have been covered. Players then use their calculators to find their total scores. The player with the higher total score wins the game.

Factor Captor
Grid 1

1	2	2	2	2	2
2	3	3	3	3	3
3	4	4	4	4	5
5	5	5	6	6	7
7	8	8	9	9	10
10	11	12	13	14	15
16	18	20	21	22	24
25	26	27	28	30	32

2-4-5-10 Frac-Tac-Toe

Advance Preparation: Separate the cards into two piles—a numerator pile and a denominator pile. Place two each of the 2, 4, 5, and 10 cards in the denominator pile. All other cards are placed on the numerator pile.

Shuffle the cards in each pile. Place the piles facedown. When the numerator pile is completely used, reshuffle that pile, and place it facedown. When the denominator pile is completely used, turn it over, and place it facedown without reshuffling it.

1. Players take turns. When it is your turn:

   ◆ Turn over the top card from each pile to form a fraction (numerator card over denominator card).

   ◆ Try to match the fraction shown with one of the grid squares on the gameboard. (Use either of the gameboards shown.) If a match is found, cover that grid square with your counter and your turn is over. If no match is found, your turn is over.

2-4-5-10 Frac-Tac-Toe
Gameboards

> 1.0	0 or 1	> 2.0	0 or 1	> 1.0
0.1	0.2	0.25	0.3	0.4
> 1.5	0.5	> 1.5	0.5	> 1.5
0.6	0.7	0.75	0.8	0.9
> 1.0	0 or 1	> 2.0	0 or 1	> 1.0

>100%	0% or 100%	>200%	0% or 100%	>100%
10%	20%	25%	30%	40%
>100%	50%	>200%	50%	>100%
60%	70%	75%	80%	90%
>100%	0% or 100%	>200%	0% or 100%	>100%

369

2. To change the fraction shown by the cards to a decimal or percent, players *may* use a calculator.

3. **Scoring** The first player covering three squares in a row in any direction (horizontal, vertical, diagonal) is the winner.

Variations:

◆ For a *2-4-8* game, place two each of the 2, 4, and 8 cards in the denominator pile. Use the gameboards shown in the margin.

◆ For a *3-6-9* game, place two each of the 3, 6, and 9 cards in the denominator pile. Use the gameboards shown in the margin.

Multiplication Bull's-eye

1. Shuffle a deck of number cards (4 each of the numbers 0–9) and place them facedown on the playing surface.

2. Players take turns. When it is your turn:

   ◆ Roll a six-sided die. Look up the target range of the product in the table.

   ◆ Take four cards from the top of the deck.

   ◆ Use the cards to try and form two numbers whose product falls within the target range. **Do not use a calculator.**

   ◆ Multiply the two numbers on your calculator to determine whether the product falls within the target range. If it does, you have hit the bull's-eye and score 1 point. If it doesn't, you score 0 points.

   ◆ Sometimes it is impossible to form two numbers whose product falls within the target range. If this happens, you score 0 points for that turn.

3. The game ends when each player has had five turns.

4. The player scoring more points wins the game.

Example:

Tom rolls a 3, so the target range of the product is from 1,001 to 3,000.

He turns over a 5, a 7, a 2, and a 9.

Tom uses estimation to try to form two numbers whose product falls within the target range, for example, 97 and 25.

He finds the product on the calculator:
97 * 25 = 2,425.

Because the product is between 1,001 and 3,000, Tom has hit the bull's-eye and scores 1 point.

Some other possible winning products from the 5, 7, 2, and 9 cards are:
25 * 79, 27 * 59, 9 * 257, and 2 * 579.

Number on Die	Target Range of Product
1	500 or less
2	501–1,000
3	1,001–3,000
4	3,001–5,000
5	5,001–7,000
6	more than 7,000

2-4-8 Frac-Tac-Toe
Gameboards

>2.0	0 or 1	>1.5	0 or 1	>2.0
1.5	0.125	0.25	0.375	1.5
>1.0	0.5	0.25 or 0.75	0.5	>1.0
2.0	0.625	0.75	0.875	2.0
>2.0	0 or 1	1.125	0 or 1	>2.0

>200%	0% or 100%	>150%	0% or 100%	>200%
150%	12½%	25%	37½%	150%
>100%	50%	25% or 75%	50%	>100%
200%	62½%	75%	87½%	200%
>200%	0% or 100%	112½%	0% or 100%	>200%

3-6-9 Frac-Tac-Toe
Gameboards

> 1.0	0 or 1	0.$\overline{1}$	0 or 1	> 1.0
0.1$\overline{6}$	0.$\overline{2}$	0.$\overline{3}$	0.$\overline{3}$	0 $\overline{4}$
> 2.0	0.$\overline{5}$	> 1.0	0.$\overline{6}$	> 2.0
0.$\overline{6}$	0.$\overline{7}$	0.8$\overline{3}$	0.$\overline{8}$	1.$\overline{3}$
> 1.0	0 or 1	1.$\overline{6}$	0 or 1	> 1.0

>100%	0% or 100%	11.1%	0% or 100%	>100%
16⅔%	22.2%	33⅓%	33.3%	44.4%
>200%	55.5%	>100%	66.6%	>200%
66⅔%	77.7%	83⅓%	88.8%	133⅓%
>100%	0% or 100%	166⅔%	0% or 100%	>100%

Vacation Reading with a Mathematical Twist

Books can contribute to children's learning by presenting mathematics in a combination of real-world and imaginary contexts. The titles listed below were recommended by teachers who use *Everyday Mathematics* in their classrooms. They are organized by mathematical topics. Visit your local library and check out these mathematics-related books with your child.

Numeration
The Rajah's Rice: A Mathematical Folktale from India by David Barry

Operations and Computation
Counting on Frank by Rod Clement

Data and Chance
Jumanji by Chris Van Allsburg

Geometry
A Cloak for the Dreamer by Aileen Friedman; *Flatland* by Edwin Abbott; *The Boy Who Reversed Himself* by William Sleator

Measurement and Reference Frames
Spaghetti and Meatballs for All!: A Mathematical Story by Marilyn Burns; *Mr. Archimedes' Bath* by Pamela Allen

Looking Ahead: *Sixth Grade Everyday Mathematics*

Next year your child will ...

◆ continue to collect, display, describe, and interpret data.

◆ maintain and extend skills for comparing, adding, subtracting, multiplying, and dividing fractions and mixed numbers.

◆ use scientific notation to write large and small numbers, and explore scientific notation on a calculator.

◆ continue the study of variables, expressions, equations, and other topics in algebra; use variables in spreadsheets; and solve equations and inequalities.

◆ extend skills in geometry, including constructions, transformations of figures, and finding volumes of 3-dimensional figures.

◆ maintain and apply skills for adding, subtracting, multiplying, and dividing whole numbers, decimals, and positive and negative numbers.

Project Masters

Project Masters

Name   Date   Time

PROJECT 2 — A Perfect-Number Challenge

Perfect numbers become big very quickly. The third perfect number has 3 digits, the fourth has 4 digits, the fifth has 8 digits, the sixth has 10 digits, and the thirty-second has 455,663 digits! In other words, perfect numbers are hard to find.

You can find perfect numbers without having to find the sum of the proper factors of every number. Here is what you do:

1. Complete the pattern of starting numbers in the first column in the table.

2. List the factors of each starting number in the second column.

3. Write the sum of the factors of each starting number in the third column.

4. If the sum of the factors of the starting number is prime, multiply this sum by the starting number itself. The product is a perfect number. Record it in the last column.

The first perfect number is 6. Try to find the next three perfect numbers.

Starting Number	Factors	Sum of Factors	Perfect Number
2	1 2	3	6
4			
8			

People have been fascinated by perfect numbers for centuries. The ancient Greeks knew the first four. The fifth perfect number was not found until the year 1456. The search for perfect numbers is now carried out on computers. When this book went to press, 42 perfect numbers had been identified. All the perfect numbers found so far are even numbers.

382

Name   Date   Time

PROJECT 6 — Ground Areas of Famous Large Buildings

The ground areas of buildings, their footprints, are almost always given in square feet or square meters. Some buildings have very large ground areas. When their areas are given in square feet, the numbers are so large that it is hard to imagine how big the buildings really are.

For large buildings, if you convert the area in square feet to an estimate in acres, you can get a better idea of the size of the building.

Estimate the ground area, in acres, of each building in the table below:

Reference

1 acre = 43,560 square feet

For estimating, think of 1 acre as about 50,000 square feet.

A football field (excluding the end zones) is approximately 1 acre.

Example: The Colosseum, in Italy, covers an area of about 250,000 ft².

One acre is about 50,000 ft².

So 5 acres is about 250,000 ft².

The Colosseum covers an area of about 5 acres (5 football fields).

Building	Country	Date Built	Ground Area (ft²)	Estimated Area (in acres)
Colosseum	Italy	70–224	250,000 ft²	5 acres
Pyramid of Cheops	Egypt	c. 2600 B.C.	571,500 ft²	acres
Chartres Cathedral	France	1194–1514	60,000 ft²	acres
St. Peter's Basilica	Vatican City	1506–1626	392,300 ft²	acres
Taj Mahal	India	1636–1653	78,000 ft²	acres
Pentagon	U.S. (Virginia)	1941–1943	1,263,000 ft²	acres
Ford Parts Center	U.S. (Michigan)	1936	2,800,000 ft²	acres

403

PROJECT 1

The Search for Prime Numbers

You probably know the following definitions of prime and composite numbers:

A **prime number** is a whole number that has exactly two **factors.** The factors are 1 and the number itself. For example, 7 is a prime number because its only factors are 1 and 7. A prime number is divisible by only 1 and itself.

A **composite number** is a whole number that has more than two factors. For example, 10 is a composite number because it has four factors: 1, 2, 5, and 10. A composite number is divisible by at least three whole numbers.

The number 1 is neither prime nor composite.

For centuries, mathematicians have been interested in prime and composite numbers because they are the building blocks of whole numbers. They have found that every composite number can be written as the product of prime numbers. For example, 18 can be written as $2 * 3 * 3$.

Around 300 B.C., the Greek mathematician Euclid (yOO´klid) proved that there is no largest prime number. No matter how large a prime number you find, there will always be larger prime numbers. Since then, people have been searching for more prime numbers. In 1893, a mathematician was able to show that there are more than 50 million prime numbers between the numbers 1 and 1 billion.

The Greek mathematician Eratosthenes (ĕr´ ə-tŏs´ thə-nēz´), who lived around 200 B.C., devised a simple method for finding prime numbers. His strategy was based on the fact that every **multiple of a number** is divisible by that number. For example, the numbers 2, 4, 6, 8, and 10 are multiples of 2, and each of these numbers is divisible by 2. Here is another way to say it: A whole number is a factor of every one of its multiples. For example, 2 is a factor of 2, 4, 6, 8, and 10. The number 2 has only one other factor, the number 1, so 2 is a prime number. All other multiples of 2 are composite numbers.

Eratosthenes' method is called the **Sieve of Eratosthenes.** The directions for using the sieve to find prime numbers are given on *Math Masters,* page 375.

Since the time of Eratosthenes, mathematicians have invented more powerful methods for finding prime numbers. Some methods use formulas. Today, people use computers. The largest prime number known when this book went to press had 12,978,189 digits. If that number were printed in a book with pages the same size as this page, in the same size type, the book would be about 1,900 pages long.

374

PROJECT 1

The Sieve of Eratosthenes

Follow the directions below for *Math Masters,* page 376. When you have finished, you will have crossed out every number from 1 to 100 that is not a prime number.

1. Because 1 is not a prime number, cross it out.

2. Circle 2 with a colored marker or crayon. Then count by 2, crossing out all multiples of 2; that is, 4, 6, 8, 10, and so on.

3. Circle 3 with a different colored marker or crayon. Cross out every third number after 3—6, 9, 12, and so on. If a number is already crossed out, make a mark in a corner of the box. The numbers you have crossed out or marked are multiples of 3.

4. Skip 4, because it is already crossed out, and go on to 5. Use a new color to circle 5, and cross out multiples of 5.

5. Continue in the same pattern. Start each time by circling the next number that is not crossed out. Cross out all multiples of that number. If a number is already crossed out, make a mark in a corner of the box. Use a different color for each new set of multiples.

6. Stop when there are no more numbers to be circled or crossed out. The circled numbers are the prime numbers from 1 to 100.

7. List all the prime numbers from 1 to 100.

_____

_____

_____

The Sieve of Eratosthenes continued

1	2	3	4	5	6	7	8	9	10
11	12	13	14	15	16	17	18	19	20
21	22	23	24	25	26	27	28	29	30
31	32	33	34	35	36	37	38	39	40
41	42	43	44	45	46	47	48	49	50
51	52	53	54	55	56	57	58	59	60
61	62	63	64	65	66	67	68	69	70
71	72	73	74	75	76	77	78	79	80
81	82	83	84	85	86	87	88	89	90
91	92	93	94	95	96	97	98	99	100

The Sieve of Eratosthenes *continued*

1. What are the crossed-out numbers greater than 1 called?

_____

2. Notice that 6 is a multiple of both 2 and 3. Find two other numbers that are multiples of both 2 and 3.

_____

3. Find a number that is a multiple of 2, 3, and 5. (*Hint:* Look at the colors.)

_____

4. Find a number that is a multiple of 2, 3, 4, and 5. _____

5. Choose any crossed-out number between 50 and 60. List its factors.

_____

6. List the crossed-out numbers that have no marks in the corners of their boxes.

_____

7. Find a pair of consecutive prime numbers. _____

Are there any others? _____ If yes, list them.

_____

8. The numbers 3 and 5 are called **twin primes** because they are separated by just one composite number. List all the other twin primes from 1 to 100.

_____

_____

9. Why do you think this grid is called a sieve?

_____

_____

_____

377

The Sieve of Eratosthenes *continued*

101	102	103	104	105	106	107	108	109	100
111	112	113	114	115	116	117	118	119	120
121	122	123	124	125	126	127	128	129	130
131	132	133	134	135	136	137	138	139	140
141	142	143	144	145	146	147	148	149	150
151	152	153	154	155	156	157	158	159	160
161	162	163	164	165	166	167	168	169	170
171	172	173	174	175	176	177	178	179	180
181	182	183	184	185	186	187	188	189	190
191	192	193	194	195	196	197	198	199	200

PROJECT 2

Deficient, Abundant, and Perfect Numbers

A **factor** of a whole number N is any whole number that can be multiplied by a whole number to give N as the product. For example, 5 is a factor of 30 because $6 * 5 = 30$. Also, 6 is a factor of 30. Every whole number has itself and 1 as factors.

A **proper factor** of a whole number is any factor of that number except the number itself. For example, the *factors* of 10 are 1, 2, 5, and 10. The *proper factors* of 10 are 1, 2, and 5.

A whole number is a **deficient number** if the sum of its proper factors is less than the number. For example, 10 is a deficient number because the sum of its proper factors is $1 + 2 + 5 = 8$, and 8 is less than 10.

A whole number is an **abundant number** if the sum of its proper factors is greater than the number. For example, 12 is an abundant number because the sum of its proper factors is $1 + 2 + 3 + 4 + 6 = 16$, and 16 is greater than 12.

A whole number is a **perfect number** if the sum of its proper factors is equal to the number. For example, 6 is a perfect number because the sum of its proper factors is $1 + 2 + 3 = 6$.

Exploration

List the proper factors of each number from 1 to 50 in the table on *Math Masters,* pages 380 and 381. Then find the sum of the proper factors of each number, and record it in the third column of the table. Finally, make a check mark in the appropriate column to show whether the number is deficient, abundant, or perfect.

Divide the work with the other members of your group. Have partners use factor rainbows to check each other's work. When you are satisfied that all the results are correct, answer the questions on page 381.

PROJECT 2

Deficient, Abundant, and Perfect Numbers *cont.*

Number	Proper Factors	Sum of Proper Factors	Deficient	Abundant	Perfect
1		0	✔		
2					
3					
4					
5					
6	1, 2, 3	6			✔
7					
8					
9					
10	1, 2, 5	8	✔		
11					
12	1, 2, 3, 4, 6	16		✔	
13					
14					
15					
16					
17					
18					
19					
20					
21					
22					
23					
24					
25					
26					
27					
28					
29					
30					
31					
32					
33					
34					

PROJECT 2

Deficient, Abundant, and Perfect Numbers *cont.*

Number	Proper Factors	Sum of Proper Factors	Deficient	Abundant	Perfect
35					
36					
37					
38					
39					
40					
41					
42					
43					
44					
45					
46					
47					
48					
49					
50					

Source: *The Math Teacher's Book of Lists.* San Francisco: Jossey-Bass, 2005.

Refer to the results in your table.

1. What are the perfect numbers up to 50? _____

2. Is there an abundant number that is
   not an even number? _____

3. Are all deficient numbers odd numbers? _____

4. What is the next number greater than 50 for which
   the sum of its proper factors is 1? _____

5. The sum of the proper factors of 4 is 1 less than 4.
   List all the numbers through 50 for which the sum
   of the proper factors is 1 less than the number itself. _____

6. What do you think is the next number greater than 50
   for which the sum of its proper factors is 1 less than
   the number itself? _____

381

PROJECT 2

A Perfect-Number Challenge

Perfect numbers become big very quickly. The third perfect number has 3 digits, the fourth has 4 digits, the fifth has 8 digits, the sixth has 10 digits, and the thirty-second has 455,663 digits! In other words, perfect numbers are hard to find.

You can find perfect numbers without having to find the sum of the proper factors of every number. Here is what you do:

1. Complete the pattern of starting numbers in the first column of the table.

2. List the factors of each starting number in the second column.

3. Write the sum of the factors of each starting number in the third column.

4. If the sum of the factors of the starting number is prime, multiply this sum by the starting number itself. The product is a perfect number. Record it in the last column.

The first perfect number is 6. Try to find the next three perfect numbers.

Starting Number	Factors	Sum of Factors	Perfect Number
2	1, 2	3	6
4			
8			

People have been fascinated by perfect numbers for centuries. The ancient Greeks knew the first four. No one found the fifth perfect number until the year 1456. Computers now carry on the search for perfect numbers. When this book went to press, 42 perfect numbers had been identified. All the perfect numbers found so far are even numbers.

382

PROJECT 3 | **An Ancient Multiplication Method**

Thousands of years ago, the Egyptians developed one of the earliest multiplication methods. Their method uses an idea from number theory.

Every positive whole number can be expressed as a sum of powers of 2.

2^0	2^1	2^2	2^3	2^4	2^5	2^6
1	2	4	8	16	32	64

Write a number sentence to show each of the numbers below as the sum of powers of 2. For example, $13 = 1 + 4 + 8$.

1. $19 = $ _____   **2.** $67 = $ _____

Follow the steps below to use the Egyptian method to multiply $19 * 62$.

Step 1 List the powers of 2 that are less than the first factor, 19.

Step 2 List the products of the powers of 2 and the second factor, 62. Notice that each product is double the product before it.

Step 3 Put a check mark next to the powers of 2 whose sum is the first factor, 19.

Step 4 Cross out the remaining rows.

Step 5 Add the partial products that are not crossed out.
$62 + 124 + 992 = 1,178$
So $19 * 62 = 1,178$

$19 * 62 = $	
1	62
2	124
4	248
8	496
16	992

$19 * 62 = 1,178$	
✓ 1	62
✓ 2	124
~~4~~	~~248~~
~~8~~	~~496~~
✓ 16	992

3. Explain why you don't have to multiply by any number other than 2 to write the list of partial products when you use the Egyptian method.

_____

_____

_____

_____

_____

_____

_____

383

PROJECT 3 **An Ancient Multiplication Method** *cont.*

4. Try to solve these problems using the Egyptian method.

85 * 14 = _____	38 * 43 = _____	45 * 29 = _____

Try This

5. Here is another ancient multiplication method, based on the Egyptian method. People living in rural areas of Russia, Ethiopia, and the Near East still use this method. See whether you can figure out how it works. Then try to complete the problem in the third box, using this method.

13 * 25 = _325_	38 * 43 = _1,634_	45 * 29 = _____
13 25	38 43	45 29
6 50	19 86	22 58
3 100	9 172	11 116
1 200	4 344	5 232
325	2 688	2 464
	1 1,376	1 928
	1,634	_____

384

PROJECT 3
Comparing Multiplication Algorithms

Think about the advantages and disadvantages of each multiplication method that you know. Record your thoughts in the chart below.

Algorithm	Advantages	Disadvantages
Partial Products 43 $*62$ $60\ [40s] =2,400$ $60\ [3s] =180$ $2\ [40s] =80$ $2\ [3s] =6$ $2,666$		
Lattice		
Egyptian $43*62$ ✓ 162 ✓ 2124 4248 ✓ 8496 16992 ✓ $321,984$ $2,666$		

Lattice diagram:

$$4 \quad 3$$
$$2 \begin{array}{|c|c|} \hline {}^{\ }2 & {}^{1}1 \\ \hline 4 & 8 \\ \hline \end{array} 6$$
$$6 \begin{array}{|c|c|} \hline 0 & 0 \\ \hline 8 & 6 \\ \hline \end{array} 2$$
$$6 \quad 6$$

PROJECT 3 · Ancient Math Symbols

1. The ancient Egyptians used picture symbols, called hieroglyphs, to write numbers. Here is how they might have multiplied 11 * 13 using the algorithm you learned in this project.

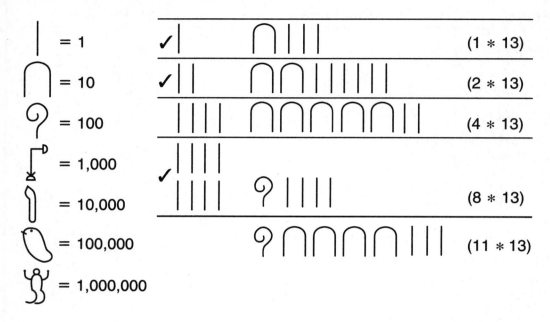

On the back of this sheet, try to multiply 21 * 16 using the Egyptian algorithm and Egyptian numerals.

2. Do you know any Roman numerals? They were used in Europe for centuries until Hindu-Arabic numerals replaced them. Today, Roman numerals appear mainly in dates on cornerstones and in copyright notices.

It is sometimes said that "multiplication with Roman numerals was impossible." Is that true? See whether you can multiply 12 * 15 using Roman numerals and the Egyptian algorithm. Use the back of this sheet.

Examples of Roman Numerals:

I = 1	II = 2	III = 3
IV = 4	V = 5	VI = 6
IX = 9	X = 10	XX = 20
XL = 40	L = 50	LX = 60
C = 100	D = 500	M = 1,000

PROJECT 4

Computation Trick #1—Super Speedy Addition

Set the Stage: Tell a friend that you have become a whiz at addition. To prove it, you are going to add five 3-digit numbers in your head within seconds.

Props Needed: calculator

Performing the Trick:

Examples:

	Trial 1	Trial 2	Trial 3
1. Ask your friend to jot down a 3-digit number on a piece of paper. Each digit must be different.	493	261	682
2. Ask your friend to write another 3-digit number below the first number. Each digit must be different.	764	503	149
3. One more time. (This is the "notice-me number.")	175	935	306
4. Now it is your turn. Write a number so that the sum of your number and the first number is 999. (For example, in Trial 1, 493 + 506 = 999.)	506	738	317
5. Write another number so that the sum of this number and the second number is 999. (For example, in Trial 1, 764 + 235 = 999.)	+ 235	+ 496	+ 850
6. Pause a few seconds, and then give the sum of the five numbers. Have your friend check your super speedy addition on a calculator.	2,173	2,933	2,304

Figure out how to do this trick. How does it work?

_____

_____

_____

_____

_____

PROJECT 4

Computation Trick #2—Subtraction Surprise

Set the Stage: Tell a friend that your subtraction skills have soared. You are now able to give the answer to a subtraction problem without ever seeing the problem.

Props Needed: calculator

Performing the Trick:

Examples:

	Trial 1	Trial 2

1. Ask your friend to secretly write a 3-digit number on a piece of paper. Each digit must be different.

| | 135 | 562 |

2. Tell your friend to reverse the digits and write the new number below the first number.

| | 531 | 265 |

3. Now have your friend use a calculator to subtract the smaller number from the larger number.

	531	562
	− 135	− 265
	396	297

4. Say: *Tell me either the digit in the hundreds place or the digit in the ones place.*

| | 3 in the hundreds place | 7 in the ones place |

5. Pause a few seconds, and then give the answer.

| | 396 | 297 |

Figure out how to do this trick. How does it work?

_____

_____

_____

_____

388

PROJECT 4

Computation Trick #3—Crazy Calendar Addition

Set the Stage: Tell a friend that you have become so good at addition that you can tell what an addition problem is by merely looking at the answer.

Props Needed: calculator and a calendar

Performing the Trick:

Examples:

Give your friend a calendar.

Sun.	Mon.	Tue.	Wed.	Thu.	Fri.	Sat.
		1	2	3	4	5
6	7	8	9	10	11	12
13	14	15	16	17	18	19
20	21	22	23	24	25	26
27	28	29	30	31		

1. Ask your friend to choose a month and to secretly circle any three dates that are next to each other, either in a row or in a column.

	Trial 1	**Trial 2**	**Trial 3**
2. Now ask your friend to add the three dates on a calculator and to give you the calculator showing the sum in the display.	30	27	39
3. Ask: *Are the three dates you circled in a row or in a column?*	column	row	column
4. Pause a few seconds, and then give the answer.	3, 10, 17	8, 9, 10	6, 13, 20

Figure out how to do this trick. How does it work?

_____

_____

_____

_____

_____

PROJECT 4

12-Month Calendar

JANUARY
S	M	T	W	T	F	S
1	2	3	4	5	6	7
8	9	10	11	12	13	14
15	16	17	18	19	20	21
22	23	24	25	26	27	28
29	30	31				

FEBRUARY
S	M	T	W	T	F	S
			1	2	3	4
5	6	7	8	9	10	11
12	13	14	15	16	17	18
19	20	21	22	23	24	25
26	27	28				

MARCH
S	M	T	W	T	F	S
			1	2	3	4
5	6	7	8	9	10	11
12	13	14	15	16	17	18
19	20	21	22	23	24	25
26	27	28	29	30	31	

APRIL
S	M	T	W	T	F	S
						1
2	3	4	5	6	7	8
9	10	11	12	13	14	15
16	17	18	19	20	21	22
23	24	25	26	27	28	29
30						

MAY
S	M	T	W	T	F	S
	1	2	3	4	5	6
7	8	9	10	11	12	13
14	15	16	17	18	19	20
21	22	23	24	25	26	27
28	29	30	31			

JUNE
S	M	T	W	T	F	S
				1	2	3
4	5	6	7	8	9	10
11	12	13	14	15	16	17
18	19	20	21	22	23	24
25	26	27	28	29	30	

JULY
S	M	T	W	T	F	S
						1
2	3	4	5	6	7	8
9	10	11	12	13	14	15
16	17	18	19	20	21	22
23	24	25	26	27	28	29
30	31					

AUGUST
S	M	T	W	T	F	S
		1	2	3	4	5
6	7	8	9	10	11	12
13	14	15	16	17	18	19
20	21	22	23	24	25	26
27	28	29	30	31		

SEPTEMBER
S	M	T	W	T	F	S
					1	2
3	4	5	6	7	8	9
10	11	12	13	14	15	16
17	18	19	20	21	22	23
24	25	26	27	28	29	30

OCTOBER
S	M	T	W	T	F	S
1	2	3	4	5	6	7
8	9	10	11	12	13	14
15	16	17	18	19	20	21
22	23	24	25	26	27	28
29	30	31				

NOVEMBER
S	M	T	W	T	F	S
			1	2	3	4
5	6	7	8	9	10	11
12	13	14	15	16	17	18
19	20	21	22	23	24	25
26	27	28	29	30		

DECEMBER
S	M	T	W	T	F	S
					1	2
3	4	5	6	7	8	9
10	11	12	13	14	15	16
17	18	19	20	21	22	23
24	25	26	27	28	29	30
31						

PROJECT 4 | **Computation Trick #1—Super Speedy Addition**

Why Does It Work?

All you need to do to solve this addition problem is to look at the notice-me number. Here is why:

Remember that you created two pairs of numbers—each with a sum of 999. These two pairs of numbers add up to 1,998 (999 + 999 = 1,998). This is 2 short of 2,000. The remaining number is the notice-me number. If you subtract 2 from the notice-me number and add the result to 2,000, you will always get the answer!

The total will always be:

(notice-me number − 2)
_____ + 2,000

Example:

```
        493
        764
        175      (175 − 2) + 2,000
        506
      + 235
      2,173
```

If you want to do more:

Here are some variations you might want to try. You might use 7 or 9 numbers instead of 5. The trick is done in exactly the same way. However, think about how your formula would change if you did this.

You might also try this with 6-digit numbers. Once again, the procedure is the same, but the formula would change.

Record your findings below.

_____

_____

_____

_____

_____

_____

_____

_____

_____

**PROJECT
4**

Computation Trick #2—Subtraction Surprise

Why Does It Work?

The trick depends on the way in which you had your classmate create the subtraction problem. There are only 9 possible solutions to a subtraction problem created in that way:

99   198   297   396   495   594   693   792   891

You might have noticed that the digit in the tens place is always 9 and that the digits in the hundreds place and the ones place always add up to 9.

For example, if your classmate tells you that the digit in the hundreds place is 4, then you know that the digit in the ones place must be 5, since $4 + 5 = 9$. You know that the digit in the tens place is always 9. Therefore the answer is 495.

What is the answer if your classmate tells
you that the digit in the ones place is 9? _____

If you want to do more:

Will this trick work with a 4-digit number? With a 5-digit number?
Describe your findings.

_____

_____

_____

_____

_____

_____

PROJECT 4

Computation Trick #3—Crazy Calendar Addition

Why Does It Work?

If three numbers are evenly spaced, you can find the middle number by dividing the sum of the numbers by 3.

Example:

Sun.	Mon.	Tue.	Wed.	Thu.	Fri.	Sat.
		1	2	3	4	5
6	7	8	9	10	11	12
13	14	15	16	17	18	19
20	21	22	23	24	25	26
27	28	29	30	31		

The numbers in a row and the numbers in a column of a calendar are evenly spaced.

◆ The numbers in a row are consecutive whole numbers. They are 1 apart.

◆ The numbers in a column are 7 apart. This is because there are 7 days in a week.

After you find the middle number by dividing the sum of the numbers by 3, it is easy to find the other two numbers.

◆ If the three numbers are in a row, subtract 1 from the middle number to get the first number. Add 1 to the middle number to get the third number.

◆ If the three numbers are in a column, subtract 7 from the middle number to get the first number. Add 7 to the middle number to get the third number.

If you want to do more:

What would happen if the three dates chosen were on a diagonal? Would the trick still work? Why or why not?

_____

_____

_____

_____

_____

_____

393

PROJECT 5

How Would You Spend $1,000,000?—Emily's Idea

Emily decided that if she had $1,000,000 she would spend it on a fabulous 10-day trip to Florida for her, 19 of her friends, and 4 chaperones—24 people altogether. With $1,000,000, she knew that she could make this a trip no one would ever forget.

Emily began by thinking about everything she and her friends might need for their trip. She visited a local department store to find out how much different items cost. She decided to purchase a **vacation wardrobe** for everyone, including the chaperones, at a cost of $50,750. Her next stop was a **sporting goods** store for items such as snorkel gear, swimsuits, and sunglasses. The store clerk calculated that all of her purchases there would cost $24,100.

Emily knew that she would need **transportation** to Florida and for traveling around while there. She made a few telephone calls to find out the prices for transportation. Emily found that when she politely explained her project to people, most of them were willing to help her. After doing some research, she chartered an airplane for a flight from Chicago to Orlando and back ($54,780). She purchased two stretch limos to use in Florida ($165,160 + $10,000 for gas and two around-the-clock chauffeurs). She also purchased a minivan to carry the chaperones and the luggage ($20,700) while in Florida.

Lodging was another consideration. Emily decided that her group would stay at one of the resorts inside a theme park ($33,550). She went to a travel agency to get some information about the **activities** that she and her friends might try while they were there. For $177,200, Emily made reservations for several special breakfasts as well as dinner shows, rented a water park for 12 hours, and purchased 10-day passes to the theme park where she and her group were staying.

PROJECT 5 — How Would You Spend $1,000,000? *cont.*

Emily decided to keep a record of the money she was spending by listing her purchases in major categories. At the right is part of the chart that she made.

Major Category	Cost
Vacation Wardrobe	$ 50,750
Sports Equipment	$ 24,100
Transportation	$ 250,640
Lodging	$ 33,550
Activities	$ 177,200

Emily also decided that for each category she would keep a detailed record so that she would know exactly how she was spending the $1,000,000.

Below is an example of her record for one category.

Major Category—Vacation Wardrobe			
Item	Quantity	Unit Price	Total Price
Boxer shorts	100	$ 12.50	$ 1,250.00
Socks	200	$ 5.50	$ 1,100.00
Shorts	240	$ 38.00	$ 9,120.00
T-shirts	200	$ 32.00	$ 6,400.00
Swimsuits	100	$ 36.00	$ 3,600.00
Jeans	100	$ 34.00	$ 3,400.00
Shoes	60	$ 50.00	$ 3,000.00
Flip-flops	60	$ 24.00	$ 1,440.00
Sunglasses	20	$ 29.50	$ 590.00
Long-sleeve shirts	40	$ 57.00	$ 2,280.00
Tax			$ 2,570.00
Chaperones' Wardrobe Allotment		$4,000.00 per person	$ 16,000.00
		Total	$50,750.00

These are examples of just a few of the expenses for Emily's amazing trip.

About how much money has Emily spent so far? _____

About how much money does Emily have left to spend? _____

PROJECT 5

How Would You Spend $1,000,000? *cont.*

Project Guidelines

Imagine that you have just inherited $1,000,000. One of the conditions for receiving the money is that you must investigate, research, and present exactly how you will spend it. You must follow the guidelines below.

Theme   The $1,000,000 must be spent carrying out one particular plan.

For example: A plan that would help save the rain forest; a plan to build new parks and playgrounds in your city; a plan for a trip around the world; or a plan to open a ballet studio.

Goal   Spend as close to $1,000,000 as possible, but not more than $1,000,000.

Research   Include all of the expenses involved in carrying out the details of your plan.

For example: If you are opening a ballet studio, you must consider how many teachers you will need and how much you will pay them. If you are buying a car, you will need to consider the cost of gas, maintenance, and insurance for the length of time you will own the car.

Accounting   In an organized way, record exactly how you will spend the $1,000,000. The purchases needed to carry out your plan should be organized in several major categories. Each major category must total at least $10,000.

For example: Think about how Emily organized the purchases for her Florida vacation, as described on *Math Masters,* pages 394 and 395.

Display   Present the research and accounting for your plan in a report, on a display board, on a poster, or in a portfolio. You might even make a video production.

For example: Emily presented her project as a report. In addition to her calculations, she included pictures and sample receipts whenever possible.

PROJECT 5

How Would You Spend $1,000,000?—Totals

Accounting Sheet	
Totals of Major Categories	
Major Category	**Cost**
Total	**$1,000,000**

How Would You Spend $1,000,000?—Itemized

Accounting Sheet

A Major Category Itemized

Category: _____

Item	Quantity	Unit Price	Total Price
		Total Price	**$** _____

PROJECT 5

How Would You Spend $1,000,000?—Categories

In the table below, list all of your major expense categories and the total amount for each. (Refer to your accounting sheets—*Math Masters,* pages 397 and 398.) Write each amount as a fraction, decimal, and percent of $1,000,000. Round each decimal to the nearest hundredth. Round each percent to the nearest whole percent.

Category	Total $ Spent	Fraction	Decimal	Percent
		⎯⎯⎯⎯ 1,000,000		
		⎯⎯⎯⎯ 1,000,000		
		⎯⎯⎯⎯ 1,000,000		
		⎯⎯⎯⎯ 1,000,000		
		⎯⎯⎯⎯ 1,000,000		
		⎯⎯⎯⎯ 1,000,000		
		⎯⎯⎯⎯ 1,000,000		
		⎯⎯⎯⎯ 1,000,000		
		⎯⎯⎯⎯ 1,000,000		
		⎯⎯⎯⎯ 1,000,000		
		⎯⎯⎯⎯ 1,000,000		
		⎯⎯⎯⎯ 1,000,000		
		⎯⎯⎯⎯ 1,000,000		

PROJECT 5

How Would You Spend $1,000,000?—Graph

Make a circle graph of your categories for spending $1,000,000. Use your Percent Circle and the information on *Math Masters,* page 399.

Begin by drawing the section for the smallest part of the $1,000,000. Continue with the larger parts. Mark the largest part last. Because of rounding, the percents may not add up to exactly 100%.

Give the graph a title and label each section.

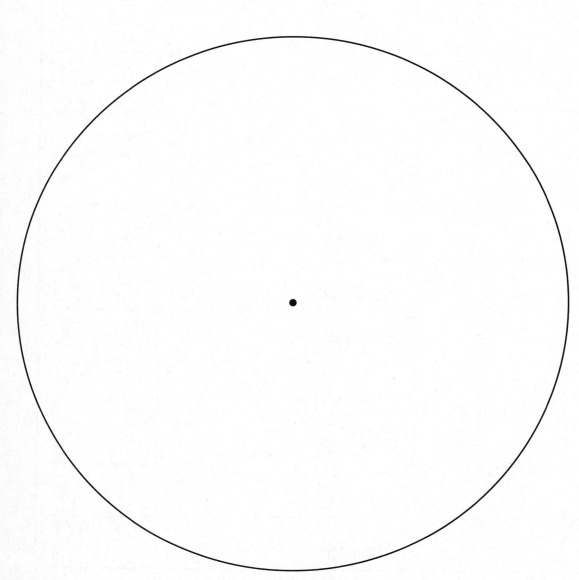

PROJECT 6

Playing Areas for Five Contact Sports

Use your calculator to find each playing area.

Scale:

1 mm (drawing) represents 1 ft (actual)

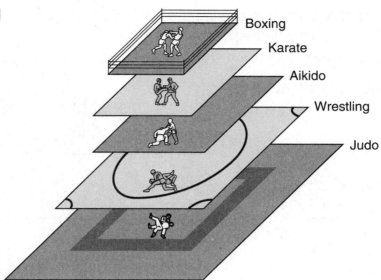

Sport	Dimensions	Playing Area
Boxing	20 ft by 20 ft	ft²
Karate	26 ft by 26 ft	ft²
Aikido	29 ft 6 in. by 29 ft 6 in.*	ft²
Wrestling	39 ft 3 in. by 39 ft 3 in.*	ft²
Judo	52 ft 6 in. by 52 ft 6 in.*	ft²

*Calculate with decimals. For example, 29 ft 6 in. is equal to 29.5 ft.

Source: *COMPARISONS* by the Diagram Group. Reprinted by permission of St. Martin's Press.

PROJECT 6

Playing Areas for Other Sports

Use your calculator to find each playing area.
Circle *more* or *less* to tell whether each
area is more or less than 1 acre.

1 acre = 43,560 square feet

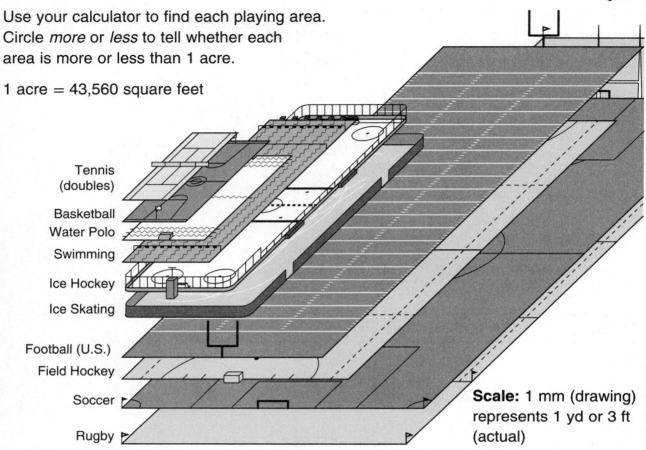

Tennis (doubles)

Basketball
Water Polo
Swimming

Ice Hockey

Ice Skating

Football (U.S.)

Field Hockey

Soccer ▷

Rugby ▷

Scale: 1 mm (drawing)
represents 1 yd or 3 ft
(actual)

Sport	Dimensions	Playing Area	More or Less than 1 Acre?	
Tennis (doubles)	78 ft by 36 ft	ft^2	more	less
Basketball	94 ft by 50 ft	ft^2	more	less
Water Polo	98 ft by 65 ft	ft^2	more	less
Swimming	165 ft by 69 ft	ft^2	more	less
Ice Hockey	200 ft by 85 ft	ft^2	more	less
Ice Skating	200 ft by 100 ft	ft^2	more	less
Football (U.S.)	300 ft by 160 ft*	ft^2	more	less
Field Hockey	300 ft by 180 ft	ft^2	more	less
Soccer	360 ft by 240 ft	ft^2	more	less
Rugby	472 ft by 226 ft	ft^2	more	less

*Not including end zones

Source: *COMPARISONS* by the Diagram Group. Reprinted by permission of St. Martin's Press.

PROJECT 6 — Ground Areas of Famous Large Buildings

The ground areas of buildings, their footprints, are almost always given in square feet or square meters. Some buildings have very large ground areas. When their areas are given in square feet, the numbers are so large that it is hard to imagine how big the buildings really are.

For large buildings, if you convert the area in square feet to an estimate in acres, you can get a better idea of the size of the building.

Estimate the ground area, in acres, of each building in the table below:

Reference

1 acre = 43,560 square feet

For estimating, think of 1 acre as about 50,000 square feet.

A football field (excluding the end zones) is approximately 1 acre.

Example: The Colosseum, in Italy, covers an area of about 250,000 ft².

One acre is about 50,000 ft².

So 5 acres is about 250,000 ft².

The Colosseum covers an area of about 5 acres (5 football fields).

Building	Country	Date Built	Ground Area (ft²)	Estimated Area (in acres)	
Colosseum	Italy	70–224	250,000 ft²	5	acres
Pyramid of Cheops	Egypt	c. 2600 B.C.	571,500 ft²		acres
Chartres Cathedral	France	1194–1514	60,000 ft²		acres
St. Peter's Basilica	Vatican City	1506–1626	392,300 ft²		acres
Taj Mahal	India	1636–1653	78,000 ft²		acres
Pentagon	U.S. (Virginia)	1941–1943	1,263,000 ft²		acres
Ford Parts Center	U.S. (Michigan)	1936	2,800,000 ft²		acres

PROJECT 7

Finding Areas with Standard Methods

Use any method you want to find the area of each polygon below. Record the area in the table to the right. You can use different methods with different figures. If you use any area formulas, remember that height is always measured perpendicular to the base you choose. Measure base and height very carefully.

Figure	Area
A	about _____ cm²
B	about _____ cm²
C	about _____ cm²
D	about _____ cm²
E	about _____ cm²
F	about _____ cm²

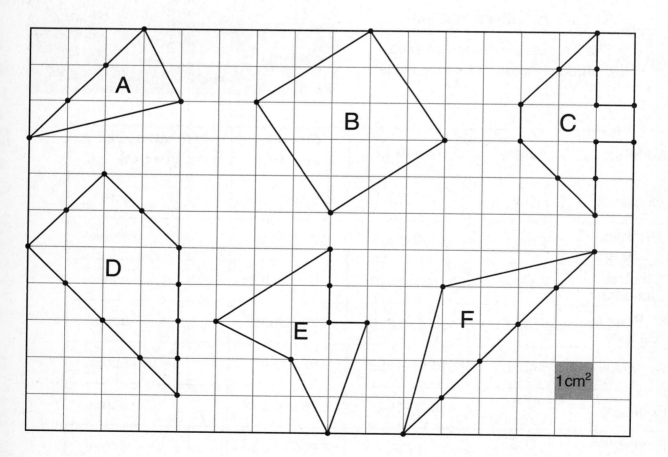

1 cm²

PROJECT 7 | Finding Areas with Pick's Formula

Read the paragraphs below, and then use Pick's Formula to find the areas of the polygons on the previous page. Record your results in the table below. Compare them to the results you recorded in the table on the previous page. You should expect some differences—measures are always estimates.

Pick's Formula for Finding Polygon Areas by Counting

In 1899, Georg Pick, an Austrian mathematician, discovered a formula for finding the area of a polygon on a square grid (such as graph paper). If a polygon has its vertices at grid points, its area can be found by counting the number of grid points on the polygon (P) and the number of grid points in the interior of the polygon (I) and then by using the formula $A = (\frac{1}{2} * P) + I - 1$. The unit of area is one square on the grid.

For figure B on the previous page, the unit of area is cm^2.

$P = 4$ (grid points on polygon)

$I = 12$ (grid points in interior)

$A = (\frac{1}{2} * P) + I - 1$

$= (\frac{1}{2} * 4) + 12 - 1$

$= 13 \ cm^2$

Figure	P	I	Area $= (\frac{1}{2} * P) + I +- 1$
A			cm^2
B			cm^2
C			cm^2
D			cm^2
E			cm^2
F			cm^2

Draw two polygons. Be sure that the vertices are at grid points.
Use Pick's Formula to find the areas of the polygons.

1 cm²

Area: _____   Area: _____

405

PROJECT 7

Finding Areas with Pick's Formula *cont.*

You might have found the area of this shaded path in Lesson 9-6.

Now use Pick's Formula to find the area.

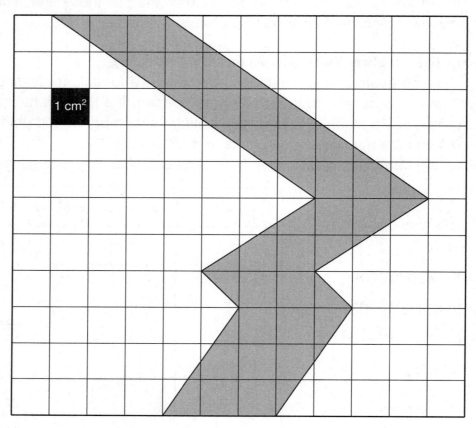

1 cm²

1. The area of the path is _____ cm².

2. Do you think Pick's Formula is a good way to find this area? _____

Explain. _____

_____

_____

_____

_____

PROJECT 8

The Swing Time of Pendulums

1. Your teacher will demonstrate an experiment with a pendulum that is 50 cm long. Record the results below.

   a. It took about _____ seconds for 10 complete swings of the pendulum.

   b. About how much time did it take for one swing? Round your answer to the nearest 0.1 second.

   _____ second(s)

2. Form a pendulum that is 75 cm long. Time 10 complete swings of the pendulum. Time the swings to the nearest second.

   Practice timing 10 complete swings several times. Then time 10 swings and record the results below.

   a. It took about _____ seconds for 10 complete swings of the pendulum.

   b. About how much time did it take for one swing? Round your answer to the nearest 0.1 second. _____ second(s)

3. Record the results for a 50-cm and a 75-cm pendulum in the table at the right.

4. Experiment with different lengths of pendulum string.

   Find the time for 10 complete swings for each of the other pendulum lengths. Time the 10 swings to the nearest 0.1 second. Record your results in the table.

   After collecting your data, divide each of the times by 10 to estimate the time for one complete swing. Record your answers in the table, rounded to the nearest 0.1 second.

Length of Pendulum	Time for: Ten Complete Swings (to nearest 0.1 sec)	Time for: One Complete Swing (to nearest 0.1 sec)
5 cm	_____ sec	_____ sec
10 cm	_____ sec	_____ sec
20 cm	_____ sec	_____ sec
30 cm	_____ sec	_____ sec
50 cm	_____ sec	_____ sec
75 cm	_____ sec	_____ sec
100 cm	_____ sec	_____ sec
200 cm	_____ sec	_____ sec

407

The Swing Time of Pendulums *cont.*

Wait for instructions from your teacher before drawing the graph in Problem 5.

5. Construct a graph to show the amount of time it took for each length of the pendulum to complete one swing.

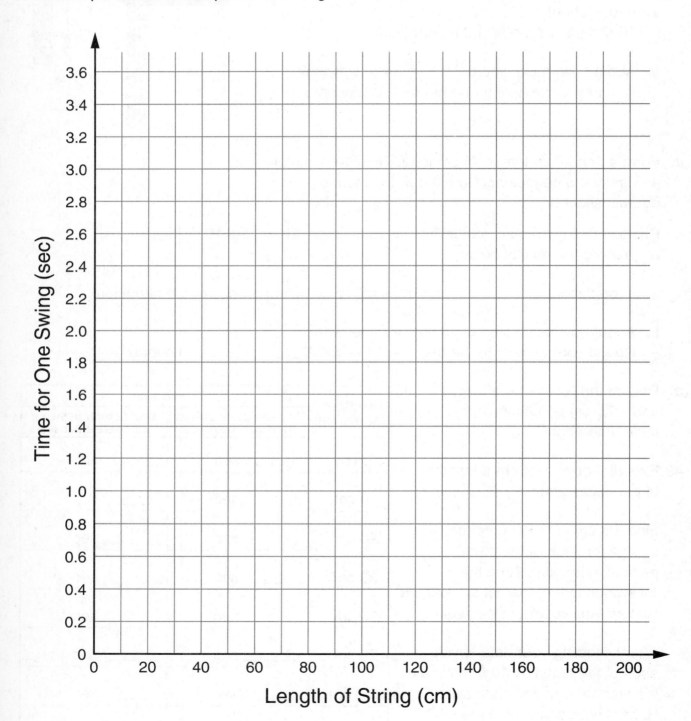

PROJECT 8 **The Swing Time of Pendulums** *cont.*

6. Experiment with different arc sizes. The largest arc is formed when the string of the pendulum is in a horizontal position. Does the size of the arc make much difference in the amount of time it takes for 10 complete swings?

_____

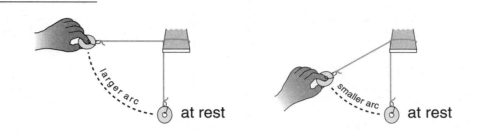

larger arc   at rest   smaller arc   at rest

7. Does the weight of the object at the end of a pendulum affect the time for a complete swing? Using a pendulum with a string 50 cm long, try different numbers of objects to find out if weight makes a difference in the time of the swing.

Length of Pendulum	Number of Weights (washers or other objects)	Time for 10 Swings (to nearest 0.1 sec)	Time for One Swing (to nearest 0.1 or 0.01 sec)
50 cm	1	sec	sec
50 cm	3	sec	sec
50 cm	5	sec	sec
50 cm	10	sec	sec

My conclusion: It seems that _____

_____

_____

_____

_____

_____

PROJECT 9 | **Building a Solid Figure to Find Volume**

For Problems 1–3, do the following:

a. Use centimeter cubes to build each rectangular prism.

b. Find the volume of each rectangular prism.

c. Find the volume of the solid figure formed by the two rectangular prisms.

1.

	Length *l*	Width *w*	Height *h*	Volume *V* (cubic units)
Rectangular Prism A	1	2	3	
Rectangular Prism B	2	3	4	
Solid Figure Formed by Prisms A and B				

2.

	Length *l*	Width *w*	Height *h*	Volume *V* (cubic units)
Rectangular Prism C	5	3	2	
Rectangular Prism D	2	3	5	
Solid Figure Formed by Prisms C and D				

3.

	Length *l*	Width *w*	Height *h*	Volume *V* (cubic units)
Rectangular Prism E	12	3	1	
Rectangular Prism F	3	3	3	
Solid Figure Formed by Prisms E and F				

4. Explain how to find the volume of a solid figure made from two rectangular prisms, one with dimensions 3 cm by 4 cm by 5 cm and one with dimensions 2 cm by 5 cm by 4 cm.

_____

_____

_____

PROJECT 9

Finding the Volume of Willis Tower

At 1,450 feet tall, Willis Tower in Chicago is the tallest building in the United States. It is composed of nine rectangular prisms known as "tubes." The tubes are built in a 3-by-3 arrangement. Although the tubes are of various heights, each one has a square base that measures 75 feet on a side.

1. What is the area of the base of each tube?

_____ ft²

The table below shows the approximate heights of the tubes. Only two of them reach all the way to the top.

2. What formula could you use to find the volume

of one tube? _____

Willis Tower

3. Complete the table to find the volume of one tube at each given height. Then find the total volume of the tubes for each height.

Approximate Height of Tube	Number of Tubes at this Height	Volume of One Tube at this Height (ft³)	Total Volume of Tubes at this Height (ft³)
646 ft	3		
672 ft	2		
1,200 ft	2		
1,450 ft	2		

4. Describe what you will do to find the total approximate volume of Willis Tower.

_____

_____

5. The total volume of Willis Tower is about _____ ft³.

Teaching Aid Masters

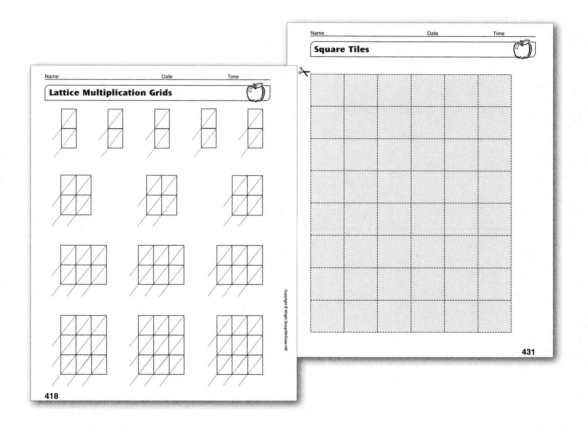

Name   Date   Time

Square Tiles

431

Name   Date   Time

Lattice Multiplication Grids

418

Math Boxes (4 cells)

1.

2.

3.

4.

Array Dot Paper

Exit Slip

Exit Slip

Computation Grid

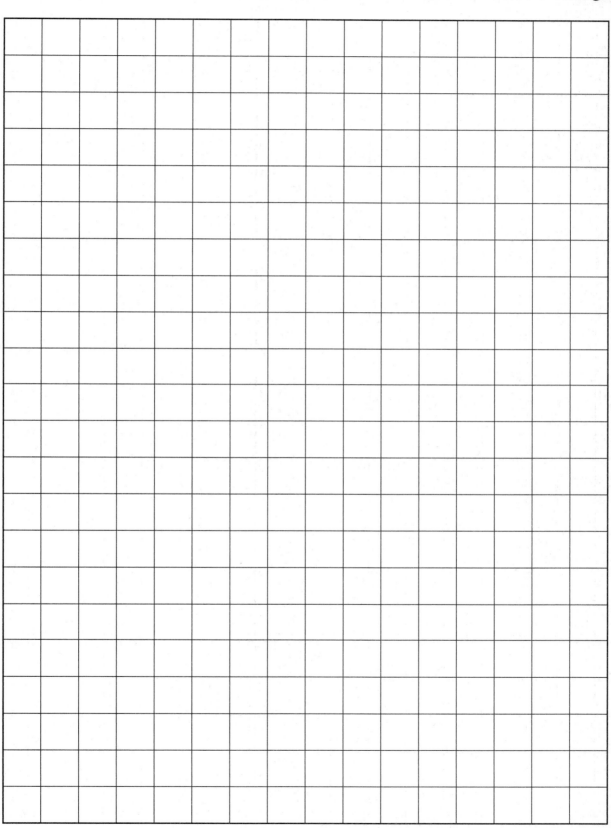

Array Grid

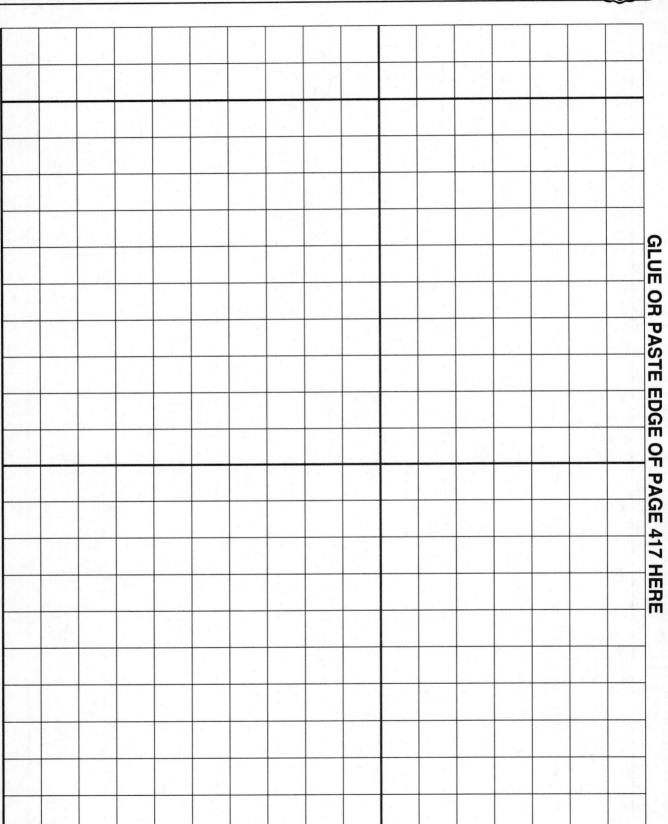

GLUE OR PASTE EDGE OF PAGE 417 HERE

Start here.

Array Grid *continued*

Lattice Multiplication Grids

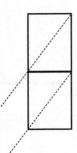 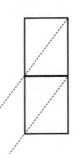 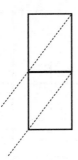  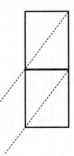

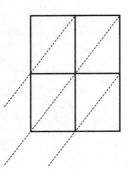 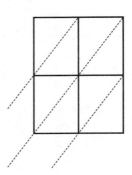 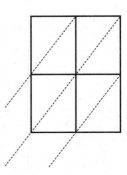

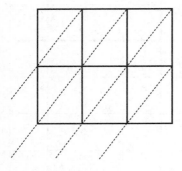 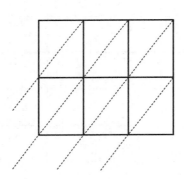 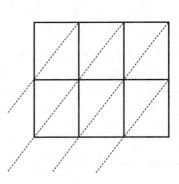

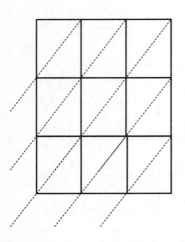 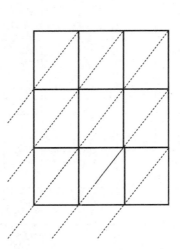 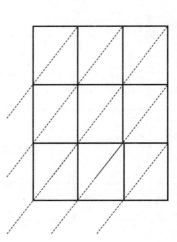

Geometry Template

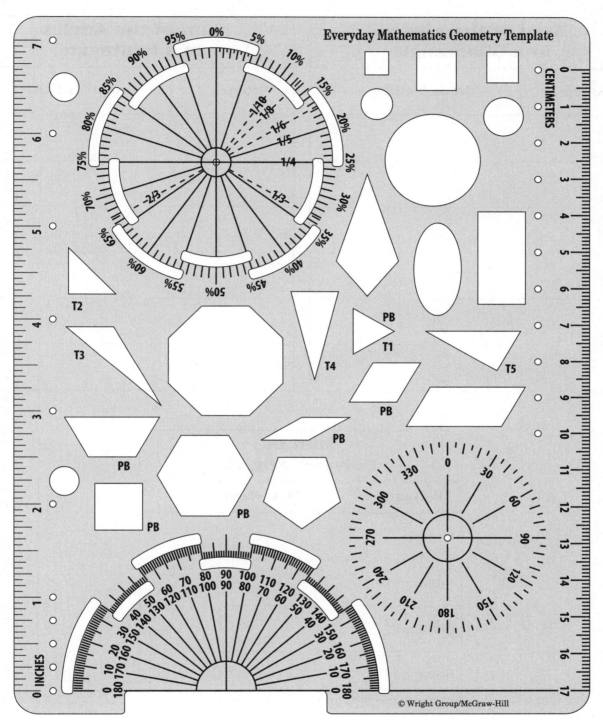

Everyday Mathematics Geometry Template

© Wright Group/McGraw-Hill

Angles in Quadrangles and Pentagons

Sum of the Angles in a Quadrangle	
Group	**Group Median**

Sum of the Angles in a Pentagon	
Group	**Group Median**

Sum of Polygon Angles	
Polygon	**Class Median**
triangle	
quadrangle	
pentagon	
hexagon	

Equivalent Names for Numbers

Ruler Close-Up

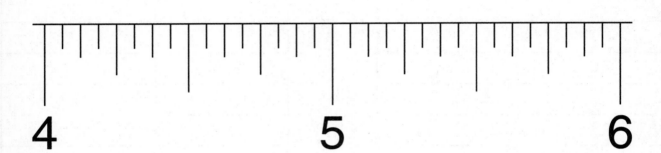

4   5   6

Name Date Time

A Number Story

SRB 226 243

Title:

Mathematical Number Model:

Solution:

Base-10 Grids

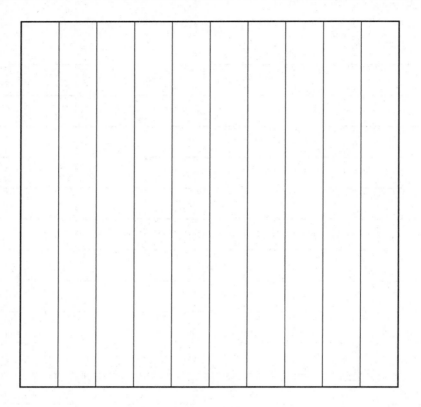

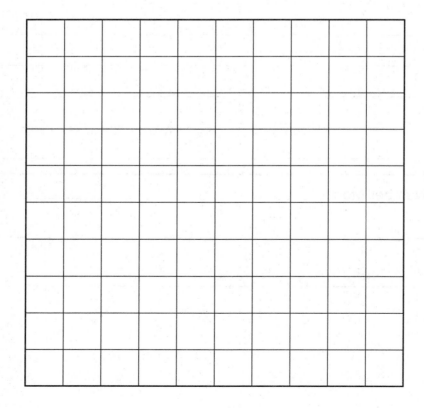

Name _____ Date _____ Time _____

Number Stories

Data Bank													
8	40	2.5	90%	12	$4\frac{3}{2}$	75%	$\frac{5}{3}$	98	8.25	25	$9\frac{1}{2}$	10%	$\frac{9}{8}$

Use at least 4 numbers from the data bank to write a number story. Be sure to include units.

_____

_____

_____

_____

_____

_____

 -

Name _____ Date _____ Time _____

Number Stories

Data Bank													
8	40	2.5	90%	12	$4\frac{3}{2}$	75%	$\frac{5}{3}$	98	8.25	25	$9\frac{1}{2}$	10%	$\frac{9}{8}$

Use at least 4 numbers from the data bank to write a number story. Be sure to include units.

_____

_____

_____

_____

_____

Percent Circle

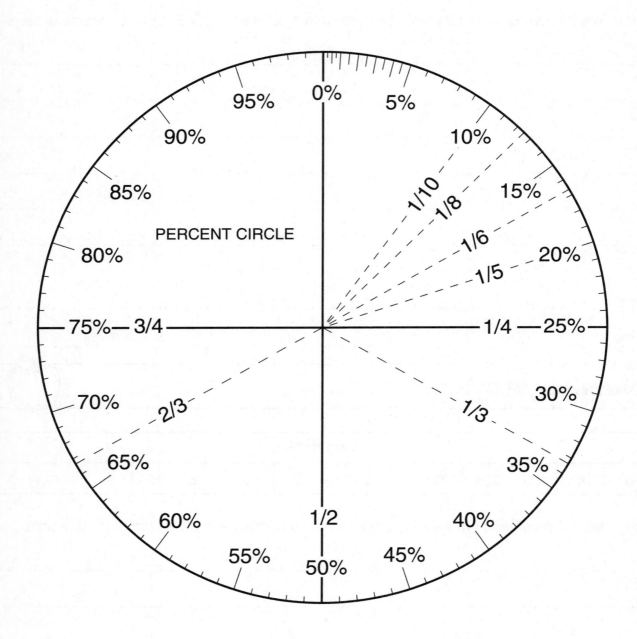

PERCENT CIRCLE

Percent Circles

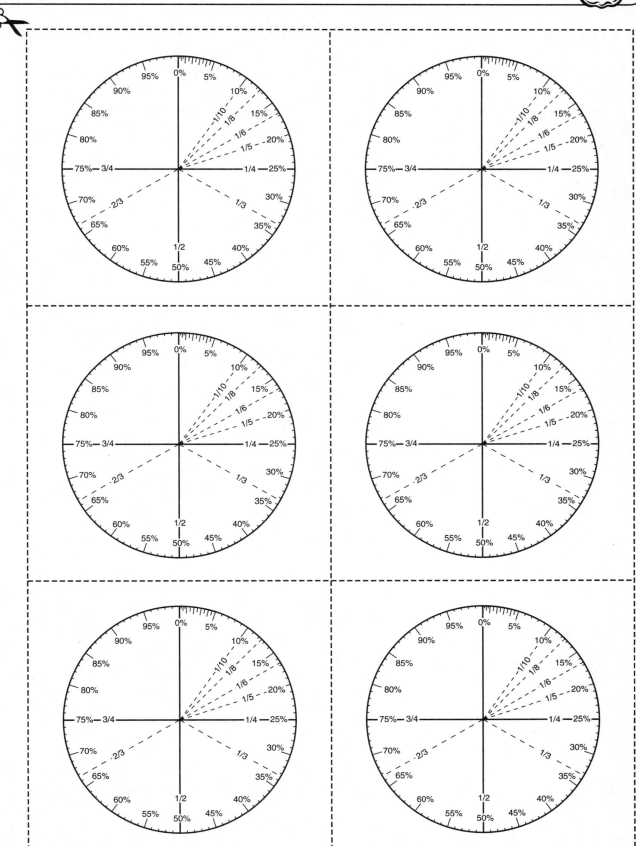

Measuring Circle-Graph Sections

Use your Percent Circle to find the percent of each piece (sector) within the whole circle.

1.

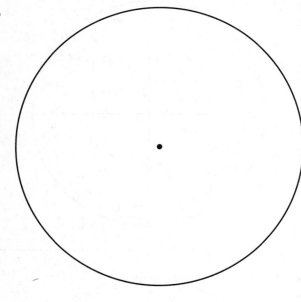

☐ _____ %   ☐ _____ %

☐ _____ %   ☐ _____ %

2.

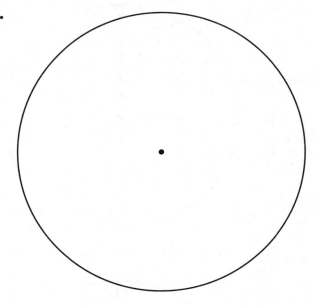

☐ _____ %   ☐ _____ %

☐ _____ %   ☐ _____ %

3.

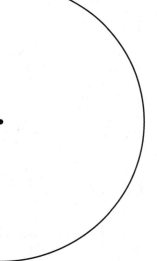

☐ _____ %   ☐ _____ %

☐ _____ %   ☐ _____ %

4.

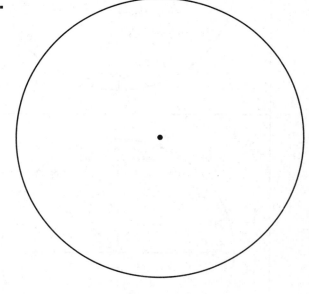

☐ _____ %   ☐ _____ %

☐ _____ %   ☐ _____ %

Grid Paper (1 in.)

Circles

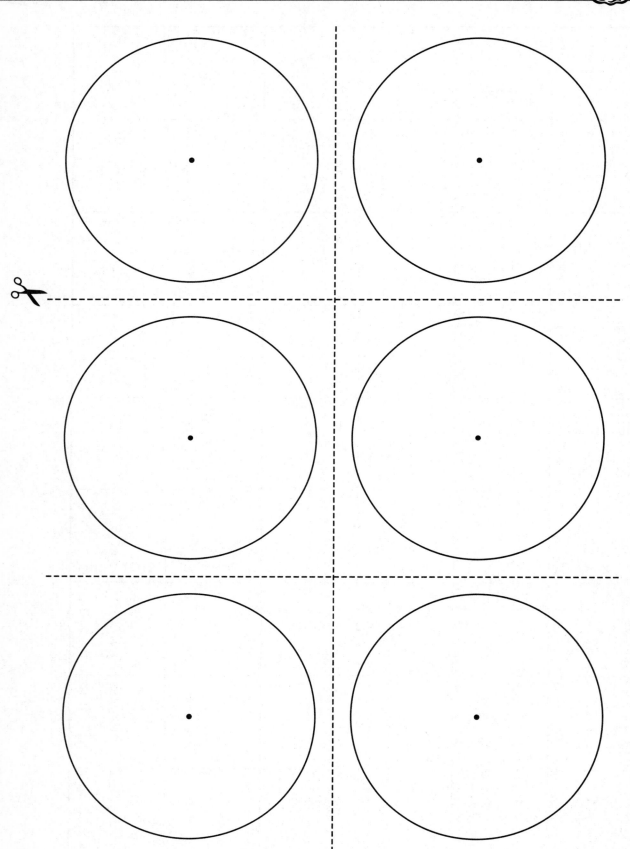

Square Tiles

Cash and Debt Cards

+	+	−	−
$1 Cash	**$1 Cash**	**$1 Debt**	**$1 Debt**
+	+	−	−
$1 Cash	**$1 Cash**	**$1 Debt**	**$1 Debt**
+	+	−	−
$1 Cash	**$1 Cash**	**$1 Debt**	**$1 Debt**
+	+	−	−
$1 Cash	**$1 Cash**	**$1 Debt**	**$1 Debt**
+	+	−	−
$1 Cash	**$1 Cash**	**$1 Debt**	**$1 Debt**

Exponential Notation Place-Value Chart

billions	hundred millions	ten millions	millions	hundred thousands	ten thousands	thousands	hundreds	tens	ones	.	tenths	hundredths
10^9	10^8	10^7	10^6	10^5	10^4	10^3	10^2	10^1	10^0	.	10^{-1}	10^{-2}
										.		
										.		
										.		
										.		
										.		

billions	hundred millions	ten millions	millions	hundred thousands	ten thousands	thousands	hundreds	tens	ones	.	tenths	hundredths
10^9	10^8	10^7	10^6	10^5	10^4	10^3	10^2	10^1	10^0	.	10^{-1}	10^{-2}
										.		
										.		
										.		
										.		
										.		

Number-Line Models

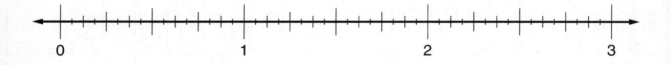

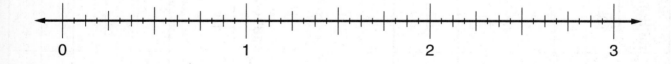

100 Grid

Grid Paper (1 cm)

Coordinate Grid

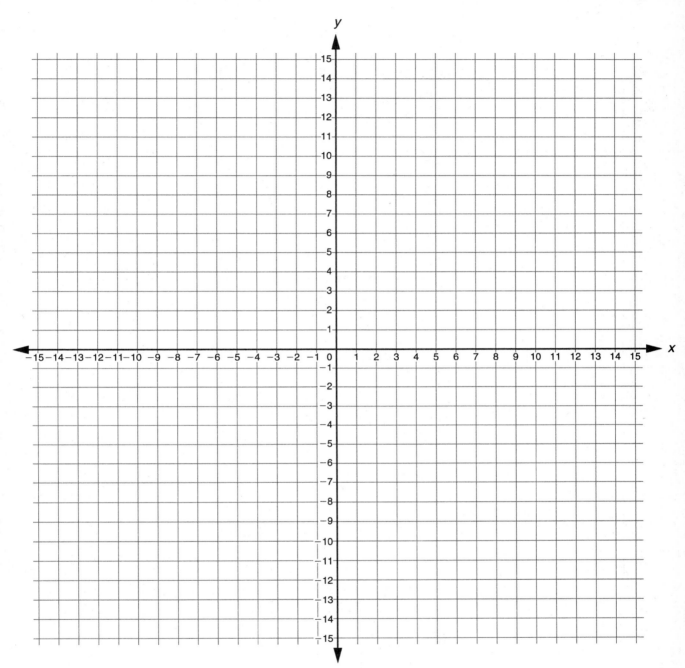

First-Quadrant Grid

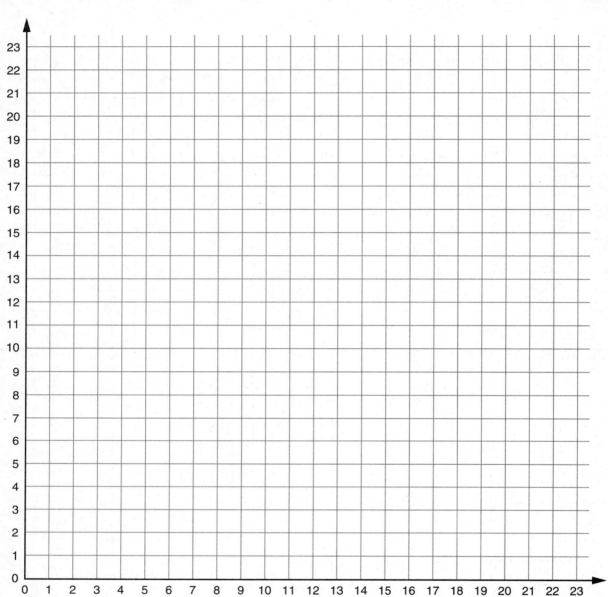

Distance/Time Graph

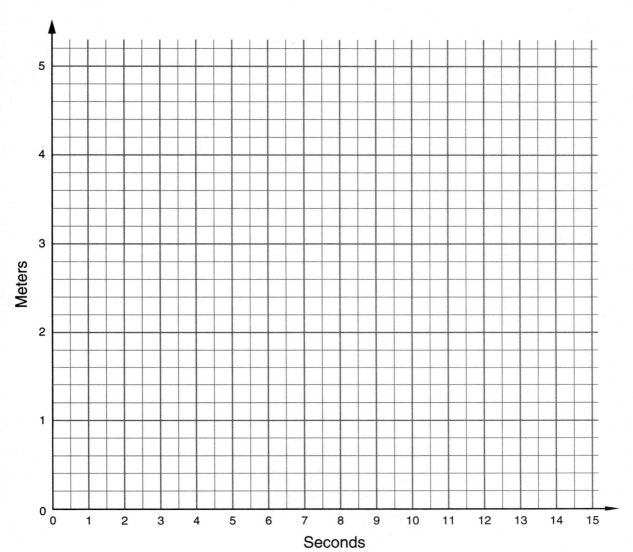

Cone Pattern

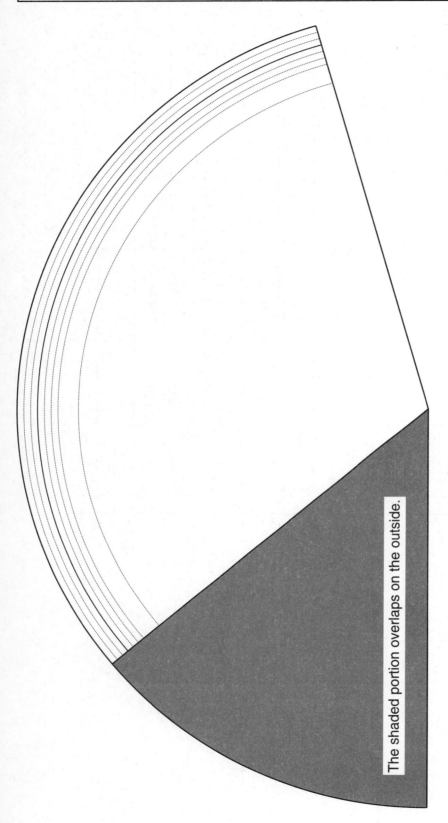

The shaded portion overlaps on the outside.

1. Cut out the pattern.

2. Curl the cone into position by lining up the two heavy black lines and the sets of gray lines.

3. Tape the cone by sealing the seams on the inside and outside.

Venn Diagram

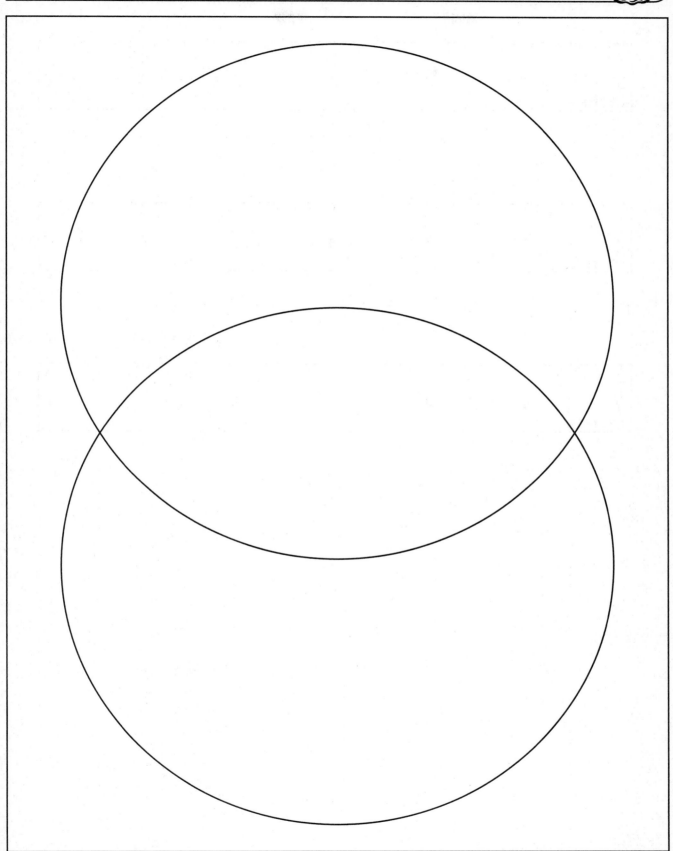

Rulers

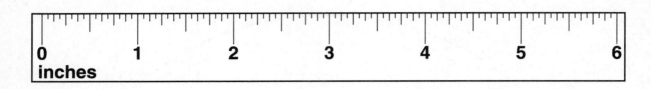

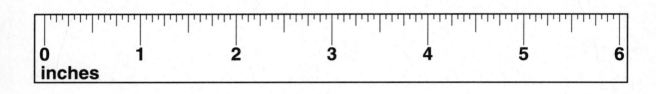

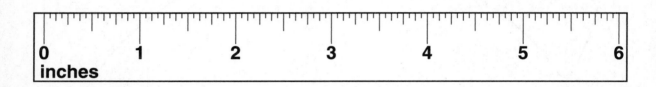

440B

Game Masters

Name _____ Date _____ Time _____

Factor Captor 1–110 Grid

1	2	3	4	5	6	7	8	9	10
11	12	13	14	15	16	17	18	19	20
21	22	23	24	25	26	27	28	29	30
31	32	33	34	35	36	37	38	39	40
41	42	43	44	45	46	47	48	49	50
51	52	53	54	55	56	57	58	59	60
61	62	63	64	65	66	67	68	69	70
71	72	73	74	75	76	77	78	79	80
81	82	83	84	85	86	87	88	89	90
91	92	93	94	95	96	97	98	99	100
101	102	103	104	105	106	107	108	109	110

Name _____ Date _____ Time _____

What's My Attribute Rule?

Directions

1. Label one sheet of paper **These fit the rule.**

2. Label another sheet of paper **These do NOT fit the rule.**

3. Take turns. Roll the six-sided die once. The player with the lowest number is the first "Rule Maker."

4. The Rule Maker shuffles and places the Attribute Rule Cards facedown.

5. The Rule Maker turns over the top Attribute Rule Card, but does not show it to the other players or tell them what the rule is. For example: *large shapes, but not triangles.*

6. The Rule Maker chooses 3 or 4 attribute blocks that fit the rule on the card. The Rule Maker puts them on the sheet labeled *These fit the rule.*

> These fit the rule.
>
> **These fit the rule.**

7. The Rule Maker chooses 3 or 4 blocks that do NOT fit the rule. The Rule Maker puts them on the sheet labeled *These do NOT fit the rule.*

> These do NOT fit the rule.
>
> **These do NOT fit the rule.**

8. The other players take turns choosing a block that they think might fit the rule and placing it on that sheet.

9. If the Rule Maker says "No," the player puts the block on the correct sheet. If "Yes," the player gets to suggest what the rule might be. The Rule Maker then tells the player whether his or her rule is correct.

10. The round continues until someone figures out the rule. That person becomes the Rule Maker for the next round.

Algebra Election Gameboard

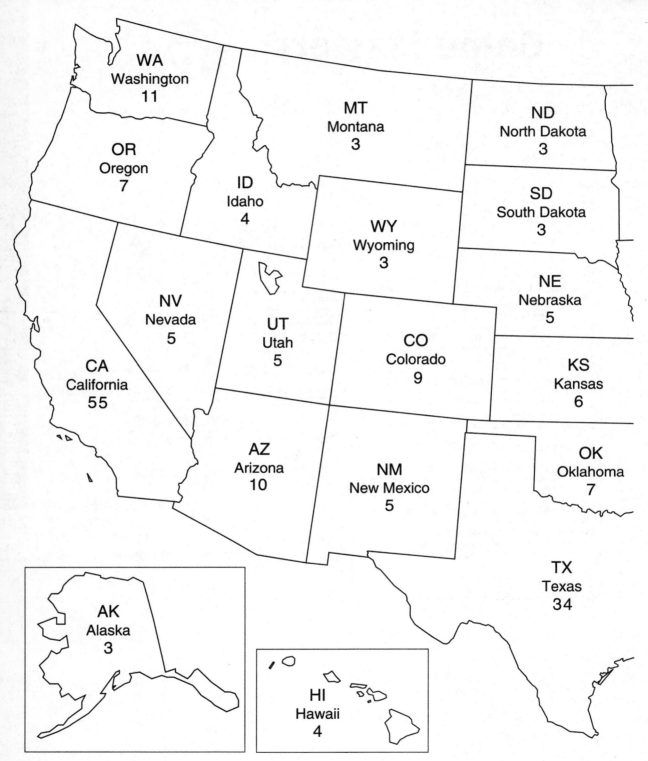

NOTE: Alaska and Hawaii are not drawn to scale.

Algebra Election Gameboard *continued*

Minnesota
MN
10

WI
Wisconsin
10

MI
Michigan
17

IA
Iowa
7

IL
Illinois
21

IN
Indiana
11

OH
Ohio
20

MO
Missouri
11

KY
Kentucky
8

TN   11
Tennessee

AR
Arkansas
6

MS
Mississippi
6

AL
Alabama
9

GA
Georgia
15

LA
Louisiana
9

Vermont *

ME
Maine
4

VT
3

NH
4

New Hampshire *

NY
New York
31

MA

Massachusetts *
12

CT

RI
Rhode Island *
4

PA
Pennsylvania
21

Connecticut *
7

NJ

New Jersey *
15

WV
West
Virginia
5

VA
Virginia
13

MD

DE

Delaware *
3

Maryland *
10

NC
North Carolina
15

DC
District of Columbia *
3

SC
South
Carolina
8

FL
Florida
27

*If your marker does not fit on the state, put your marker on the state's name.

Angle Tangle **Record Sheet**

Round	Angle	Estimated measure	Actual measure	Score
1		_____ °	_____ °	
2		_____ °	_____ °	
3		_____ °	_____ °	
4		_____ °	_____ °	
5		_____ °	_____ °	
			Total Score	

Baseball Multiplication Game Mat

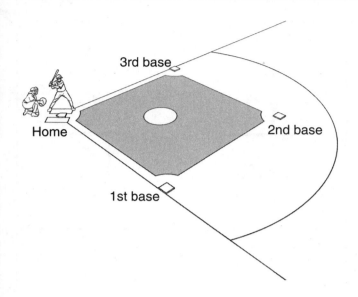

3rd base

Home

1st base

2nd base

Hitting Table 1-to-6 Facts	
1 to 9	Out
10 to 19	Single (1 base)
20 to 29	Double (2 bases)
30 to 35	Triple (3 bases)
36	Home Run (4 bases)

Inning		1	2	3	Total
Team 1	Outs				
	Runs				
Team 2	Outs				
	Runs				

Inning		1	2	3	Total
Team 1	Outs				
	Runs				
Team 2	Outs				
	Runs				

Inning		1	2	3	Total
Team 1	Outs				
	Runs				
Team 2	Outs				
	Runs				

445

Build-It **Card Deck**

$\dfrac{5}{9}$	$\dfrac{1}{3}$	$\dfrac{11}{12}$	$\dfrac{1}{12}$
$\dfrac{7}{12}$	$\dfrac{3}{8}$	$\dfrac{1}{4}$	$\dfrac{1}{5}$
$\dfrac{2}{3}$	$\dfrac{3}{7}$	$\dfrac{4}{7}$	$\dfrac{3}{4}$
$\dfrac{3}{5}$	$\dfrac{4}{5}$	$\dfrac{7}{9}$	$\dfrac{5}{6}$

Build-It Gameboard

Closest
to 1

Closest
to 0

Closest
to 1

Closest
to 0

Coordinate Search Grid

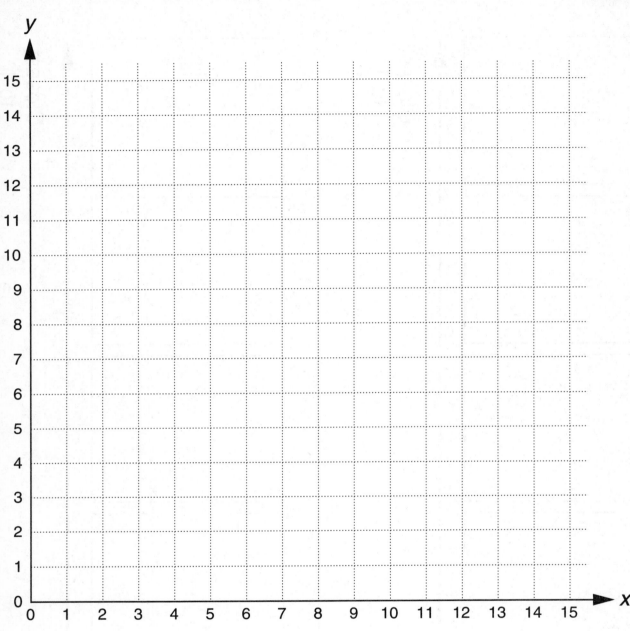

Coordinate Search

You are sailing a yacht in the Caribbean Sea. Unfortunately, you are caught in a tropical storm, and your navigation charts are damaged. You know that there are several physical landmarks to watch for. All the landmarks are located northeast of your current position in one quadrant of the damaged charts.

You will need to locate the following physical landmarks:

2 large islands   2 small islands   1 atoll   4 buoys

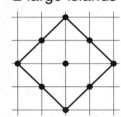

Use the tables from the navigation charts you salvaged. Graph the points of the missing physical landmarks onto the coordinate grid on *Math Masters,* page 448.

Here are some clues to help you:

The center of a large island is at (13,13). The center of another large island is at (2,6). The center of a small island is at (5,13). The center of the second small island is at (10,8).

Physical Landmarks		Physical Landmarks	
X-axis value	Number of points	*Y*-axis value	Number of points
0	1	0	0
1	2	1	0
2	3	2	3
3	3	3	2
4	3	4	3
5	3	5	3
6	1	6	3
7	0	7	3
8	0	8	4
9	2	9	1
10	5	10	1
11	4	11	1
12	4	12	3
13	4	13	6
14	2	14	4
15	1	15	1

449

Credits/Debits Game (Advanced Version) Record Sheets

Game 1

	Start	Change		End and Next Start
		Addition or Subtraction	Credit or Debit	
1				
2				
3				
4				
5				
6				
7				
8				
9				
10				

Game 2

	Start	Change		End and Next Start
		Addition or Subtraction	Credit or Debit	
1				
2				
3				
4				
5				
6				
7				
8				
9				
10				

Exponent Ball Gameboard

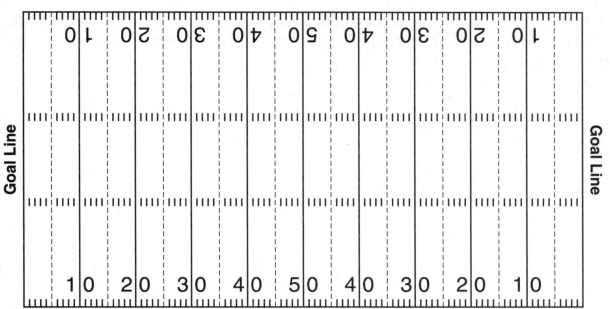

Table 1: Runs

Value of Roll	Move Ball	Chances of Gaining on the Ground
1	−15 yd	−15 yards: 1 out of 6, or about 17%
2 to 6	+10 yd	10 yards or more: 5 out of 6, or about 83%
8 to 81	+20 yd	20 yards or more: 4 out of 6, or about 67%
in the 100s	+30 yd	30 yards or more: 13 out of 36, or about 36%
in the 1,000s	+40 yd	40 yards or more: 7 out of 36, or about 19%
in the 10,000s	+50 yd	50 yards: 1 out of 18, or about 6%

Table 2: Kicks

Value of Roll	Move Ball	Chances of Kicking
1	+10 yd	10 yards or more: 6 out of 6, or 100%
2	+20 yd	20 yards or more: 5 out of 6, or about 83%
3	+30 yd	30 yards or more: 4 out of 6, or about 67%
4	+40 yd	40 yards or more: 3 out of 6, or about 50%
5	+50 yd	50 yards or more: 2 out of 6, or about 33%
6	+60 yd	60 yards: 1 out of 6, or about 17%

Factor Bingo Game Mat

Fill in the squares on the game mat grid with any 25 numbers from 2–90. Write one number in each square on the grid. Every square must contain a different number. Be careful to mix the numbers so they are not in order on the grid.

	2	3	4	5	6	7	8	9	10
11	12	13	14	15	16	17	18	19	20
21	22	23	24	25	26	27	28	29	30
31	32	33	34	35	36	37	38	39	40
41	42	43	44	45	46	47	48	49	50
51	52	53	54	55	56	57	58	59	60
61	62	63	64	65	66	67	68	69	70
71	72	73	74	75	76	77	78	79	80
81	82	83	84	85	86	87	88	89	90

Factor Captor **Grid 1**

1	2	2	2	2	2
2	3	3	3	3	3
3	4	4	4	4	5
5	5	5	6	6	7
7	8	8	9	9	10
10	11	12	13	14	15
16	18	20	21	22	24
25	26	27	28	30	32

Factor Captor Grid 2

1	2	2	2	2	2	3
3	3	3	3	4	4	4
4	5	5	5	5	6	6
6	7	7	8	8	9	9
10	10	11	12	13	14	15
16	17	18	19	20	21	22
23	24	25	26	27	28	30
32	33	34	35	36	38	39
40	42	44	45	46	48	49
50	51	52	54	55	56	60

Factor Captor 1–110 Grid

1	2	3	4	5	6	7	8	9	10
11	12	13	14	15	16	17	18	19	20
21	22	23	24	25	26	27	28	29	30
31	32	33	34	35	36	37	38	39	40
41	42	43	44	45	46	47	48	49	50
51	52	53	54	55	56	57	58	59	60
61	62	63	64	65	66	67	68	69	70
71	72	73	74	75	76	77	78	79	80
81	82	83	84	85	86	87	88	89	90
91	92	93	94	95	96	97	98	99	100
101	102	103	104	105	106	107	108	109	110

First to 100 **Problem Cards**

How many inches are there in *x* feet? How many centimeters are there in *x* meters? 1	How many quarts are there in *x* gallons? 2	What is the smallest number of *x*'s you can add to get a sum greater than 100? 3	Is $50 * x$ greater than 1,000? Is $\frac{x}{10}$ less than 1? 4
$\frac{1}{2}$ of $x = ?$ $\frac{1}{10}$ of $x = ?$ 5	$1 - x = ?$ $x + 998 = ?$ 6	If *x* people share 1,000 stamps equally, how many stamps will each person get? 7	What time will it be *x* minutes from now? What time was it *x* minutes ago? 8
It is 102 miles to your destination. You have gone *x* miles. How many miles are left? 9	What whole or mixed number equals *x* divided by 2? 10	Is *x* a prime or a composite number? Is *x* divisible by 2? 11	The time is 11:05 A.M. The train left *x* minutes ago. What time did the train leave? 12
Bill was born in 1939. Freddy was born the same day, but *x* years later. In what year was Freddy born? 13	Which is larger: $2 * x$ or $x + 50$? 14	There are *x* rows of seats. There are 9 seats in each row. How many seats are there in all? 15	Sargon spent *x* cents on apples. If she paid with a $5 bill, how much change should she get? 16

First to 100 Problem Cards *continued*

The temperature was 25°F. It dropped x degrees. What was the new temperature? 17	Each story in a building is 10 ft high. If the building has x stories, how tall is it? 18	Which is larger: $2 * x$ or $\frac{100}{x}$? 19	$20 * x = ?$ 20
Name all the whole-number factors of x. 21	Is x an even or an odd number? Is x divisible by 9? 22	Shalanda was born on a Tuesday. Linda was born x days later. On what day of the week was Linda born? 23	Will had a quarter plus x cents. How much money did he have in all? 24
Find the perimeter and area of this square. x cm — x cm 25	What is the median of these weights? 5 pounds 21 pounds x pounds What is the range? 26	$x°$ $?°$ 27	$x^2 = ?$ 50% of $x^2 = ?$ 28
$(3x + 4) - 8 = ?$ 29	x out of 100 students voted for Ruby. Is this more than 25%, less than 25%, or exactly 25% of the students? 30	There are 200 students at Wilson School. x% speak Spanish. How many students speak Spanish? 31	People answered a survey question either Yes or No. x% answered Yes. What percent answered No? 32

First to 100 Record Sheet

Example: A student rolls a 5 and a 6. The product is 30. So $x = 30$.

The student draws card number 29.

x	Card Number	Number Model/ Response	Score
30	29	$(3 * 30 + 4) - 8 = 86$	30

x	Card Number	Number Model/ Response	Score

Fraction Action, Fraction Friction Cards

$\dfrac{1}{2}$	$\dfrac{1}{3}$	$\dfrac{2}{3}$	$\dfrac{1}{4}$
$\dfrac{3}{4}$	$\dfrac{1}{6}$	$\dfrac{1}{6}$	$\dfrac{5}{6}$
$\dfrac{1}{12}$	$\dfrac{1}{12}$	$\dfrac{5}{12}$	$\dfrac{5}{12}$
$\dfrac{7}{12}$	$\dfrac{7}{12}$	$\dfrac{11}{12}$	$\dfrac{11}{12}$

Fraction Capture Gameboard

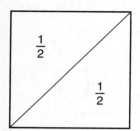 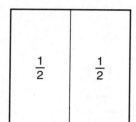 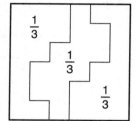 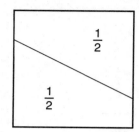

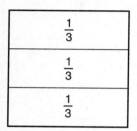 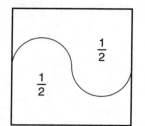 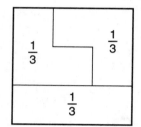

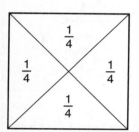 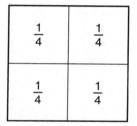 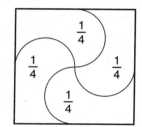 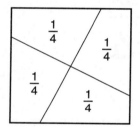

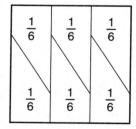

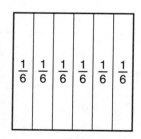 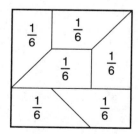

Fraction Capture Record Sheet

Player 1

Round	Dice Roll	Fraction	Fraction Addition Expression
1			
2			
3			
4			
5			

✂ -

Name   Date   Time

Fraction Capture Record Sheet

Player 2

Round	Dice Roll	Fraction	Fraction Addition Expression
1			
2			
3			
4			
5			

Fraction Top-It **Cards 1**

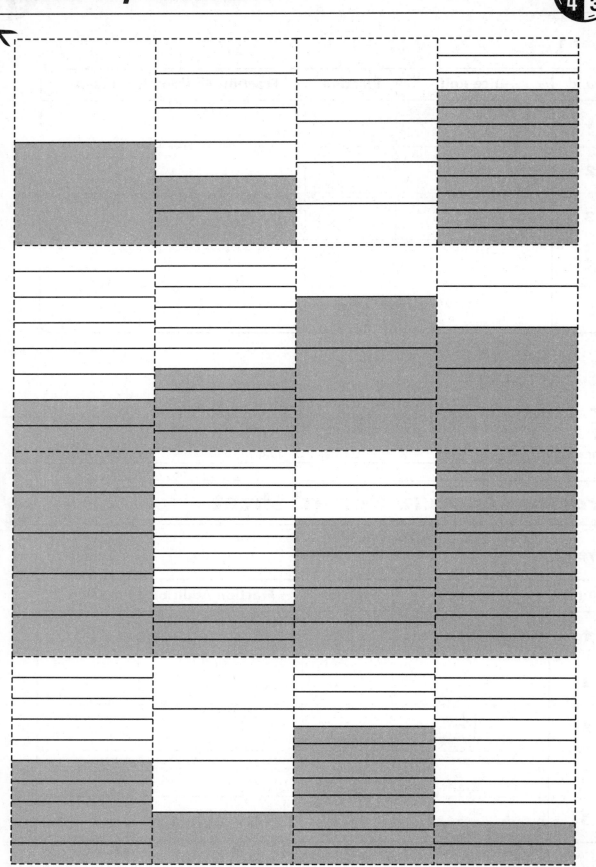

Fraction Top-It Cards 2

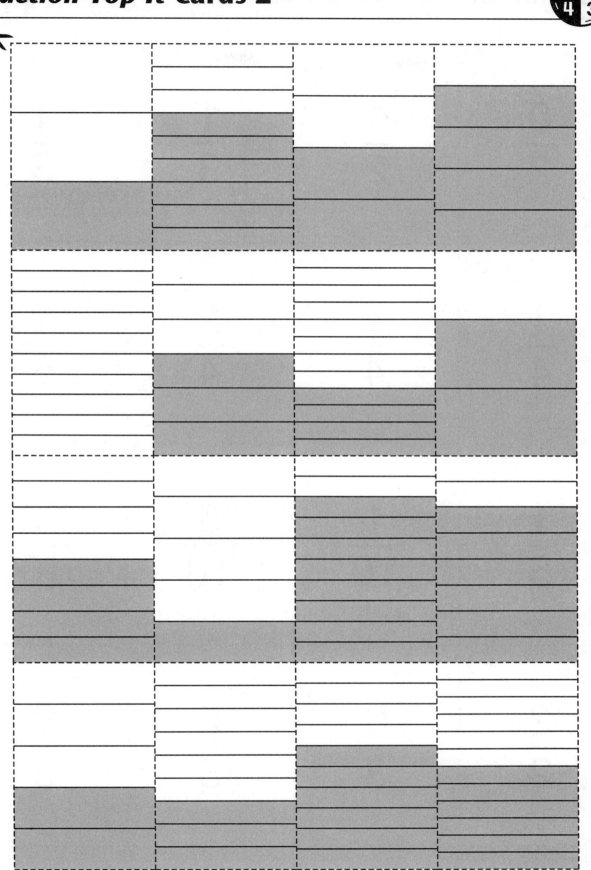

463

Fraction Of **Fraction Cards 1**

$\dfrac{0}{2}$ $\dfrac{1}{2}$ $\dfrac{1}{3}$ $\dfrac{1}{3}$

$\dfrac{1}{4}$ $\dfrac{1}{4}$ $\dfrac{2}{4}$ $\dfrac{1}{5}$

$\dfrac{1}{5}$ $\dfrac{1}{10}$ $\dfrac{5}{10}$ $\dfrac{10}{10}$

$\dfrac{2}{2}$ $\dfrac{0}{3}$ $\dfrac{2}{3}$ $\dfrac{3}{3}$

Fraction Of Fraction Cards 2

$\dfrac{0}{4}$	$\dfrac{3}{4}$	$\dfrac{4}{4}$	$\dfrac{0}{5}$
$\dfrac{2}{5}$	$\dfrac{3}{5}$	$\dfrac{4}{5}$	$\dfrac{5}{5}$
$\dfrac{1}{10}$	$\dfrac{2}{10}$	$\dfrac{3}{10}$	$\dfrac{4}{10}$
$\dfrac{6}{10}$	$\dfrac{7}{10}$	$\dfrac{8}{10}$	$\dfrac{9}{10}$

Fraction Of Gameboard and Record Sheet

```
┌─────────────────────┐                    ┌─────────────────────┐
│                     │                    │       WHOLE         │
│                     │                    │ (Choose 1 of these  │
│                     │                    │      sets.)         │
│                     │                    │                     │
│                     │                    │                     │
│    Fraction         │        of          │       Set           │
│     card            │                    │      card           │
│                     │                    │                     │
│                     │                    │                     │
│                     │                    │                     │
│                     │                    │                     │
└─────────────────────┘                    └─────────────────────┘
```

Round	"Fraction-of" Problem	Points
Sample	$\frac{1}{5}$ of 25	5
1		
2		
3		
4		
5		
6		
7		
8		
	Total Score	

Fraction/Percent Concentration Tiles (Front)

10%	20%	25%	30%
40%	50%	60%	70%
75%	80%	90%	100%
$\frac{1}{2}$	$\frac{1}{4}$	$\frac{3}{4}$	$\frac{1}{5}$
$\frac{2}{5}$	$\frac{3}{5}$	$\frac{4}{5}$	$\frac{1}{10}$
$\frac{3}{10}$	$\frac{7}{10}$	$\frac{9}{10}$	$\frac{2}{2}$

Fraction/Percent Concentration Tiles (Back)

%	%	%	%
%	%	%	%
%	%	%	%
$\dfrac{a}{b}$	$\dfrac{a}{b}$	$\dfrac{a}{b}$	$\dfrac{a}{b}$
$\dfrac{a}{b}$	$\dfrac{a}{b}$	$\dfrac{a}{b}$	$\dfrac{a}{b}$
$\dfrac{a}{b}$	$\dfrac{a}{b}$	$\dfrac{a}{b}$	$\dfrac{a}{b}$

Fraction Of Set Cards

3 counters 20 counters 15 counters	4 counters 21 counters 30 counters	5 counters 12 counters 20 counters	6 counters 28 counters 40 counters
8 counters 27 counters 20 counters	10 counters 32 counters 24 counters	12 counters 30 counters 25 counters	15 counters 36 counters 20 counters
18 counters 36 counters 10 counters	20 counters 4 counters 3 counters	21 counters 30 counters 24 counters	25 counters 6 counters 40 counters
28 counters 35 counters 30 counters	30 counters 32 counters 15 counters	36 counters 20 counters 24 counters	40 counters 18 counters 25 counters

Fraction Spin Record Sheet

Name	Name

_____ + _____ < 1   _____ + _____ < 1

_____ + _____ > 1   _____ + _____ > 1

_____ − _____ < $\frac{1}{2}$ _____ − _____ < $\frac{1}{2}$

_____ − _____ > $\frac{1}{2}$ _____ − _____ > $\frac{1}{2}$

_____ + _____ < 1   _____ + _____ < 1

_____ + _____ < $\frac{1}{4}$ _____ + _____ < $\frac{1}{4}$

_____ + _____ > $\frac{1}{4}$ _____ + _____ > $\frac{1}{4}$

_____ + _____ = 1   _____ + _____ = 1

_____ − _____ < $\frac{1}{4}$ _____ − _____ < $\frac{1}{4}$

_____ − _____ > $\frac{1}{4}$ _____ − _____ > $\frac{1}{4}$

_____ + _____ < $\frac{3}{4}$ _____ + _____ < $\frac{3}{4}$

_____ + _____ > $\frac{3}{4}$ _____ + _____ > $\frac{3}{4}$

Fraction Spin

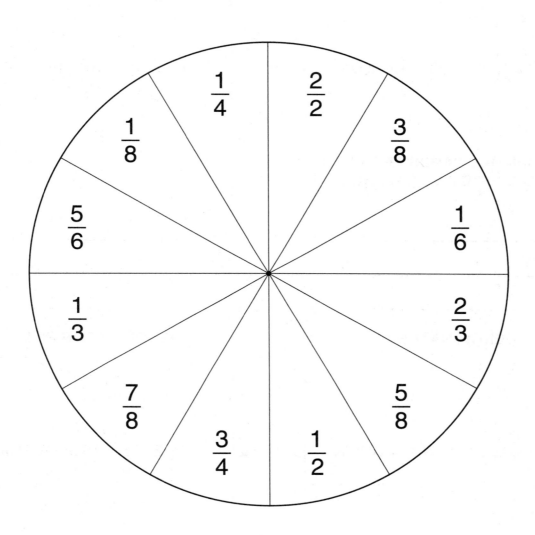

Frac-Tac-Toe **Number-Card Board**

NUMERATOR PILE

PLACE CARDS FACEDOWN.

**WHEN ALL CARDS ARE USED,
SHUFFLE AND REPLACE.**

NUMERATOR PILE

PLAY EACH CARD FACEUP.

DENOMINATOR PILE

PLACE CARDS FACEDOWN.

**WHEN ALL CARDS ARE USED,
JUST REPLACE.
DO NOT SHUFFLE!**

DENOMINATOR PILE

PLAY EACH CARD FACEUP.

2-4-5-10 Frac-Tac-Toe (Decimal Bingo Version)

If you use a standard deck of playing cards:

◆ Use Queens as zeros (0).

◆ Use Aces as ones (1).

◆ Discard Jacks, Kings, and Jokers.

If you use an Everything Math Deck, discard cards greater than 10.

Fill in the gameboard by entering these numbers in the empty spaces:

0	0	0.1	0.2	0.25	0.3	0.4	0.5
0.5	0.6	0.7	0.75	0.8	0.9	1	1

Numerator Pile

All remaining cards

Denominator Pile

Two each of 2, 4, 5, and 10 cards

> 1.0		> 2.0		> 1.0
> 1.5		> 1.5		> 1.5
> 1.0		> 2.0		> 1.0

473

2-4-5-10 Frac-Tac-Toe (Decimal Version)

If you use a standard deck of playing cards,

◆ use queens as zeros (0);

◆ use aces as ones (1);

◆ discard jacks, kings, and jokers.

If you use an Everything Math Deck, discard cards greater than 10.

Use different color counters or coins as markers. If you use coins, one player is "heads" and the other player is "tails."

If you use a pencil to initial the squares, print lightly so you can erase and use the board again.

Numerator Pile

All remaining cards

Denominator Pile

Two each of 2, 4, 5, and 10 cards

>1.0	0 or 1	>2.0	0 or 1	>1.0
0.1	0.2	0.25	0.3	0.4
>1.5	0.5	>1.5	0.5	>1.5
0.6	0.7	0.75	0.8	0.9
>1.0	0 or 1	>2.0	0 or 1	>1.0

2-4-5-10 Frac-Tac-Toe (Percent Bingo Version)

If you use a standard deck of playing cards:

◆ Use Queens as zeros (0).

◆ Use Aces as ones (1).

◆ Discard Jacks, Kings, and Jokers.

If you use an Everything Math Deck, discard cards greater than 10.

Fill in the gameboard by entering these numbers in the empty spaces:

0%	0%	10%	20%	25%	30%	40%	50%
50%	60%	70%	75%	80%	90%	100%	100%

Numerator Pile

All remaining cards

Denominator Pile

Two each of 2, 4, 5, and 10 cards

>100%		>200%		>100%
>100%		>200%		>100%
>100%		>300%		>100%

2-4-5-10 Frac-Tac-Toe (Percent Version)

If you use a standard deck of playing cards,

- ◆ use queens as zeros (0);

- ◆ use aces as ones (1);

- ◆ discard jacks, kings, and jokers.

If you use an Everything Math Deck, discard cards greater than 10.

Use different color counters or coins as markers. If you use coins, one player is "heads" and the other player is "tails."

If you use a pencil to initial the squares, print lightly so you can erase and use the board again.

Numerator Pile
All remaining cards

Denominator Pile
Two each of 2, 4, 5, and 10 cards

>100%	0% or 100%	>200%	0% or 100%	>100%
10%	20%	25%	30%	40%
>100%	50%	>200%	50%	>100%
60%	70%	75%	80%	90%
>100%	0% or 100%	>200%	0% or 100%	>100%

2-4-8 Frac-Tac-Toe (Decimal Bingo Version)

If you use a standard deck of playing cards:

◆ Use Queens as zeros (0).

◆ Use Aces as ones (1).

◆ Discard Jacks, Kings, and Jokers.

Numerator Pile
All remaining cards

If you use an Everything Math Deck, discard cards greater than 10.

Fill in the gameboard by entering these numbers in the empty spaces:

| 0 | 0 | 0.125 | 0.25 | 0.375 | 0.5 | 0.5 | 0.625 |
| 0.75 | 0.875 | 1 | 1 | 1.5 | 1.5 | 2 | 2 |

Denominator Pile
Two each of 2, 4, and 8 cards

> 2.0		> 1.5		> 2.0
> 1.0		0.25 or 0.75		> 1.0
> 2.0		1.125		> 2.0

477

2-4-8 Frac-Tac-Toe (Decimal Version)

If you use a standard deck of playing cards,

- ◆ use queens as zeros (0);

- ◆ use aces as ones (1);

- ◆ discard jacks, kings, and jokers.

If you use an Everything Math Deck, discard cards greater than 10.

Use different color counters or coins as markers. If you use coins, one player is "heads" and the other player is "tails."

If you use a pencil to initial the squares, print lightly so you can erase and use the board again.

Numerator Pile

All remaining cards

Denominator Pile

Two each of 2, 4, and 8 cards

>2.0	0 or 1	>1.5	0 or 1	>2.0
1.5	0.125	0.25	0.375	1.5
>1.0	0.5	0.25 or 0.75	0.5	>1.0
2.0	0.625	0.75	0.875	2.0
>2.0	0 or 1	1.125	0 or 1	>2.0

2-4-8 Frac-Tac-Toe (Percent Bingo Version)

If you use a standard deck of playing cards:

◆ Use Queens as zeros (0).

◆ Use Aces as ones (1).

◆ Discard Jacks, Kings, and Jokers.

Numerator Pile
All remaining cards

If you use an Everything Math Deck, discard cards greater than 10.

Fill in the gameboard by entering these numbers in the empty spaces:

0%	0%	$12\frac{1}{2}$%	25%	$37\frac{1}{2}$%	50%	50%	$62\frac{1}{2}$%
75%	$87\frac{1}{2}$%	100%	100%	150%	150%	200%	200%

Denominator Pile
Two each of 2, 4, and 8 cards

>200%		>150%		>200%
>100%		25% or 75%		>100%
>200%		$112\frac{1}{2}$%		>200%

2-4-8 Frac-Tac-Toe (Percent Version)

If you use a standard deck of playing cards:

◆ Use Queens as zeros (0).

◆ Use Aces as ones (1).

◆ Discard Jacks, Kings, and Jokers.

If you use an Everything Math Deck, discard cards greater than 10.

Use different color counters or coins as markers. If you use coins, one player is HEADS and the other player is TAILS.

If you use a pencil to initial the squares, print lightly so you can erase and use the board again.

Numerator Pile
All remaining cards

Denominator Pile
Two each of 2, 4, and 8 cards

>200%	0% or 100%	>150%	0% or 100%	>200%
150%	$12\frac{1}{2}$%	25%	$37\frac{1}{2}$%	150%
>100%	50%	25% or 75%	50%	>100%
200%	$62\frac{1}{2}$%	75%	$87\frac{1}{2}$%	200%
>200%	0% or 100%	$112\frac{1}{2}$%	0% or 100%	>200%

3-6-9 *Frac-Tac-Toe* (Decimal Bingo Version)

If you use a standard deck of playing cards:

◆ Use Queens as zeros (0).

◆ Use Aces as ones (1).

◆ Discard Jacks, Kings, and Jokers.

If you use an Everything Math Deck, discard cards greater than 10.

Fill in the gameboard by entering these numbers in the empty spaces:

0	0	$0.1\overline{6}$	$0.\overline{3}$	$0.\overline{3}$	$0.\overline{6}$
$0.\overline{6}$	$0.8\overline{3}$	1	1	$1.\overline{3}$	$1.\overline{6}$

Numerator Pile

All remaining cards

Denominator Pile

Two each of 3, 6, and 9 cards

> 1.0		$0.\overline{1}$		> 1.0
	$0.\overline{2}$			$0.\overline{4}$
> 2.0	$0.\overline{5}$	> 1.0		> 2.0
	$0.\overline{7}$		$0.\overline{8}$	
> 1.0				> 1.0

3-6-9 Frac-Tac-Toe (Decimal Version)

If you use a standard deck of playing cards,

- ◆ use queens as zeros (0);

- ◆ use aces as ones (1);

- ◆ discard jacks, kings, and jokers.

If you use an Everything Math Deck, discard cards greater than 10.

Use different color counters or coins as markers. If you use coins, one player is "heads" and the other player is "tails."

If you use a pencil to initial the squares, print lightly so you can erase and use the board again.

Numerator Pile
All remaining cards

Denominator Pile
Two each of 3, 6, and 9 cards

>1.0	0 or 1	$0.\overline{1}$	0 or 1	>1.0
$0.1\overline{6}$	$0.\overline{2}$	$0.\overline{3}$	$0.\overline{3}$	$0.\overline{4}$
>2.0	$0.\overline{5}$	>1.0	$0.\overline{6}$	>2.0
$0.\overline{6}$	$0.\overline{7}$	$0.8\overline{3}$	$0.\overline{8}$	$1.\overline{3}$
>1.0	0 or 1	$1.\overline{6}$	0 or 1	>1.0

3-6-9 Frac-Tac-Toe (Percent Bingo Version)

If you use a standard deck of playing cards:

◆ Use Queens as zeros (0).

◆ Use Aces as ones (1).

◆ Discard Jacks, Kings, and Jokers.

If you use an Everything Math Deck, discard cards greater than 10.

Fill in the gameboard by entering these numbers in the empty spaces:

0%	0%	100%	$16\frac{2}{3}\%$	$33\frac{1}{3}\%$	$33\frac{1}{3}\%$
$66\frac{2}{3}\%$	$83\frac{1}{3}\%$	100%	$133\frac{1}{3}\%$	$166\frac{2}{3}\%$	$166\frac{2}{3}\%$

Numerator Pile

All remaining cards

Denominator Pile

Two each of 3, 6, and 9 cards

>100%		11.1%		>100%
	22.2%			44.4%
>200%	55.5%	>100%		>200%
	77.7%		88.8%	
>100%				>100%

3-6-9 Frac-Tac-Toe (Percent Version)

If you use a standard deck of playing cards:

◆ Use Queens as zeros (0).

◆ Use Aces as ones (1).

◆ Discard Jacks, Kings, and Jokers.

If you use an Everything Math Deck, discard cards greater than 10.

Use different color counters or coins as markers. If you use coins, one player is HEADS and the other player is TAILS.

If you use a pencil to initial the squares, print lightly so you can erase and use the board again.

> **Numerator Pile**
>
> All remaining cards

> **Denominator Pile**
>
> Two each of 3, 6, and 9 cards

>100%	0% or 100%	11.1%	0% or 100%	>100%
$16\frac{2}{3}\%$	22.2%	$33\frac{1}{3}\%$	33.3%	44.4%
>200%	55.5%	>100%	66.6%	>200%
$66\frac{2}{3}\%$	77.7%	$83\frac{1}{3}\%$	88.8%	$133\frac{1}{3}\%$
>100%	0% or 100%	$166\frac{2}{3}\%$	0% or 100%	>100%

Hidden Treasure Gameboards 1

Each player uses Grids 1 and 2.

Grid 1: Hide your point here.

Grid 2: Guess other player's point here.

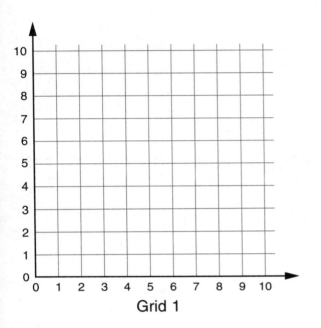

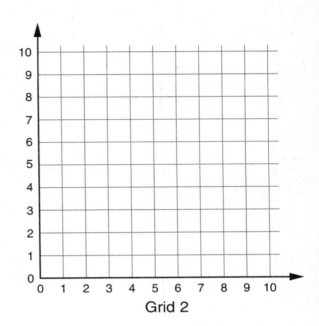

Use this set of grids to play another game.

Grid 1: Hide your point here.

Grid 2: Guess other player's point here.

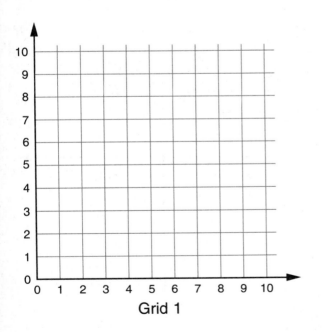

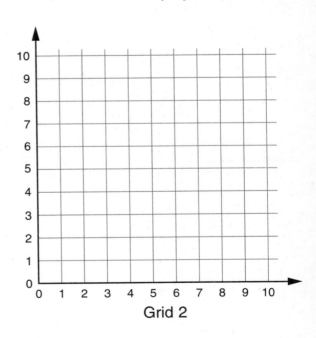

Hidden Treasure Gameboards 2

Each player uses Grids 1 and 2.

Grid 1: Hide your point here.

Grid 2: Guess other player's point here.

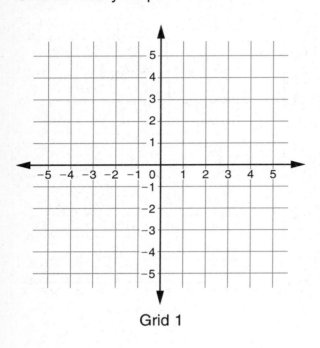

Grid 1

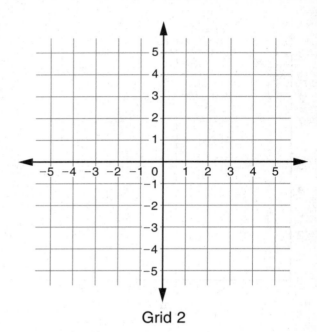

Grid 2

Use this set of grids to play another game.

Grid 1: Hide your point here.

Grid 2: Guess other player's point here.

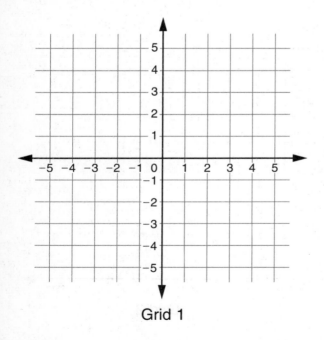

Grid 1

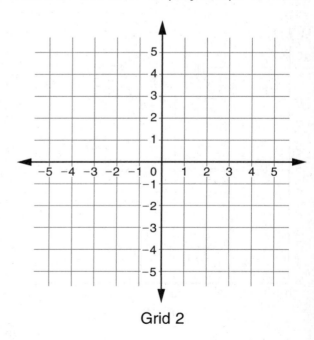

Grid 2

High-Number Toss Record Sheet

Hundred Millions	Ten Millions	Millions	,	Hundred Thousands	Ten Thousands	Thousands	,	Hundreds	Tens	Ones

Round	Player 1	>, <, =	Player 2
Sample	<u>1</u> <u>3</u> <u>2</u> , <u>6</u> *132,000,000*	>	<u>3</u> <u>5</u> <u>6</u> , <u>4</u> *3,560,000*
1	— — — ╷ — _____		— — — ╷ — _____
2	— — — ╷ — _____		— — — ╷ — _____
3	— — — ╷ — _____		— — — ╷ — _____
4	— — — ╷ — _____		— — — ╷ — _____
5	— — — ╷ — _____		— — — ╷ — _____

487

Mixed-Number Spin

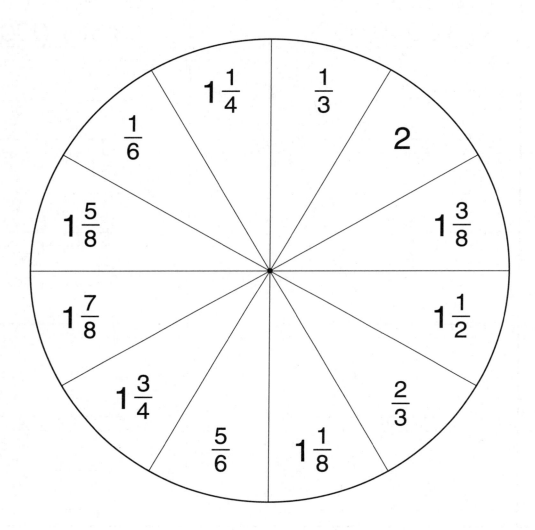

Mixed-Number Spin **Record Sheet**

Name	Name

_____ + _____ < 3   _____ + _____ < 3

_____ + _____ > 3   _____ + _____ > 3

_____ − _____ < 1   _____ − _____ < 1

_____ − _____ < $\frac{1}{2}$ _____ − _____ < $\frac{1}{2}$

_____ + _____ < 1   _____ + _____ > 1

_____ + _____ < 1   _____ + _____ < 1

_____ + _____ < 2   _____ + _____ < 2

_____ − _____ = 3   _____ − _____ = 3

_____ − _____ > 1   _____ − _____ > 1

_____ + _____ > $\frac{1}{2}$ _____ + _____ > $\frac{1}{2}$

_____ + _____ < 3   _____ + _____ < 3

_____ + _____ > 2   _____ + _____ > 2

Name That Number **Record Sheet**

Round 1

Target number: _____   My cards: _____   _____   _____   _____   _____   _____

My best solution (number model): _____

Number of cards used: _____

Round 2

Target number: _____   My cards: _____   _____   _____   _____   _____   _____

My best solution (number model): _____

Number of cards used: _____

- -

Name That Number **Record Sheet**

Round 1

Target number: _____   My cards: _____   _____   _____   _____   _____   _____

My best solution (number model): _____

Number of cards used: _____

Round 2

Target number: _____   My cards: _____   _____   _____   _____   _____   _____

My best solution (number model): _____

Number of cards used: _____

Number Top-It Mat

Millions

Hundred-Thousands

Ten-Thousands

Thous...

Number Top-It Mat *continued*

Ones

Tens

Hundreds

ands

Name   Do not cut. Paste or tape to Math Masters, page 491

492

Name   Date   Time

Top-It Record Sheet

Round	Player 1	>, <, =	Player 2
Sample			
1			
2			
3			
4			
5			

✂ -

Name   Date   Time

Top-It Record Sheet

Round	Player 1	>, <, =	Player 2
Sample			
1			
2			
3			
4			
5			

Polygon Capture Pieces

Polygon Capture Property Cards

There is only one right angle.	There are one or more right angles.	All angles are right angles.	There are no right angles.
There is at least one acute angle.	At least one angle is more than 90°.	All angles are right angles.	There are no right angles.
All opposite sides are parallel.	Only one pair of sides is parallel.	There are no parallel sides.	All sides are the same length.
All opposite sides are parallel.	Some sides have the same length.	All opposite sides have the same length.	**Wild Card:** Pick your own side property.

Polygon Capture Property Cards

Angles	Angles	Angles	Angles
Angles	Angles	Angles	Angles
Sides	Sides	Sides	Sides
Sides	Sides	Sides	Sides

Polygon Capture Record Sheet

Round	Properties	List Polygons Captured	Number of Polygons
1			
2			
3			
4			
5			
		Total	

Rugs and Fences Area and Perimeter Deck

A Find the area of the polygon.	**A** Find the area of the polygon.	**A** Find the area of the polygon.	**A** Find the area of the polygon.
P Find the perimeter of the polygon.	**P** Find the perimeter of the polygon.	**P** Find the perimeter of the polygon.	**P** Find the perimeter of the polygon.
A or P Opponent's Choice	**A or P** Opponent's Choice	**A or P** Opponent's Choice	**A or P** Opponent's Choice
A or P Player's Choice	**A or P** Player's Choice	**A or P** Player's Choice	**A or P** Player's Choice

Rugs and Fences Polygon Deck B

1

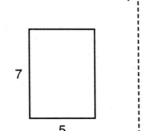

7   5

2

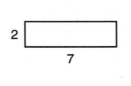

4   9

3

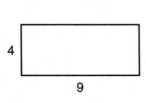

2   7

4

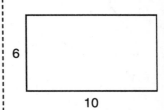

6   10

5

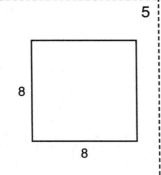

8   8

6

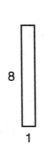

8   1

7

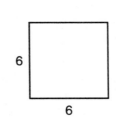

6   6

8

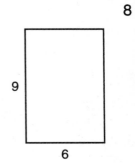

9   6

9

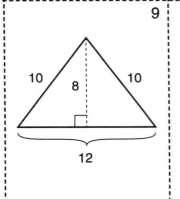

10   8   10   12

10

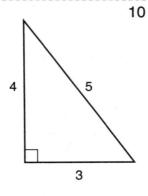

4   5   3

11

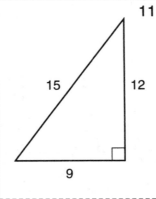

15   12   9

12

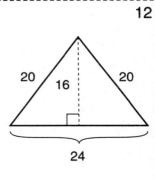

20   16   20   24

13

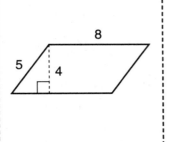

8   5   4

14

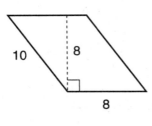

10   8   8

15

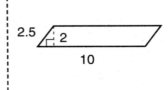

2.5   2   10

16

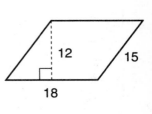

12   15   18

499

Rugs and Fences **Polygon Deck C**

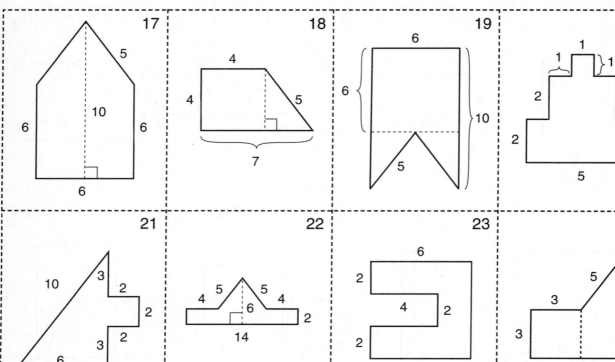

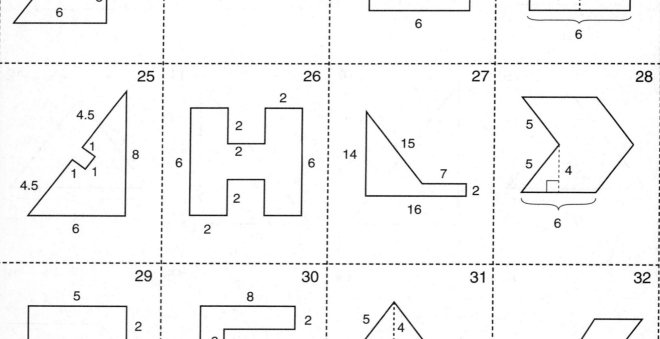

Rugs and Fences Record Sheet

Round	Card number	Circle A (area) or P (perimeter)	Number model	Score
Sample	3	A or Ⓟ	10 + 10 + 2 + 2 = 24	24
1		A or P		
2		A or P		
3		A or P		
4		A or P		
5		A or P		
6		A or P		
7		A or P		
8		A or P		
			Total Score	

Round	Card number	Circle A (area) or P (perimeter)	Number model	Score
Sample	3	A or Ⓟ	10 + 10 + 2 + 2 = 24	24
1		A or P		
2		A or P		
3		A or P		
4		A or P		
5		A or P		
6		A or P		
7		A or P		
8		A or P		
			Total Score	

Sides and Angles: Triangles

1. Cut out the cards. Place the 4 triangle cards in a row. Shuffle the remaining cards.

2. Partners take turns drawing cards and placing them in groups to build a triangle. If a card cannot be placed (a 4th angle or side in the column, for example), return it to the bottom of the deck. Continue until all cards have been drawn.

3. The partner who places the final card to build a triangle takes all the cards in that pile.

4. When all cards have been drawn, use your protractor and straightedge to draw the triangles that match your cards.

Equilateral Triangle	Isosceles Triangle	Scalene Triangle	Right Triangle	2" Line Segment	2" Line Segment
90° Angle	20° Angle	35° Angle	125° Angle	3" Line Segment	35° Angle
55° Angle	2" Line Segment	40° Angle	40° Angle	100° Angle	2" Line Segment
2" Line Segment	7 cm Line Segment	4 cm Line Segment	7 cm Line Segment	4 cm Line Segment	4 cm Line Segment
5 cm Line Segment	6 cm Line Segment	3 cm Line Segment	60° Angle	60° Angle	60° Angle

Spoon Scramble Record Sheet

Player Name:

Record your letters on the lines below.

_____   _____   _____   _____   _____   _____

Winning Combinations

In each row, record the four cards that are of equal value from two of the rounds that you won.

✂ -

Name   Date   Time

Spoon Scramble Record Sheet

Player Name:

Record your letters on the lines below.

_____   _____   _____   _____   _____   _____

Winning Combinations

In each row, record the four cards that are of equal value from two of the rounds that you won.

503

Triangle Sort

1. Cut out the 16 triangle cards below.

2. Sort them into two different groups. Explain how you sorted them.

3. Sort them into three groups. Explain how you sorted them.

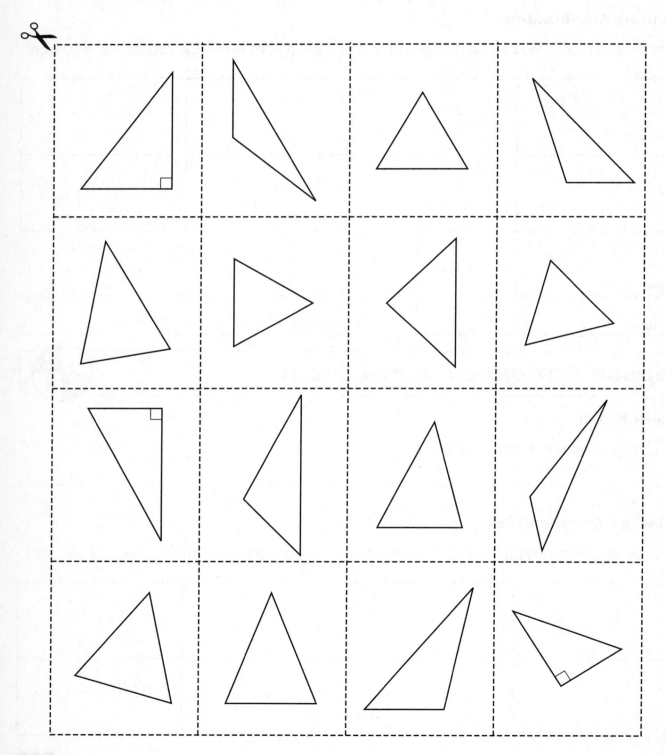

3-D Shape Sort Property Cards

I have an even number of vertices.	I have no vertices.	I have at least 2 edges that are parallel to each other.	I have an odd number of edges.
One of my vertices is formed by an even number of edges.	I have at least 1 curved edge.	I have fewer than 6 vertices.	I have at least 2 edges that are perpendicular to each other.
All of my surfaces are polygons.	I have at least 1 face (flat surface).	I have at least 1 curved surface.	All of my faces are triangles.
All of my faces are regular polygons.	At least 1 of my faces is a circle.	I have at least 1 pair of faces that are parallel to each other.	**Wild Card:** Pick your own surface property.

3-D Shape Sort **Property Cards** *continued*

Vertex/Edge	Vertex/Edge	Vertex/Edge	Vertex/Edge

Vertex/Edge	Vertex/Edge	Vertex/Edge	Vertex/Edge

Surface	Surface	Surface	Surface

Surface	Surface	Surface	Surface

3-D Shape Sort Shape Cards

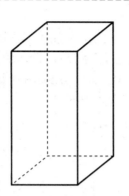

Rectangular Prism

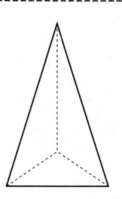

Triangular Pyramid

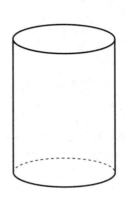

Cylinder

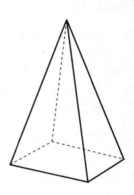

Rectangular Pyramid

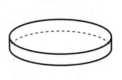

Cylinder

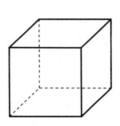

Cube

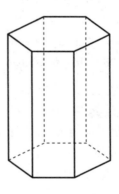

Hexagonal Prism

Sphere

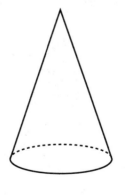

Cone

Truncated Cone

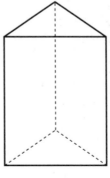

Triangular Prism

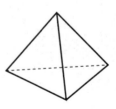

Tetrahedron

What's My Attribute Rule?

Directions

1. Label one sheet of paper *These fit the rule.*

2. Label another sheet of paper *These do NOT fit the rule.*

3. Take turns. Roll the six-sided die once. The player with the lowest number is the first "Rule Maker."

4. The Rule Maker shuffles and places the Attribute Rule Cards facedown.

5. The Rule Maker turns over the top Attribute Rule Card, but does not show it to the other players or tell them what the rule is. For example: *large shapes, but not triangles.*

6. The Rule Maker chooses 3 or 4 attribute blocks that fit the rule on the card. The Rule Maker puts them on the sheet labeled *These fit the rule.*

These fit the rule.

7. The Rule Maker chooses 3 or 4 blocks that do NOT fit the rule. The Rule Maker puts them on the sheet labeled *These do NOT fit the rule.*

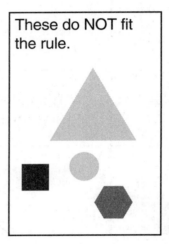

These do NOT fit the rule.

8. The other players take turns choosing a block that they think might fit the rule and placing it on that sheet.

9. If the Rule Maker says "No," the player puts the block on the correct sheet. If "Yes," the player gets to suggest what the rule might be. The Rule Maker then tells the player whether his or her rule is correct.

10. The round continues until someone figures out the rule. That person becomes the Rule Maker for the next round.

What's My Attribute Rule? Cards

small blue shapes	large red shapes	large shapes, but not triangles	circles, but not red
blue and yellow shapes, but not circles	red and yellow small shapes	not triangles or squares	large triangles, but not yellow
large circles, but not red	large circles or squares		

Where Do I Fit In?

1. Cut along the dotted line to separate the Activity Mat from the property cards.

2. Cut out the property cards.

3. Partners each roll a die: the higher roll stands for angles; the lower roll stands for sides.

4. Shuffle and deal all 12 property cards (6 cards to each player).

5. If a partner rolls angles, that partner places all of his or her angle cards under the appropriate triangles. If a partner rolls sides, that partner places all of his or her side cards under the appropriate triangles.

6. Shuffle the cards again and repeat Steps 3 through 5.

Activity Mat

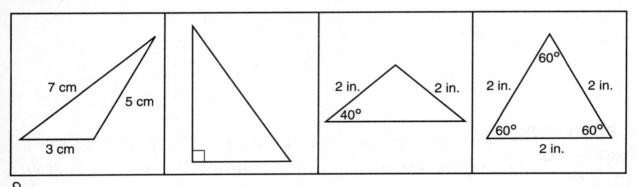

3 acute angles	3 equal angles	sides all the same length	no two angles with the same measure
sides all with different lengths	two sides with the same length	at least two angles with the same measure	one right angle
two acute angles	no more than two equal sides	one 90° angle	3 acute angles

High-Number Toss: Decimal Version Record Sheet

Circle the winning number for each round. Fill in the Score column each time you have the winning number.

SRB
321

Player 1 _____
(Name)

Player 2 _____
(Name)

Round	Player 1	<, >, =	Player 2	Score
Sample	0. 6 5 4	<	0. 7 5 3	0.753 − 0.654 0.099
1	0.___ ___ ___		0.___ ___ ___	
2	0.___ ___ ___		0.___ ___ ___	
3	0.___ ___ ___		0.___ ___ ___	
4	0.___ ___ ___		0.___ ___ ___	
5	0.___ ___ ___		0.___ ___ ___	
			Total Score	

511

Spoon Scramble Cards

$\frac{1}{4}$ of 24	$\frac{3}{4} * 8$	50% of 12	0.10 * 60
$\frac{1}{3}$ of 21	$3\frac{1}{2} * 2$	25% of 28	0.10 * 70
$\frac{1}{5}$ of 40	$2 * \frac{16}{4}$	1% of 800	0.10 * 80
$\frac{3}{4}$ of 12	$4\frac{1}{2} * 2$	25% of 36	0.10 * 90